THE SEC...

Andrew Collins was born in 1957. After an uneventful school career at Wickford in Essex, he became a shipping clerk in London and joined the 1976 punk rock explosion by forming his own, now forgotten band.

Giving up his anarchic ideals in favour of his life-long interest in the mysteries of life, Andrew became an investigator of UFO sightings, studying their apparent link with psychics and psychic abilities. In 1979 he entered a journalistic career, writing for the magazine *Strange Phenomena* with parapsychologist and author Graham Phillips. Working together, they played out what has become one of the century's most controversial supernatural dramas – the search to find a green talismanic stone, once belonging to Mary Queen of Scots, and a short sword bearing her personal monogram. The discovery of these historical artefacts is told in Andrew's book *The Seventh Sword*, published in 1991.

In 1981 Andrew became a researcher and writer on the earth mysteries, a parascience studying man's relationship to the sacred and ancient places of our landscape. Three years later he initiated the subject of psychic questing, a term coined to describe his own unique brand of discovering hidden artefacts and solving historical enigmas using psychic and mystical processes.

By the same author

**THE BLACK ALCHEMIST
THE CIRCLEMAKERS
THE SEVENTH SWORD**

THE SECOND COMING

Andrew Collins

This edition published by Arrow Books Limited 1994

1 3 5 7 9 10 8 6 4 2

Copyright © 1994 Andrew Collins

All rights reserved

The right of Andrew Collins to be identified as the author of this work has been asserted by him in accordance with the Copyright, Designs and Patents Act, 1988

This book is sold subject to the condition that it shall not, by way of trade or otherwise, be lent, resold, hired out, or otherwise circulated without the publisher's prior consent in any form of binding or cover other than that in which it is published and without a similar condition including this condition being imposed on the subsequent purchaser

First published in the United Kingdom in 1993 by Century
Random House UK Ltd, 20 Vauxhall Bridge Road, London SW1V 2SA

Arrow Books Limited
Random House UK Ltd, 20 Vauxhall Bridge Road, London SW1V 2SA

Random House Australia (Pty) Limited
20 Alfred Street, Milsons Point, Sydney,
New South Wales 2061, Australia

Random House New Zealand Limited
18 Poland Road, Glenfield
Auckland 10, New Zealand

Random House South Africa (Pty) Limited
PO Box 337, Bergvlei, South Africa

Random House UK Limited Reg. No. 954009

A CIP catalogue record for this book
is available from the British Library

ISBN 0 09 925151 5

Printed and bound in Great Britain by
Cox & Wyman Ltd, Reading, Berkshire

Contents

Acknowledgements   7

Preface   8

Is it Black Magic?   9

The Proclamation   13

PART ONE – Kickback

1	Changing Times	17
2	The Foul Pit	27
3	The Voice of Fire	37
4	Paradise Lost	40
5	Forbidden Fruit	50
6	The Hosts of Hekate	59
7	The Summoning	65
8	The Venus of Regret	69

PART TWO – The Dark Council

9	The Wheel of Destruction	81
10	Markus of the Miz-maze	90
11	The Energy Matrix	94
12	The First Doubt	101
13	The Ides of March	105
14	Octavia's Hill	112
15	Cracking the Crucible	125
16	Midnight Sun	133
17	Brave Faces	143
18	Rachel's Anguish	149
19	The Dark Pool	159
20	The Serpent's Egg	164

PART THREE – Hexe

21	The Bygone Village	173
22	The People of Hexe	180
23	The Doom of the Gods	187
24	The First Seal	198
25	The Black Cross of the Flame	205
26	A Last Goodbye	211
27	Trouble at Stonehenge	217
28	The Bone Man	227
29	The Walking Bone	233
30	The Angry Moon	241
31	The Well of Revealing	247
32	Portents of Danger	252

PART FOUR – Hellbound

33	The Coming Fear	257
34	Night Stalker	260
35	Nosferatu	265
36	Something Silver	271
37	Harbinger of Destruction	275
38	Omens of Despair	283
39	The Form of the Wolf	288
40	The Lantern's Force	297

Epilogue	307
Appendix I – The Cult of St Catherine	310
Notes and References	314
Bibliography	325
Index	328

To Stella Eik
Thanks for everything

Acknowledgements

Thanks to, in alphabetical order, Arthur and Jenny Benstead, Bernard, David, Karl and Lisa Dawkins, Tim Dedopulos, Fiona, Ingrid Fischer, Gary and staff at Photofen, Bob Gilbert, Helen, John and Kerry Horrigan, Rory Kee, Alex Langstone, Johnny Merron, Toyne and Joan Newton, Ian Read, Angela Reeve, Geoff Roberts, Charles Topham, Cara Trimarco, Charles Walker, Paul Weston, Steve Wilson and last, but not least, Caroline Wise. I must also thank those at Century and Arrow who have supported my publishing ventures in recent years, especially Mark Booth, Andrea Henry, Tracey Jennings and Oliver Johnson.

Most important of all, I wish to thank Debbie for her undivided support and the many hours she spent checking and rechecking the manuscript.

Preface

The Second Coming is not a work of fiction. Each chapter has been constructed from the extensive diaries, tapes and notes accumulated over the four-year period reflected in the text. Where possible exact conversations have been used to reconstruct the situations and settings in question. Sometimes it has been necessary to blend together or re-arrange events for reading purposes. When this occurs it has been clearly marked and explained in the Notes at the end of the book.

The Second Coming features my working relationship with various talented individuals who display rare and quite unique psychic abilities. For the purposes of anonymity, some of them have asked me to use their first names only. This decision I have dutifully respected, since their positions in daily life, as well as their cherished privacy, would be jeopardised should knowledge of their psychic activities become widely known.

Many readers will question the authenticity of the book's extraordinary and, on some occasions, quite disturbing contents. This I accept and appreciate, although I would ask them to read and absorb the whole book before drawing any final conclusions.

Andrew Collins, 21 March 1993

Is it Black Magic?

Following the release of my book *The Black Alchemist* in 1988 I suddenly found myself at the centre of a major row highlighted in the local media. Fundamentalist Christians objected to the promotion and sale of the book claiming, without due consideration, that it encouraged its readers to indulge in occult practices incompatible with their own understanding of the Christian faith.

Over a period of two years I was hounded at every level and on every possible occasion. Bookshops were forced to remove the book from display following complaints from customers. Talks were banned in most major towns in the south of England. Pickets said prayers outside lecture halls and turned people away whenever possible. One venue in Brentwood, Essex, was told its windows would be smashed if a day of lectures by myself was allowed to go ahead. Another venue at Colchester in the same county was informed that if a similar all-dayer were to take place the building would be fire-bombed and right-wing Christian extremists would break up the event.

In my home town of Leigh-on-Sea I was threatened by an obviously disturbed born-again Christian who claimed he would carry out God's work and kill me if I did not cancel an up-coming conference.

The list goes on and on; so why all the fuss? There have been plenty of books on the occult before, and *their* authors have not suffered a similar fate, so why object to me?

Well, this is the way I see it.

The Black Alchemist openly popularised the idea of using psychic abilities in a modern day-to-day context, in this case to uncover and expose the corrupt magical activities of a sinister

THE SECOND COMING

occultist known only as the Black Alchemist. Yet despite its gripping story-line the book said more about my working relationship with a psychic than it did about any alleged black magic activities in Britain today.

The Black Alchemist attempted to highlight the current interest in a subject we refer to as psychic questing – a process that might be defined as the acceptance and use of psychically gained information to achieve a predetermined goal, be it the retrieval of an object, the solving of a historical enigma, or the search for spiritual enlightenment.

Psychic questing is not a religion or a belief system, it is a set of techniques enabling the human mind to interact and communicate with the hidden energies and intelligences existing beyond the normal reaches of space-time. Such abilities were once understood by our distant ancestors, those great builders of the stone and earthen monuments that are found throughout Britain and stand as stark reminders of our own ignorance of the subtleties of nature.

Anthropological studies have shown that past and present cultures across the world have always revered and respected gifted individuals who withdraw from the mundane world to commune with supernatural forces and ancestral spirits on behalf of their tribe or community. These people are generally referred to as shamans, although popular culture has remembered them only as 'medicine men' and 'witch-doctors', terms ill-describing their full functions and quite extraordinary paranormal capabilities.

In the civilised world such wild talents did not just fade away with the rise of world religions or with the arrival of the age of reason. If not sanctioned by the Church itself, such gifts were generally suppressed or repressed by society through superstitious fear and blind ignorance. In seventeenth-century Europe a person could be condemned to death as a witch for displaying even the vaguest hint of supernatural powers. Countless millions of innocent people were persecuted in the name of witchcraft, and even today psychics run the risk of ridicule and torment simply for showing an interest in their own unique abilities.

The Black Alchemist came under immediate attack from

fundamentalist Christians because it promoted a kind of urban shamanism by demonstrating that the functions once deemed as essential to tribal communities are now resurfacing in a format acceptable to a very wide audience indeed. Furthermore, it shattered the whole seance-room illusion by showing that you don't need to be in a trance or standing on a Spiritualist platform to obtain psychically inspired information. Powerful dreams and visions can occur anywhere at all – in a crowded pub, at an ancient stone circle or inside a speeding car.

The off-the-cuff attitude of *The Black Alchemist* appealed to a mostly youthful audience at a time when alternative thought and New Age concepts were gaining momentum hand-in-hand with the phenomenal growth of the rave culture of the late 1980s and early 1990s. It made perfect sense to read the book and it was becoming hip to be a psychic.

It is a process continuing today, and it is this situation that poses a major threat to world religions. Suddenly people are once again thinking for themselves and, worse still, are attempting to communicate with unseen energies and intelligences previously considered as taboo, and even heretical, by established faiths.

This is why the Christian fundamentalists objected to *The Black Alchemist*.

So much for their side of the story, but what about the equally venomous attacks made on the book by certain elements of the occult community. What was their argument?

The book's main story-line concerned our efforts to uncover the nefarious activities of the Black Alchemist and his shady associates in the Friends of Hekate. Both parties had been conducting very questionable magical rites at sanctified sites in the south of England and these I plainly referred to as acts of 'black magic'. It was a term I did not use lightly, in spite of which various sensation-seeking newspapers hijacked the book's findings to print grossly inaccurate stories suggesting that the south of England was rife with black magic rings and human sacrifice. Unfortunately, certain extracts from the book had, in their view, suggested such conclusions, placing the blame firmly in my court. This I greatly regret, for – as influential bodies such as the Sorcerer's Apprentice Fighting Fund (SAFF) readily point out – false claims of this nature are fuelling the causes of the fundamentalist Christians.

Over the past five years Britain has witnessed the debacles surrounding various alleged ritual child-abuse cases following accusations made to the police by children in the care of social workers. Despite extensive police investigations *not one* single case has resulted in a court conviction, which is just as well as there is mounting evidence pointing to Christian fundamentalists being involved in the often clandestine groups now advising social workers on questioning procedures for allegations of ritual child abuse.

If just one of these test cases were to produce a conviction then, with the mounting 'evidence' for 'black magic' rings in Britain today, Christian fundamentalists would lobby the Houses of Parliament for changes in the laws governing occult practices. Unfortunately such a Bill, if passed, would not only affect practitioners of the black arts, it would also affect pagans, psychics, witches, Tarot readers and ritual magicians, and many more besides. It would also affect the freedom to communicate knowledge on such topics. One recent report claims that leading publishers are already steering away from new books on 'witchcraft' owing to the growing unease caused by recent ritual child-abuse cases.

The Second Coming does not wish to contribute to this quite disturbing situation. The author would like to make it clear that the people referred to in its text cannot be seen as exponents of 'black magic'. There is *no such thing* as black or white magic, only magic – the ability of the human mind to effect change through ritual processes. It is up to the individual practitioner how he or she uses or interprets such prized knowledge.

The Black Alchemist, the Friends of Hekate, the Dark Council and the People of Hexe all possess an immense understanding of magical practices. This they have utilised for their own purposes, often on behalf of commercial enterprises which have no active involvement in the occult themselves.

The actions of these groups and individuals – particularly their concealment of fixing markers at ancient and sanctified sites – is, in my opinion, highly dangerous. It has therefore been the choice of myself and my colleagues to investigate and, where possible, disrupt or curtail the magical operations set in motion by such people.

The Proclamation

Thursday, 5 November 1987. Out of the muted darkness emerged a plain, unmarked car that rolled gently to a halt in front of the imposing country church, its tall, conical spire ablaze with the silver light of a full moon.

Slowly, the doors of the vehicle opened – though no interior light was seen – and into view came two silhouetted figures, both male, the taller of whom carried a black leather Gladstone bag.

The vehicle was left unlocked, and the sound of gravel crunching underfoot was clearly heard as they walked swiftly into the shadows cast by this towering Christian edifice.

Skirting the outside of the medieval stone building they soon reached the eastern wall. Beyond this was the high altar on which stood the Cross of Christ – the focus of Godly power and the greatest threat to their success.

The tall figure holding the bag now crouched down and withdrew from its interior a large rectangular stone plate. Scratched into its surface was the image of a serpent biting its own tail, its coiled body encircling a magical symbol portraying the ultimate goal of the ancient alchemist – the creation of black life through the forces of fire and menstruation.

It had been prepared well and its sheer presence here, beneath the majestic east window, would ensure that no interference could be expected from the congregation of this idyllic Essex parish.

Picking up the bag again, the two men moved on to their final destination – a gaping hole in the very womb of the earth itself, exposed by the force of *Lykaina*, the she-wolf, whose raw power had been felt by so many on the night of the Great Storm, just three weeks before. Through her the prophecies would now be

THE SECOND COMING

fulfilled and the doom of the life-bearing fire could begin in earnest. But first the new seed must be welcomed into the sterile womb of the barren bitch.

Lykaina's foul breath had smitten the sacred tree in front of them, just as it had done to the millions of others that fell to their deaths in the forests and woods of southern England. Yet here, at this place of earthly power, she had taken out just one solitary tree. Beneath its charred stump was where it would be placed. The priestess of Hekate had prepared an earthen hollow on the feast of Samhain and now it was ready to accept this final gift.

Placing his black leather bag on the soft muddy earth, the tall, silent figure reached inside and explored with his fingers. They found the object of his search – it felt spongy and just a little slippery.

His hand emerged clutching a large blood-soaked heart, its distinctive shape dimly visible in the pale moonlight. Balancing the fleshy organ on his palm, he reached in with the other hand and withdrew a long black dagger, its ebony handle fashioned into the crude likeness of the Cynocephalus – the grotesque baboon revered by the ancient Egyptians because it emitted menstrual blood at the exact moment of a full-moon eclipse.[1] Scratched carefully into the surface of its long, slim blade was his proclamation to the hosts of the night: 'All haile to the noble companie a parfet master made them call'. On its reverse was a magical formula, an alchemical catalyst that would germinate and protect the black seed.

Clenching the dagger tightly, he pierced its pinion-like blade into the soft flesh until it reached the ventricles which once pumped the life-blood through the body of some poor animal. Puncturing the tough gristle necessitated one final thrust, but finally the hideous act was complete.

With congealing blood on cold hands, both dark figures dropped to their knees and placed the gruesome gift in the ugly fissure left when the tree's thick roots had been wrenched violently from their earthen socket.

'It is done,' a low voice uttered in the faint lunar light. 'Let the gestation begin.'

PART ONE
Kickback

1
Changing Times

Monday, 1 August 1988. Bernard gulped down the remains of his pint of Guinness and placed the empty glass on the table with a look of contented satisfaction on his beaming face. 'Here, you might as well take it.'

Shaking my head once more, I reached across and picked up the strange image carved in soft green stone. It was an amazing story, no one could deny that. Having vowed to cast aside his remarkable psychic talents in the wake of the harrowing experiences suffered during the Black Alchemist affair, Bernard had booked a package holiday to Malta with his wife and daughter. Halfway through their two-week stay on this lazy Mediterranean isle, they went on a day trip to the neighbouring island of Gozo, where they visited the huge temple complex at Ggantija.

After spending an hour listening to the guide giving a cock-eyed rendition of the megalithic monument's supposed history, Bernard's wife and daughter retired to the café for an ice-cool Coke, leaving him to explore. It was then that he encountered the radiant spectre of a tall, native priestess. He caught glimpses of her past life and of her eventual slaughter at the hands of two smaller men – invading marauders, he decided, of a foreign, hostile race. From around her neck they swiped a carved pendant fastened to a leather thong. This they discarded, yet intuitively Bernard knew exactly where to look and, after using his fingers to dig between two great stones, he unearthed a dirt-caked stone around three inches long. Rubbing away its hardened coating, his heart nearly missed a beat when he realised it was a face carved out of soft green rock with a hole for a thong and crude spirals scratched into the rear surface of the neck.

The antiquity's long, flattened features and angular nose gave it the distinct appearance of the carved faces seen on statues belonging to the palace-building Cycladic culture, whose distinctive artistic style was common in the Aegean islands from around 2600 BC onwards. If correct, then it strongly suggested that Bernard's curious find could come from this age.

'So what do we do with it?' he asked, glancing towards the ancient artefact placed next to the dirty ashtray. 'Take it to the British Museum?'

I would get it checked. His whole story needed verification, but for the moment his word was good enough. Working with Bernard for several years had shown me the deadly accurate nature of his psychic powers, especially his capability to find lost or hidden artefacts.

Leaving the Gozo head for a moment, I turned our attentions to more immediate matters that evening, as we sat supping beer in the corner of The Griffin public house at Danbury, a small village somewhere in the heart of Essex.

Today was 1 August, the festival of Lugnasadh in the yearly calendar of our Celtic ancestors as well as the eve of Lammastide in rural Christian tradition. In Iron Age Britain and Ireland great bonfires would be kindled upon hilltops across the land in honour of Lugh, the Gaelic god of light. For these pagan people it was a time of change, a time of cosmic renewal, a point of transition not just in an agricultural cycle, but in the subtle rhythms of the body clock. Such times were seen as periods of uncertainty when the invisible veils between this world and the next wore very thin, and even today they could be utilised by witches and occultists to manipulate the powerful psychic energies and spirits of the astral domains.

Perhaps it was an opportune moment to leave the comfort of the less than crowded bar and venture into the churchyard to see if he was receptive to this transition point in the seasonal cycle. It was a pleasant summer's evening and it seemed a shame to lose this golden opportunity to obtain new psychic information.

It took some convincing, but finally Bernard relented and went to stand up. 'Come on then,' he sighed. 'Don't forget the face, and your sword-stick!'

Grabbing the 3,500-year-old Maltese artefact, I slipped it into my document case, picked up the Indian sword-stick and followed him towards the exit.

Outside, the low orange sun was losing its warmth, and a slight chill in the evening air prompted me to slip on an old cardigan while Bernard waited in the car-park.

Crossing the busy main road, the psychic stamped out his cigarette butt and began ascending the gravel track that passed between two Victorian, brick-built houses. The tall lead-grey spire of Danbury's church of St John the Baptist came into view and at a leisurely pace we entered the churchyard.

Passing below the medieval stone tower, I could not help but remember the many occasions in which Bernard and I had used this sacred place for reasons beyond the jurisdiction of canonical church practices. Everywhere around us was some unobvious spot where a bizarre psychic incident had taken place since we first began working together in 1984.

The dry dirt path took us to the foot of a lone silver birch. Its gently shifting shadows offered a natural area of diminished light ideal for achieving altered states of consciousness. Bernard lowered himself to the dry earth and leaned back against the slim tree trunk.

I was not entirely sure what I expected to happen. Picking a position on the nearby gravel path I pushed down on the sword-stick, like some tap dancer swivelling on a black cane, and closed my eyes. The power of creative visualisation could – I knew from years of experience – excite not only the subtle life energies of our own physical bodies, but trigger into motion the site's inherent energy matrix.

The whole of Danbury churchyard was enclosed within a virtually demolished Iron Age encampment over 2,500 years old, showing the site's ancient sanctity. Indeed, Bernard felt that a pagan temple of the sun had once been located in the middle of the prehistoric earthwork, close to where the 1987 hurricane had taken out the old horse-chestnut tree which had acted as our much-loved place of meditation until that time. This honour had now been transferred to this somewhat younger tree on the other side of the path which, although narrower in girth, was quite adequate for our purposes.

With conviction, I mentally pushed golden light through the length of the sword-stick, down into the earth beneath my feet. It flowed away like the spokes of a fiery wheel until the whole place was ablaze with vibrant energy. Every cross-shaft, grave-slab and tombstone became enlivened with blinding light.

This is what I imagined, but what about Bernard? What could he see with his *psychic* eyes?

'A wheel of fire,' he mused, seemingly uninterested, as he sat beneath the tree, his eyes wide open. 'Extending to the edge of the churchyard.'

Good, the visualisation was working.

A sharp breeze blew swiftly across the pleasant hill-top setting. With it came a slight drop in temperature which lingered even after the leaves had ceased their hiss.

Bernard sensed it too and rubbed his arms before looking skyward for an explanation. Not finding one, he turned and stared at the line of low hedgerow marking the most southerly extent of the cemetery, some twenty yards away. 'Bushes are burning,' he announced casually with a grimace. There was a pause before: 'White figures, vague. In cowls, beyond the hedge.' He stopped to take in more. 'They do not encroach. Some kind of ancestral spirits, I should think.'

Opening my eyes, I moved across to the tree and clicked on the pocket cassette. Psychic sessions were always recorded these days.

A further period of silence followed, then: 'Have you ever been back to that mound?' he enquired, looking towards me.

I clenched my teeth tightly, knowing which 'mound' he was referring to, but could only ask: 'Why?'

'I see a group there. Eight to a dozen. In a circle surrounding a central figure.' Then his voice sounded more serious. 'Dark robes.'

Some ritualistic event, perhaps?

'I would think to come, wouldn't you?' He looked up. 'Associated with fire ... and gargoyles, seen as symbols of negative energy at the mound. A bit chaotic really. Brings forth other things,' he said ominously. 'Black things. Floppy things. I want to kick them out of the way.'

Was this at night?

'Night, yes . . . No, it's not. It's sunset. Getting dark. Like now.' He fell silent again.

I knelt down by his side to record his intriguing words, knowing that any further away and it would be impossible to transcribe the resulting tape. What else could he see?

He simply stared into thin air and described the mental pictures crystallising before him. 'Don't know why I should say this, but I see somebody holding a black child.'

A black child? What did he mean?

'Either that, or it's a doll of some sort.'

So far he seemed undisturbed by the nature of the rich imagery his inner mind had revealed.

'There's a man, standing on the mound, wearing the same sort of cowled black robe as we've seen before, but this one has a red lining,' he added, rising to his feet and beginning to pace. 'Quite a tall figure . . . motionless, with the dark child in his hands, and there's a slight wind . . . wafting.'

An uneasiness was growing steadily inside Bernard. He could sense that old feeling, that realisation of *his* presence, *his* influence and *his* hatred of humanity. It was him all right, Bernard recognised his tangible form, impregnated upon the secluded grassy mound so far away.

And the more they linked, the more he felt he was actually there with him, on the tumulus, their two minds becoming one as they had done so many times before. He could see him so clearly now, even the carefully turned edges of the long cuffs and the thick drapes of his black cowl; they seemed so real.

He was just there, in his head . . .

Unexpectedly, Bernard could no longer see the rising ground beneath the hem of the figure's long robe. But he knew the mound was still present, somewhere.

The dark sentinel's clear image seemed suspended in mid-air, the black child still held in his arms. Not black in skin colour, but *charred black by fire*.

The last time their minds had met Bernard saw him standing on the mound holding two daggers crossed above his head. He thought then it had been a gesture of provocation and now he was *here* . . .

Oh no, please. The spirit of the Black Alchemist was here, *in the churchyard*, between the gap in the hedge not twenty paces away. Bernard's own thoughts had pulled his presence to Danbury and he was now feeding this psychic intrusion with his own vital energy . . . and it was draining his life force, making him weaker and weaker.

He felt as though he was inside an invisible bubble.

Somewhere close by was Andrew, calling out, asking him questions, outside the bubble . . . outside the waking nightmare.

Bernard's will to move was becoming impaired. He was gradually losing consciousness and as his mind fragmented he was forced to observe the domain of the dark path, *his* world . . . *his* future . . .

He could see bonfires in woods. Many of them, now and to come. Then he saw the same figures on the mound, and silhouetted hills at night; lots of steep hills all linked as one. Flashes, glimpses, of *him* and *her* together, and gargoyles, flying in circles . . . swooping low overhead.

Soon, *he* would come again. Bernard could also see Andrew and others, and woods, and darkness. Only darkness . . . only darkness . . . and then night turning into day and the sun rising. He could see a rolling green landscape . . . the Malverns, and a line of white-cowled figures ascending towards a stone well on the ridge of a rounded hill.

And now cloisters, and an abbey. Wilton? And an abbess, dressed in white with a radiant blue nimbus around her head. She exuded only warmth and serenity and stood before him in a scented herb garden. 'Peace will reign,' she said, a calming smile on her pale face as she held out her hands for him to take.

He would be safe in her care, Bernard realised, before blacking out completely.

Nodding my thanks to the landlord, I carried the drinks across to the corner table where Bernard contemplated the events of the last hour or so.

Pulling up a seat, I waited for him to re-open the conversation.

'*Is* there somewhere called Wilton?' he asked, not even sure himself.

I said there was.

Out in the churchyard his mind had somehow managed to end up at Wilton Abbey, near Amesbury in Wiltshire. Nowadays it was a private country estate, but from what I knew it was open to the public.

'Are there cloisters?' he asked, lighting a cigarette. 'I saw cloisters and a scented herb garden.'

There are no cloisters there today, but in the past Wilton Abbey had been a very important monastic settlement. One of its most celebrated abbesses was St Edith of Wilton, the visionary daughter of King Edgar, the tenth-century Anglo-Saxon king. Medieval chroniclers accredited her with the gift of prophecy and the ability to appear in two places at once. The much-loved St Dunstan of Glastonbury took heed of her inspired visions and it was said that the Danish king Cnut, or Canute, only canonised her after her spirit appeared to him in a frightening vision. Perhaps it had been St Edith who had intervened on Bernard's behalf as he fought to regain consciousness out there in the churchyard.

'Possibly, but why see a procession of white figures climbing a green hill towards a holy well in the Malverns?'

The holy well was almost certainly one of the Malvern shrines dedicated to St Anne which once drew pilgrims from across the country. Perhaps St Edith or one of her sisters had led a pilgrimage to the Malvern Hills in Worcestershire.

'Well, whoever she was, she pulled me through after the Black Alchemist appeared out there,' he sighed, nodding his head in the direction of the church. 'I'd like to know what's going on at that mound, wouldn't you?'

All I knew was that neither of us had expected to come face to face with our old adversary tonight. Ever since Thursday, 30 May 1985, when we first unearthed one of the wretched man's inscribed stone spearheads in the secluded, hill-top churchyard at Lullington in East Sussex, our lives had been plagued by his presence. Removing this highly charged ritual artefact had upset Bernard's bodily system to such a degree that he had been repeatedly sick. It had also given him an unexpected mental link with its maker – a lone figure conducting a degenerate but highly sophisticated form of Greco-Roman alchemy and magic at holy sites across the south of England.

Soon afterwards Bernard had dreamt of this corrupt alchemist's Eastbourne home and had continued to see clairvoyant glimpses of his suspect magical activities. Upon visiting the sites seen in vision, inscribed objects were generally found to confirm Bernard's growing fears.

Gradually the figure, whom we began referring to as the Black Alchemist, targeted locations in our own home county of Essex. This had led to a series of cat and mouse confrontations aimed at stamping out our unwanted interference. At each site visited he had conducted macabre rituals that involved the concealment of different inscribed artefacts.

Despite these often disconcerting episodes Bernard and I had never physically encountered the Black Alchemist, or any of his cronies, and had never learnt his real name. To be honest, I do not think Bernard was particularly interested in establishing his identity as he knew it would only guarantee him more sleepless nights, more headaches and further consternation from his dear wife, who did not really know what was going on.

The Black Alchemist affair had come to a head at the beginning of the year, and as a writer I had decided to get the whole crazy story down on paper. One thing had led to another and I now intended publishing a self-financed book entitled, curiously enough, *The Black Alchemist*. It was currently with the typesetters and was due for release on Saturday, 5 November. I had no idea what sort of response this would prompt from BA and his associates; we would have to wait and see.

As Bernard was proof-reading the manuscript in June he had once again linked in mind with the activities of the Black Alchemist. He had 'seen' him standing upon a low tumulus in front of dense woodland located on the brow of an uncultivated hill. The shadowy figure had stood there motionless, dressed, as usual, in a black cowled robe. In his hands were two daggers crossed above his head in a gesture of defiance, a sign of provocation directed, we guessed, at Bernard and myself.

From his description of the grassy mound, I had finally tracked it down to one of the estimated fifty-six examples to be found in the Eastbourne area. Placed beyond a wooded region named Paradise, just west of the town, the mound looked down upon a natural amphitheatre, with the English Channel to the south, the

Kent Downs to the north and Eastbourne directly below. It was a perfect setting for any operation – quiet, secluded and inaccessible to most people.

On impulse I had decided to check out the Paradise Mound, as I referred to it, on Friday, 17 June. Surveying the location had allowed me to grasp the accuracy of Bernard's clairvoyant description. So, after making a thorough search of the vicinity, I had conducted a simple meditational exercise to scramble the psychic memory of BA's own magical workings at the site, and there the matter had rested until tonight.

Now Bernard had again seen the Paradise Mound and this time it looked as if it was being prepared for some kind of ritualistic event co-ordinated by the Black Alchemist. It made some kind of sense as over the past week various friends had experienced vivid dreams and waking visions which had convinced them that the Black Alchemist was on the move again. Bernard knew nothing of this as I had dismissed these experiences as the product of over-active imaginations. Now I was not so sure. Something untoward was in the air and perhaps Bernard could explain exactly what.

Having listened to the evidence, he hunched his shoulders and looked thoughtful. 'Well, I reckon they're up to something, don't you?'

I nodded in agreement.

'Just before the abbess approached me I caught a glimpse of bonfires in woods, lots of them, as if many different things were taking place, not all at the same time, but linked in some way. I get the feeling they're part of some overall scheme that will require the influence and energies produced by a number of different events across the country.'

With BA co-ordinating matters at the Paradise Mound?

He stubbed out his cigarette. 'Not sure. We'll have to wait and see.'

Would this be sooner or later? I mean, within the next few days?

Bellowing laughter emanated from a group of fashion-conscious youths seated only two tables away. The Griffin always got busier as the night wore on.

'Possibly, yes, and other things afterwards, well into the

future. It's the beginning of something new and this period of time is important to them for some reason.'

Did it concern this black child or doll he had clairvoyantly seen in the hands of the Black Alchemist?

Bernard turned his head quickly. 'Yes,' he said convincingly. 'The end of one phase and the beginning of the next.'

My churning stomach told me that some ominous event involving the Black Alchemist and his cronies was fast approaching and, whatever its purpose, it was going to make anything we had encountered before look like child's play. Exactly what, only time would tell.

2
The Foul Pit

Thursday, 4 August 1988. Leaving the comfort of the warm lounge, Bernard passed through the hallway and entered the dining room. It was here that he spent long hours, immersing himself in medieval studies and delicately painting heraldic coats of arms. He pulled out a high-backed wooden chair and sat himself down.

His interests in heraldry helped keep him from thinking too much about psychic work. Even so, there was no getting away from the subject. His unexpected revelations concerning the Black Alchemist had greatly intrigued Andrew who, perhaps not unnaturally, now wanted to know more.

He pulled across a clean glass ashtray and lit a cigarette.

It did seem important, however, and after due consideration he had decided to conduct an impromptu meditation to find out what was going on.

The background din of the television coming through from the front room gradually lessened as he sat quietly and opened his mind. He never really went for any of Andrew's protection visualisations unless he got into trouble, and thankfully that was not very often.

He pictured the Paradise Mound at Eastbourne by conjuring its image into his mind's eye. He could see the setting in the fading evening sunlight. Beyond it was dense woodland and somewhere behind him he could sense the presence of a steep slope leading down to the sea. That was all he could picture as he had never visited Eastbourne before in his life.

Having fixed the scene in his mind, he searched for further clues, but found none. There was no one to be seen; no Black Alchemist or anyone at all in dark cowled robes.

He frowned to himself, stubbed out the cigarette and decided to give it one more try.

After further concentration he could still see only the mound – no strange words and no unusual feelings came to him.

He rubbed his forehead. Something was trying to take him away from this place. Through dark undergrowth he went, across woodland and out of Eastbourne completely. He was at a new location, not far away, and here he saw only darkness. No light was cast by the moon.

Then came movement before him.

His psychic eyes perceived a silhouetted figure, standing within a secluded clearing, deep within a large wood. Although its face was hidden by a floppy cowl, he knew it was a woman. In front of her was a purpose-dug pit, some four feet across and around three feet in depth.

In her hands was a bowl; yes, a stone bowl containing a thick, golden liquid. She seemed poised to pour it into the pit as some kind of ritualistic libation to the earth. It was *her*, he was sure of it – the woman they referred to as the Black Sorceress of Arundel.

Now a change of imagery. He saw a long spearhead suspended in mid-air, point downwards. It was fashioned in metal and tied to a wooden shaft.

'Enhance birth,' an unexpected male voice proclaimed, and following this came the impression of 'white fire'; the same fire that roasted the child black.

The image was quickly replaced by another of the same robed woman. She seemed enveloped in grey mist and all of a sudden the psychic scene was lost from view.

In its place were words being said by the same male voice. He could not distinguish them clearly, for they appeared to be receding, although they sounded like some kind of proclamation.

Then there was only silence and the relief that accompanies stillness.

Opening his eyes, Bernard snapped out of the light trance. The more familiar surroundings of the small room with its framed pictures of heraldic genealogies and the constant tick-tock of the wall clock returned to comfort him.

He felt as if he had just awoken from a long sleep, but in reality he had been 'away' for no more than a few minutes.

So where was this secluded pit at which the woman had offered a libation? All he knew was that it lay somewhere deep inside a wood that exuded a distinct feeling of hopelessness and desolation. Perhaps it had been hit badly by the Great Storm of the previous year. During the early hours of Friday, 16 October 1987, the southern counties of England had been devastated by their first hurricane since 1703. Tropical winds gusting up to speeds in excess of 110mph had torn through the southern counties, ripping out countless millions of trees and leaving a trail of death and destruction in their wake. No one living today had experienced winds like these before in Britain; even more curious had been the gradual realisation that over the night of the Great Storm sensitive individuals across the country had experienced hideous nightmares and waking visions concerning frightful wolves, crone-like hags and a form of Hekate – the classical dark goddess – known as Lykaina, the she-wolf.

It had then become blatantly clear that the Black Alchemist was connected with the hurricane winds and had utilised them as part of his own diabolic mission. To achieve this form of desolation magic he had employed the services of the woman that Bernard and Andrew referred to as the Black Sorceress of Arundel, BSA for short. She, they discovered, was almost certainly the priestess of a sinister Sussex-based group known as the Friends of Hekate.

All this had happened nearly ten months ago, and now BSA had returned to haunt his visions again. She was up to no good, he could sense it, but even more disturbing was his belief that this current flurry of activity in the Sussex area was the culmination of a series of rituals the Black Alchemist had been conducting since the time of the Great Storm. For what ultimate purpose, he did not wish to know.

Friday, 5 August. I needed to speak with Bernard. So much was happening in the minds of those around me to confirm the re-emergence of the Black Alchemist, that I just had to break my silence and tell him the bad news. The strangest thing of all was that much of this visionary information was coming from individuals who did not usually experience this sort of thing, including one person I hardly even knew.

Entering the front room of my flat, in the Essex town of Leigh-on-Sea, I removed the receiver and dialled his number. His voice answered after just a couple of rings. I told him about the recent rise in psychic experiences.

'Well, before you say anything, I've got a few things scribbled down here,' he announced, before I began babbling on too much.

I allowed him to continue as it was imperative that, as the principal psychic involved, any new information he could offer should not be tainted by the imagery and impressions of others.

'I saw a woman in black about to pour a bowl of golden liquid into a purposely dug pit in a secluded clearing,' he revealed, in his usual matter-of-fact way.

Oh my God, I needed a pen. This was incredible – a teenager named Richard Davey who worked at the offices of *Psychic News*, Britain's premier Spiritualist newspaper, had experienced an extraordinary dream involving almost identical imagery just days ago; he felt it was BSA.

'I'd agree, definitely.'

Swinging around to find a pen, I became entangled in the extension lead and fell hopelessly to the floor, the telephone ringing out my plight as it too crashed to the ground. Still holding the receiver, I sat up and saw I had wrenched the wires right out of the wall! Bernard had gone and it was going to take a British Telecom engineer to fix this lot!

So, to a call box, and quick.

From the red-framed phone box two streets away, I redialled Bernard's number and embarrassedly described what had happened. I tried to explain how his words had so staggered me that I had lost my sense of balance!

Jovialities over, I scribbled down the precise contents of the previous night's clairvoyant session in the back of my diary. The similarity between what Bernard had seen in vision and what Richard had witnessed in a dreamstate during the night of Wednesday, 27 July was quite extraordinary. It had begun with the vision of a beautiful woman with long, dark hair perched on the side of a bed, dressed only in black satin lingerie. Instinctively he had known that despite her seductive, serene beauty an old crone of 'great evil' was working through her body. He could recognise it in her mocking eyes.

The setting then changed. Now Richard could see the same woman dressed in a black cowled robe standing over a small pit in a wooded clearing. She began to pour a golden liquid into the hole, not from a stone bowl as Bernard had described, but from a much taller jug of some kind. Here Richard's dream ended, but remaining in his mind was the overwhelming feeling that this woman was attempting to trick someone and that the ritualistic event he had witnessed would culminate on Monday, 8 August – a date that made little sense to him.

Richard possessed very little knowledge of the Black Alchemist affair and it was only after he had felt compelled to convey details of the dream to his work colleague, my close friend Caroline Wise, that it had been brought to my attention. Caroline and Richard were, like Bernard, convinced that this woman was BSA, the Black Sorceress of Arundel.

The same night that Richard experienced his dream, Toyne Newton – author of *The Demonic Connection*, the first book to highlight the clandestine activities of the Friends of Hekate – also experienced a quite extraordinary dream sequence. He had found himself in a long dark corridor being approached by a black-cowled figure holding aloft a long black baton. This was brought down upon Toyne's head and when just inches away from his scalp the dark figure disappeared.

The whole sequence repeated itself twice more, with the baton being lowered closer and closer to his scalp on each occasion. Toyne finally awoke in a hot sweat and knew instinctively that the robed figure of his dream was the Black Alchemist. Never before had he experienced a nightmare that created so much fear within him.

Without any knowledge of the above nocturnal experiences, a sixteen-year-old girl named Fiona, who lived in the flat directly below me, dreamt of three dark figures conducting a sinister ritualistic act on a darkened mound. Behind it a fire blazed fiercely and from the shadows she could see the edge of a field lying in front of woods. Unaware of the Paradise Mound material, she had immediately connected this scenario with the Black Alchemist, feeling he was preparing the tumulus for an event of great importance. The vivid nocturnal imagery unnerved her greatly, and a few days later she produced a page of inspired impressions on the apparent meaning of her dream. She too was now speaking of 'white fire' and a 'ring of white fire' connected with an artefact that sounded dangerously like the ancient spear glimpsed in vision by Bernard.

Could I conclude that she too had viewed the Paradise Mound during her troubled slumber?

Perhaps. More importantly both Bernard and Fiona appeared to echo material contained in an obscure treatise entitled the *Chaldean Oracles*. This important magical text of the second century AD, Neo-Platonist school outlines the potency of psychic communication and oracular divination with the deities and 'daimons' of ancient Chaldean tradition. Hekate plays a major role in these fragments, and one section refers to the imagery that a magician (the so-called 'theurgist') can expect from conducting rites to Hekate in association with the astrological sign of Leo, the 'House of the Sun', i.e. during August. It speaks of 'a Fire like unto a child', as well as a 'Formless Fire, from which a Voice rushes forth' and 'a child of fire'.[1] It goes on to add: 'But when you see the formless and very holy Fire radiantly leaping up throughout the depths of the whole world; hear the Voice of Fire.'[2] Could BA and his cronies be using the *Chaldean Oracles* to manifest some form of 'child of fire' in the 'life-generating womb'[3] of the Chaldean Hekate?

'I don't know,' Bernard admitted. 'I don't even want to think about it.'

I could have gone on to describe even more dreams and even more visions, but all these experiences had just two things in common – the Black Alchemist and a coming ritualistic event of immense importance.

'They can't all be wrong, can they?' he suggested, light-heartedly.

OK, so if we assumed that something *was* going to take place at the Paradise Mound, then what about BSA's apparent libation ceremony in the secluded clearing; what could he tell me about that?

'There was definitely a sense of chaos and destruction around, so I suspect it was somewhere hit badly by the Great Storm, somewhere like Clapham Woods, perhaps.'

Clapham Woods. Of course . . .

Reaching home, I entered the front room and made directly for my well-thumbed copy of Toyne Newton's book *The Demonic Connection*, first published in 1987. Slipping it out of the bookcase, I turned to the chapters on Clapham Woods as I padded through to the kitchen and flicked on the kettle.

My first encounter with the mysterious Clapham Woods in West Sussex was as a young UFO investigator in 1976. For some years this vast area of dense woodland had become associated with accounts of unidentified aerial lights being seen in the area as well as stories concerning the mysterious disappearance of local dogs. I had compiled a lengthy report for a national UFO organisation and there the matter had rested.

After the UFOs departed in the late 1970s other strange rumours began to circulate. Word went around that Clapham Woods were being used for obscene black magic rites. Animal sacrifices were being offered up to sanguine goddesses of the night. Mysterious deaths were also reported in the area, leading some to talk of kidnap and ritual murder.

These groundless claims were later dispelled, but Toyne Newton and his colleague Charles Walker began to accumulate a core of indisputable evidence which firmly suggested that the woods at Clapham, as well as other local ancient sites, were being worked by a shadowy group of individuals known as the Friends of Hekate. One night in 1978 Charles went to Clapham Woods and met two of its alleged members under quite unnerving circumstances, following an anonymous telephone call. Prompted by this clandestine meeting, Charles illegally entered a disused farm building bordering the entrance to the woods and chanced upon an enormous demonic mural depicting a hideous half-woman, half-demon engulfed in lapping flames and holding aloft a Catholic orb.

Further anonymous correspondence addressed to Toyne Newton suggested that the Friends of Hekate were merely a single cell in a much larger operation, located in the south of England and co-ordinated by figures living in London. The letter writer claimed there were other Hekate-style groups in places such as Avebury in Wiltshire and Winchester in Hampshire.

In October 1986 Bernard was psychically informed that some of the people now working with the Black Alchemist were associated with a place named 'Clapham' in Sussex. Even though he had never heard of Clapham Woods, or their reputation, his psychic description of the locality was uncannily accurate. After contacting Toyne and Charles in January 1988 I had come to the conclusion that the Black Alchemist was closely associated with members of the Friends of Hekate. We also realised that the dark-haired woman Bernard had seen in vision alongside BA from October 1987 onwards – and who seemed to have firm links with Arundel, just five miles west of Clapham – fitted the description of the Hekate group's high priestess.

Despite the mounting evidence for the involvement of the Friends of Hekate in the Black Alchemist's affairs, there were also growing indications that the group had now split up – probably as a result of the adverse publicity Clapham Woods had received in recent years. If this was so – and Bernard and I firmly believed it to be the case – then we could only assume that the priestess of Hekate had gone on to forge new allegiances, leaving the group to reform under another name elsewhere in the country.

Bernard's assumption that the ritual pit was in Clapham did make complete sense, however, despite the fact that vast areas of the woodland had been razed to the ground during the Great Storm. Pits were a subject already familiar to Clapham's twisted history, for the dense woods contained a large sunken pit, known only to a few, and reputed to be the burial site of Clapham's plague victims following the Black Death of 1348.[4] There is no historical verification of this chilling legend, although it is clear that the village did once support a thriving medieval community that dwindled over the centuries until Clapham became just a few scattered houses and a neglected church.

Although obviously too large to have been the ritual pit seen psychically by both Bernard and Richard, I recalled something of importance Toyne had written in connection with its presence in the woods.

Pouring boiling water on to Earl Grey tea bags, I abandoned the steaming teapot to continue the search for the chapter in question. Eventually I found it. Under the title 'Hecate, Goddess

THE FOUL PIT

of the Underworld', Toyne details an ancient Greek rite to gain the favour of the dark goddess. It reads:

> Apollonius Rhodius described in the *Argonautica* how Aeson's son, Jason, consulted Medea, 'a maiden that uses sorcery under the guidance of Hecate', who advised him that to enlist Hecate's aid he must go alone at night 'clad in dusky raiment' after washing in a river, and dig a rounded pit ('Over the graves of the dead', though this translation does not specifically mention this) in which he had built a fire and slay a sheep to propitiate 'only-begotten Hecate', leaving for her an offering of 'the hive-stored labour of bees'.[5]

I smiled in satisfaction. Neither Bernard nor Richard owned a copy of *The Demonic Connection*, and unless I was grossly mistaken, there seemed to be good reason to suggest that both psychics had glimpsed BSA, an apparent devotee of Hekate, enlisting the aid of the goddess of the underworld by using a purpose-dug pit. The 'hive-stored labour of bees' had to be a reference to honey, or perhaps royal jelly, which could both be described as the golden liquid featured in the libation ceremony. There was no way of telling whether the small pit they saw was actually located 'over the graves of the dead', but if it *was* in the vicinity of the great pit in Clapham Woods, then it would satisfy this condition.

Closing the hardback book, I stared out at the gardens and rear walls of the houses opposite. It all seemed to indicate that BSA had conducted a libation ceremony to Hekate in preparation for an intended ritual to culminate the sequence of events begun during the Great Storm over nine months before. On Thursday, 5 November 1987 Bernard and I had discovered an ebony dagger speared into an animal heart and concealed in Danbury churchyard. It had been placed among the upturned roots of the old horse-chestnut tree pulled down during the hurricane. Psychic information suggested it had been ritually placed there by two men in order to 'gestate' some form of 'black life' in the womb of Hekate until its intended birth ten months later, giving a date of around this time. So, if correct, then what the hell were they attempting to bring into manifestation?

The only clue was Richard's belief that what he saw would culminate on 8 August, just three days away. Others had also referred to this date and numerically speaking it was important since it contained the number eight no less than four times. Everyone knows that 666 is considered to be the number of the Great Beast or Antichrist, as recorded in St John's Book of Revelation. Yet this rendering of 666 is inaccurate, for in the ancient Hebrew system of numerology known as gematria this figure possesses a value denoting any solar messiah, whether Christ or Antichrist. What's more, the number 888 possesses very similar connotations; indeed, the two numbers are virtually interchangeable.

I already knew of active 'white' occultists who intended to capitalise on the believed magical potency of 8 August 1988 and were planning their own rites and rituals to herald in a new age on this date. God only knew what sort of repercussions this would create.

Our limited information could only allow us a vague glimmer of what might really take place in association with the eighth day of the eighth month of 1988. Evidence now suggested, however, that BSA would be in Clapham Woods on or before this date and that BA had prepared the Paradise Mound for a major ritual to coincide with her actions.

My mind was already made up. I was going to East Sussex this coming weekend and that was final. But where was I to go?

I contemplated the options. Because I had never visited the secluded 'plague' pit in the heart of Clapham Woods, and Toyne had already decided against any active involvement in this affair, staking ourselves out below the Paradise Mound seemed the best plan of action. If so, then when exactly? In some magical traditions a day begins and ends at sunset, suggesting that any ritualistic event could commence soon after sunset on Sunday, 7 August, giving us just forty-eight hours to prepare.

For over three years I had waited for a chance to come face to face with the Black Alchemist and his cronies and now it looked even more likely than ever before.

3
The Voice of Fire

Saturday, 6 August 1988. Once his wife had retired to bed, Bernard slipped into the dining room and readied himself for a further attempt at attuning to the ritual pit viewed on Thursday evening.

Andrew had pressed him to try and see if he could pin down its exact location, for although he had suggested Clapham Woods, he was still unsure if this was correct.

Removing his glasses, he rested his elbows on the polished surface of the table and directed his thoughts towards the same image of the secluded clearing.

It takes a good deal of concentration to link in mind with places and this he could only do late at night. The absence of distractions made it that much easier; it allowed him to seek out and hold the imagery and impressions.

So far he could see only silhouetted trees picked out from the gloom of a dense woodland. Moments passed and then he noticed a figure standing alone in the darkness. Zooming in, he realised it was the Black Alchemist, poised motionless, wearing the same thick robe he had worn upon the Paradise Mound. This time there were no daggers and no small child, and he appeared to be in deep contemplation.

Where was he now?

There was no answer.

Slowly the vision faded to leave only further darkness, until another clear image replaced it. He saw an unblemished, razor-sharp lance with a long blade. It was almost certainly the same power object he had glimpsed before, but this time it appeared infinitely more potent. Why, he could not be sure.

Then he could see the clearing with its ritual pit, but there was no one there, only fire, and the overwhelming feeling that this site was definitely being prepared for a major rite of some kind.

'*I, by my power, turning air into water, and water again into blood,*' a low menacing voice began.

It was *him*, he was sure.

'*. . . and solidifying it into flesh to form a new human creature – a boy – and produce a much nobler work than God – the so-named creator. For He made man from the earth, but I from the air, a much more difficult matter.*'

Then came only silence.

Momentarily, Bernard snapped out of his concentration. He had heard enough. This was disgusting stuff.

He lit a cigarette, convinced these were the same words spoken when he had attuned to the pit on Thursday evening; but on that occasion they had been too distant to make out. Now they were clearly audible, as if growing in strength. They were *his* words – the very thoughts of the Black Alchemist. Who in God's name did he think he was?

The thought angered him.

He gave it a while before trying again. Perhaps this time he would get more sense.

As he allowed his mind to wander, an image came into view which he held and enhanced. It was the figure of a hunched old man in a tattered grey robe, with long straggly hair and a beard, leaning on a carved walking stick. It was daylight and he seemed to be standing in a damp marshy area surrounded by woodland.

The old man gave no name, but he sensed he was a spirit guardian connected with the energies of the Paradise Mound.

'The ritual has to be done with a fire,' the old grey figure informed him.

He was referring to the Black Alchemist's intended plans; he felt sure of it.

The astral guardian began slowly to shake his head as if in complete resignation. 'It will not come to fruition. It was thought to be the only way to bring forth a demon to oppose the good and change the world,' he revealed, before slowly fading from view.

For five long minutes Bernard waited for anything more to occur, but this time he was greeted with only a calm silence.

No, sorry, there *was* something else – the strong impression of a connection between what was to occur at the Paradise Mound and the country of France. It seemed there was a French group linked directly with the Black Alchemist's activities, although who or why he did not know.

'*The wanderers are on the move*,' a melodic female voice finally proclaimed. '*The wolves cry to the night. Dark forces tear at the threads.*'

'The threads' was an Anglo-Saxon term describing the Web of Wyrd – the subtle energy matrix believed to permeate all living things. It bound together the world in a web of sublime destiny woven by the three sisters of Wyrd.

Frowning to himself, Bernard closed the intense meditation and went to make a cup of coffee. It was eleven o' clock, meaning that he had been sitting at the table for nearly an hour. The results had, as always, posed more questions than answers. However, the strength with which the information was forming in his mind convinced him even further that something major was about to occur – some kind of symbolic birth involving wolves, white fire and a blackened child brought into being through highly suspect magical activity at more than one location in Sussex. Its exact nature was beyond him, although he was certain it included the culmination of the Hekate rite glimpsed at the ritual pit and a separate ceremonial event at or close to the Paradise Mound.

What concerned him more was the thought of Andrew and his friends out there in the darkness eagerly awaiting the moment when they could leap out and shake hands with the Black Alchemist. He understood the researcher's often blind enthusiasm to try and confirm every last piece of psychic information, but whatever was currently taking place in Sussex was serious business to someone and any unwanted interference was not going to be treated very kindly. For the moment all he could do was ring him and advise extreme caution, otherwise somebody might well get hurt.

4
Paradise Lost

Sunday, 7 August 1988. Crouching down behind a thick clump of bushes, I peered through the matted web of undergrowth at the Paradise Mound, situated some thirty yards away. It was a warm, clear August evening and already the gnats and mosquitos were beginning to annoy me – and it was still only nine o'clock! The sun had set at last and so, if I had been correct in my assumption about the day beginning at sunset, we could expect company soon.

With me on the edge of the grassy slope were two members of the Earthquest group I ran in Leigh-on-Sea. One was likely lad Mike Oliver, a hefty, robust figure who enjoyed nightlife entertainment just as much as he did the mysteries of life. The other was Paul Weston, a tall, cultured man in his late twenties who was a walking encyclopaedia on all aspects of the occult. Both were well versed in the Black Alchemist affair and formed part of my inner questing group.

A fourth member of the party, long-time friend and earth mysteries' researcher Johnny Merron, had returned to Eastbourne to meet others who were arriving by car at around this very time.

Bernard's psychic session the previous night had finally convinced me that we had chosen the right location. Toyne Newton and Charles Walker had been notified of the suspected activity planned for Clapham Woods and had agreed to watch the area throughout the weekend, yet without knowing exactly where BSA had conducted her ritual libation to Hekate there was little else anyone could do.

I accepted Bernard's words of caution. We would be careful to protect ourselves not just on a physical level, but on a more subtle magical level as well. There were various meditations that could be done to strengthen the body's vital energies. Such visualisation exercises could be achieved either by forming a cone of light around the group or by seeing the body as an empty vessel and then filling it full of vibrant light. Should any problems arise then there were different forms of ritual banishment that could be conducted to alleviate awkward situations, and these Bernard and I had been forced to use on more than one occasion during the three-year Black Alchemist affair.

The Paradise Mound was an ideal location for anyone conducting magical activities, for although it looked out over Eastbourne, it was almost totally inaccessible. After parking the car in a closed road, anyone attempting to reach here had a forty-five to fifty minute uphill trek through dense woodland littered with trees razed during the Great Storm. All previous paths were now blocked, making navigation that much more difficult. Approaching from the base of the slope was an even more arduous task, due to the climb involved and the lack of access points from the housing estates on the edge of Eastbourne. What's more, the nondescript nature of the well-worn tumulus probably meant that very few local residents were even aware of its existence.

In the woods some ten yards behind the Iron Age burial mound we had discovered traces of a fire pit surrounded by a ring of scorched stones. This, of course, could have been the work of anyone, some innocent pagan group perhaps who knew the work of Gerald Gardner, the founder of the modern witchcraft revival in the 1950s, who wrote of the importance of Paradise place-names. He suggested they were sites of pre-Christian worship situated on prominent hills overlooking a town or settlement.

Fire pits were evidence of nothing, so all we could do was stake out the mound and watch to see if anything happened. Our task here was not so much to prevent or stop what might or might not occur, but to confirm the words of a psychic; nothing more. Unfortunately Bernard had declined the opportunity to attend this outing, a decision I respected. In his own words, he will never follow up his own psychic material unless an inner voice tells him to do so, which is not very often. Yet he was not going to get away with it scot-free, as I had asked him to spend the entire evening periodically attuning to our presence here at the mound. I had managed to borrow a Vodaphone for the occasion, so intended keeping in touch with him throughout the night.

'When are the others arriving?' Paul enquired in a low voice, sitting cross-legged next to Mike, who was cracking open a can of lager. 'If they don't arrive within the next half hour they'll be climbing the hill in the darkness.'

Johnny Merron would know where to go, I was sure of that.

Conversation died for a few minutes as the three unlikely figures sat quietly inside their chosen clump of brambles waiting for some kind of movement.

'Hold on,' Paul suddenly whispered, hesitantly rising to his feet and staring towards the mound. 'Who's that?'

No wild excitement followed our acknowledgement of a figure emerging into view from a minor path some yards to the left of the mound.

It was a man – five feet two to five feet three – walking briskly past the mound. He looked about fifty, was of medium build and had swept-back, receding grey hair. He wore a grey-patterned, sleeveless jumper, a blue shirt and beige slacks.

His presence seemed completely out of character with the environment and his pace was quite unusual. Despite our isolated position he appeared as if he was rushing to catch the morning train.

The unexpected visitor marched past our position, glancing from left to right as if looking for something or someone, before heading off in a northerly direction. The only possible reason for taking this course was to make the climb towards the ridge of the South Downs, a pastime usually only reserved for confirmed hikers.

His image receded as he maintained the same fast pace along the side of the woods and continued to glance from left to right as he went.

I needed to know more, so quickly emerged from the cover of the bush with Mike and Paul close behind. He had not seen us and was presumably unaware of our presence. Even now, as we watched him disappear from view, he appeared to be totally preoccupied by his route march.

And then he turned . . .

Shit. He had seen us, standing there like lemons watching him move out of sight.

'Oh well, if he's some sort of scout making sure the coast is clear, then we've blown it now,' Mike admitted, turning to me with a smile on his face.

Still we watched the lone figure. Hold on, what was this? Instead of continuing on towards the South Downs he had unexpectedly re-entered the woodland some 200 yards from where we stood. This could only mean that he was retracing his steps through the woods to where my car was parked.

Curious.

The incident over, we retired to the confines of our bramble bushes.

'Something definitely odd about him, though,' Paul admitted, mulling over the man's appearance and actions. 'I mean, we've been up here for over two hours and seen no one else at all. Then, shortly after sunset, someone marches past as if they're in a great hurry.'

Seating himself on the blanket, Mike swigged from the can. 'I must admit, he did seem to be looking for something.'

I gave out a long sigh as I too dropped to the ground and reached for a beer. Perhaps we really had buggered it up. We should have been more covert, more cautious in our actions. On the other hand, he could have been anyone. He certainly didn't match Bernard's description of the Black Alchemist, who was apparently quite tall, thin faced and in his mid-forties. The alchemist's eccentric, university-style dress sense did, however, match the clothes worn by the man we had just seen.

Still, maybe we would never know the truth of the matter. All we could do now was sit and wait; see what happened next.

Bernard drew his eyes away from the television standing in the corner of the front room. A strong urge told him to retire into the dining room and meditate for a few minutes as something was wrong. Picking up his cigarettes he made his excuses and passed through the hallway.

Having sat himself down he quickly visualised the Paradise

Mound and attempted to pinpoint the whereabouts of Andrew and his friends.

As before he saw plenty of trees, but after a moment these gave way to the sight of a track leading to the road below. Here he could see two cars, one belonging to Andrew and another unfamiliar to him.

There was a rising uneasiness about this view, he realised with a low sigh. Somebody else was around; he could sense an encroachment. A man, some kind of scout, was surveying the whole area, making sure the coast was clear. He would give Andrew a ring to let him know.

Concentrating on the mental image of the vague figure moving through the trees, he glimpsed more – a dog or hound, bounding about. Perhaps it was a man out walking his dog. It would make a perfect cover, he concluded.

No more came to him so he scribbled down a few notes before dialling the number of the mobile telephone given to him by Andrew the previous night.

I was still on the telephone to Bernard when Johnny Merron turned up with Caroline Wise, a leading supporter of psychic questing; Richard Davey, the young psychic from London; Dave Rankine, a practising occultist, and his pleasant girlfriend Helen. Dave, Caroline said, was currently engaged in a series of ritual workings featuring certain aspects of the goddess Hekate. Over the past few days he had received an uncharacteristic psychic discourse from the Mistress of the Underworld which he had felt compelled to relate to Caroline earlier that day. The extraordinary nature and vivid detail of these messages matched, almost word for word, my assessment of the current situation conveyed by telephone to Caroline only the night before. She felt convinced these messages related directly to the matter at hand, so on impulse she had asked Dave and Helen to join us tonight.

Bernard said we should be on the look-out for a lone figure, a scout, making sure the woods and mound were free from interference. He had no qualms about accepting that the character we had encountered earlier was the man in question. We thought as much, and now it was becoming blatantly clear that we really had blown it. One other interesting point he made concerned the two cars clairvoyantly pictured at the entrance to the woods. Had he psychically glimpsed the lone scout's vehicle? Or did he just see Johnny Merron's car? Either way, he strongly advised checking the vehicles when we returned in the morning.

Gradually the twilight faded, allowing the low tumulus to take on a completely new aspect – one offering us some form of magical protection from possible outside influences. Already Dave Rankine was beginning to feel the brooding presence of unseen forces and Richard Davey could clearly sense the proximity of impending danger. Whether imagination or not, we all felt a dramatic change in the atmosphere, as if a bubble were about to burst; the sensation was both electric and disconcerting for those present.

A decision had to be made. Everyone was to assemble on the top of the mound and form a circle. In meditation we would visualise a cone of blue-white light building around us and then stay there until the uncertain atmosphere had finally lifted.

So we gathered, magical instruments of protection at the ready. Dave and Helen stood side by side. Caroline was helped up by Johnny and the two readied themselves. Paul waited in bemused anticipation of what might happen next. Mike stubbed out his cigarette butt as I took up a position in the centre of the small tumulus and plunged the tip of the Indian sword-stick into the hard earth.

In the deathly silence of the warm, still night the circle of seven linked hands and prepared themselves in mind. Kneeling in the middle I visualised fiery spokes of vibrant light pulsing into the ground beneath our feet. Slowly, a spiralling cone of electric-blue light rose up and came together above our heads.

Each person followed the verbal commands and pictured the imagery as best they could. The cone of power became the extent of our magical wall of protection, outside which was the domain of the unknown, the etheric void, and with this understanding we waited for the unseen psychic danger to pass.

Richard was the first to flinch. 'There's something out there, moving closer, circling the mound,' he exclaimed, sounding a little agitated.

Others wanted to know what he could see.

'It's an animal, and it's moving towards us.'

'I see it now,' another male voice announced. 'It's a wolf.'

'A white wolf with glowing red eyes,' Richard corrected him, his hands beginning to shake. 'Its eyes are like glowing embers and it's staring straight at us.'

I told the group not to break the circle on any account and just keep visualising the cone of power. It was only a created thought form, a condensed psychic energy, gathered together by occult processes and seen clearly by sensitives such as Richard.

'Yes, I see it too,' Dave said, 'but to me it is the Cerberus, the three-headed demon hound of Hades, the familiar of Hekate.'

Clairvoyantly, Richard saw the phantom beast circle again and again. 'It's advancing towards the circle.' The intense movement in his hands showed he was close to panicking, but somehow he managed to keep his cool.

It was important that everyone kept as calm as possible.

'Quickly, do something, it's almost upon us,' he suddenly exclaimed. 'IT'S HERE, *NOW!*'

'I'll banish it in the name of Hekate,' Dave responded sensibly from the opposite side of the circle. Hounds and wolves are animals sacred to Hekate in Greek magical tradition, so can be banished in her name.

The spectral white wolf sprang into the air and, just inches from the circle, vanished in mid-flight.

'It's gone,' Richard sighed. 'That scared the living daylights out of me. I really thought it was going to break the circle.'

There were more wolves now, in the minds of other members of the assembled group. Like silhouettes stalking, encroaching, moving in closer – even I could perceive them in the mind's eye.

Another bounded forward and tried to break the circle, but as it neared the etheric light of our wall of energy, the spectre simply evaporated into darkness. Others attempted a similar trick, but none was successful in breaking our ring of protection.

Something was happening here; something beyond the norm. It was as if an external influence was using the wolfish imagery, as a vehicle of Hekate, to break our confidence and force us to move on. So was this the work of the Black Alchemist? Or was it simply the product of our own imaginations?

Time passed slowly as we waited for the psychic prowlers to

subside and leave us in peace, and then the telephone rang. Shit, I'd left it with our other belongings over by the bushes.

Rushing across I picked up the Vodaphone, pressed SEND and held it against my ear.

'It's me,' Bernard announced in his usual light-hearted manner. 'Been buggering around with the sword-stick on the mound, have you?'

I admitted we had. Why, what could he see?

'A fiery wheel of light around the mound. Figures in a circle. Plenty of light and encroachments.'

There had been several of these. It seemed Bernard could see clairvoyantly what we were only visualising with our minds. I took him across to the darkened mound, where the others quickly strengthened the circle of protection.

With the mobile telephone in one hand and the sword-stick in the other, the visualisation continued. I asked Bernard if he would attune to the mound whilst we acted as a beacon of living energy to direct his focus.

Agreeing, he fell silent for a few brief seconds before saying: 'I can still see the mound.'

Anything else?

Only silence came as a response.

The rest of the group waited in eager anticipation of what he might have to say next.

Bowing his head, Bernard, at home in Essex, searched the Eastbourne district looking for clear answers. Almost immediately he sensed a flurry of mental activity as if Andrew's presence at the Paradise Mound was being hastily debated by those involved with the ritualistic event planned for that night.

He relayed his feelings across the satellite link before breaking away to concentrate again.

He could sense more – feelings of anger, frustration even, as if the ritual could no longer take place. Bernard had not been surprised to hear that those on the Paradise Mound had repeatedly suffered problems from silhouetted wolfish thought forms. Someone wanted them to move away from the location and was using psychic attack to ensure this took place.

He had glimpsed a canine presence earlier. This, he now

realised, made complete sense of the cryptic psychic statement about 'The wanderers are on the move and the wolves cry to the night'. Hounds and wolves reflected the base energy these people were attempting to use in conjunction with a spear and 'white fire' to create 'black life', which he now believed was a supernatural entity of unimaginable potential. Yet this monstrosity went far beyond any title or description, for it would not be incarnated, but given life upon some astral domain.

In his mind's eye he could make out new imagery now. There was a large room, a small hall perhaps, either standing on its own or connected to a much larger country house.

A woman dressed in a long black cape, its hood resting on her shoulders, read from a rolled parchment or manuscript in between chanting tonal noises in a strained guttural fashion.

Sitting on dark wooden benches facing towards her was an assembly of some six to eight people, each normally attired and droning in accompaniment to some sort of organ music pumping out of a stereo cassette recorder!

The woman in black was *her*, the Black Sorceress of Arundel. He recognised her shoulder-length dark hair, her long, stern face and those piercing brown eyes. She matched the composite picture constructed over the months from the various dreams and visions in which she had featured.

Who were these people, anyway, and what were they trying to achieve?

They were tormenting them into leaving the Paradise Mound, was the only reply. Almost without realising the implications or consequences, Andrew was putting a major spanner in the works of a premeditated series of ritualistic events which should have culminated tonight. He had also been right about the Black Alchemist utilising the numerological significance of the eighth day of the eighth month of the eighty-eighth year; dates mean a lot to these people.

The ritual was off! This was the overriding feeling emanating from the group gathered in the small hall. It would not take place tonight, not here at least. And if not tonight, when next would they try? For although their plans had been spoiled, the symbolic creation of the Unborn One would still be attempted at some future date, and when it happened Bernard would know how to respond.

These words the psychic conveyed across the Vodaphone link to Andrew and his friends still standing on the Paradise Mound. Their circle of protection had held up well; they would get no more trouble tonight.

The intense meditation ended as tiredness took over and each person withdrew to the cover of the black clump of brambles some yards below the tumulus. Cigarettes were lit constantly in the hope that their heat would offer some warmth, and finally the sleeping bags were unrolled as the need for rest gradually overcame the group. Utter stillness quickly fell on the motley crew of exhausted individuals, and those unable to achieve full slumber lay in a half-conscious, hypnagogic state as their bodies fought off the cold night air.

In the uneasy stillness more than one person became vaguely aware that the night was taking shape and moving like a column of dense smoke towards the scattered group.

In slow motion it twisted and turned until it finally formed the distinctive shape of a tall cowled figure advancing at a steady pace. Its archetypal appearance required no identification. Thoughts of the Black Alchemist had allowed this bilious manifestation to exist and now it was moving among the vulnerable dreamers who were no longer within the light of protection.

No more than two feet away from Dave Rankine, the moving shadow ceased its pace and raised up a long black baton, a swordstick perhaps, which was slowly lowered towards his head. The modern-day occultist used the power of the mind to push away and dissipate the amorphous mass. The cowled spectre vanished and sanctuary fell upon the cocooned bodies until the threat of further torment was removed by the welcome approach of dawn.

5
Forbidden Fruit

Sunday, 30 October 1988. Bernard had woken up in an unknown place that smelt damp and exuded a feeling of abandonment.

He could not remember how he came to be here. Had he been kidnapped?

He seemed to be in the entrance hall of an old dilapidated house which was surely no one's home.

A staircase. There was an old wooden staircase before him. Perhaps he should climb it.

Almost involuntarily, he found himself ascending the abandoned stairs, the bare floorboards creaking underfoot.

Raising his head, he followed the banister rail and finally reached the first floor landing. Turning left, he saw only panelled doors leading into unknown rooms.

Where was he to go from here?

Pieces of discarded paper littered the grimy floor, while old paint pots and stacked wood lined the edges of walls.

Moving across to a room on the left-hand side, Bernard reached towards the door handle, only to find it slowly opening of its own accord.

From behind the bedroom door a beautiful woman walked into view. At around five-feet five, with brown eyes, shoulder-length dark hair, pale skin and sporting a blue dress suit with a white blouse open to reveal her neckline, there was no mistaking her identity – it was *her*, BSA, the priestess of Hekate. But she did not pose a threat, not this time, for it was she who had brought him here to make a gesture of respect to an equal and opposite.

Their eyes met and locked, merging together the two minds, and then he knew this was a farewell message. The Black Alchemist was leaving the country and going abroad. BSA would also disappear to escape the inevitable witch-hunt that would follow the imminent publication of Andrew's book.

Without fear, he felt an instant and quite overwhelming physical attraction towards this woman, and, following a moment of hesitation, she embraced him and their lips met.

Bernard sighed and awoke suddenly from the vivid dream about the woman in a derelict house. What the hell was she doing? Why had he been drawn to this abysmal place and why had she kissed him? It made no sense, yet the emotions felt during that moment of unexpected passion remained, and throwing caution to the wind he tried immediately to return to a state of slumber!

Flashes of mundane imagery gave way to a familiar sensation of rising out of his body and moving rapidly back to the same location. That overbearing sense of disuse and mustiness was still present, but this time it seemed unimportant.

Voluntarily, he climbed the rickety stairs to reach the chaotic landing. Where was she? Would she still be waiting for him? He needed to see her – find out who she was, this woman of his nightmares, and his dreams.

Reaching the same closed door he searched for her presence, but the place was empty.

'Where are you?' he called out. *'Where are you?'*

She was not there.

'What's your name?' He shouted to each of the four walls, their paper tattered and hanging loose in great triangular slithers.

'What's your name?'

He needed to know.

'What's your name?' He would not move until he found out her name.

'Rachel,' a female voice revealed out of nowhere.

'Rachel what? You must have a surname.'

He swivelled around looking for an answer.

'Goodison,' was the final response.

Monday, 7 November. Most of The Griffin's early evening clientele – such as the overly loud party of businessmen in the corner – were destined to move into the adjoining restaurant for a high-class meal amid genuine Tudor decor by an open-hearth fire. Hopefully, this particular group would be heading that way pretty soon.

Bernard sipped his glass of draught Guinness and stared across at the source of constant bellowing laughter. 'Anyway, so that's it. Her name appears to be Rachel Goodison,' he concluded, lighting up a cigarette.

I listened to the full version of his quite extraordinary derelict-house dream. Its briefest detail had been conveyed to me by telephone during the evening of Monday, 31 October as myself and various colleagues waited inside this very bar, our cars ready outside with full tanks of petrol. Following an uneventful Hallowe'en, I had set to work immediately. How many Rachel Goodisons could there be in this world? And what about the spelling, was it Goodison, Gooderson or possibly even Goodson? Plumping for Goodison, I scanned the West Sussex telephone directory and made a note of several entries. After various telephone calls it appeared that none of the Goodisons of Arundel knew a Rachel Goodison.

To be honest, we had no real idea where 'Rachel Goodison' actually lived or worked, making it extremely difficult to know even how to begin tracking her down. On top of all this, it could simply be a pseudonym or, worse still, BSA was deliberately trying to trick us into believing her name was Rachel Goodison.

Infinitely more important at the present time was the purpose of this clearly motivated dream sequence. How could it be interpreted? Where, if anywhere at all, was this derelict house and what did it mean to Bernard?

Before going any further, I asked him whether he had received any further inspiration about this curious psychic scenario.

He shuffled forward and leaned on the table. 'Well, the only thing I feel is that it was more a hello than a goodbye,' he said, picking up his drink. He hesitated before revealing his true thoughts. 'I just get the feeling that at some point in the not-too-distant future she will need protection.'

Protection? Was he implying that the Black Sorceress of Arundel, this priestess of Hekate, would turn to us for help? He could not be serious, surely?

He accepted my reservations; they had been expected. 'No, I just feel that when we, erm, embraced, our minds became one for a few brief moments. From this alone I now feel that she is in some sort of danger and that we may end up helping her, that's all.'

Oh, this was becoming like some sort of bad B-movie. The hero defeats his adversary only to save his or her life in the final scene so they can live to fight another day.

'We'll have to wait and see, won't we?' he said with a wry smile.

Still, if she really did need help, then I was prepared to reach out and rescue her! Having 'Rachel' on our side would do wonders for sorting out much of Bernard's earlier psychic material. The important word here was, however, not compassion, but caution. How did he know she was not leading him into temptation?

'I don't,' he confessed.

This dream sequence had the word WARNING written above it in large neon letters. I suggested he tread very carefully indeed.

'This is obviously building towards something,' he readily admitted, 'but I don't think we'll be put in any real danger.'

I was not so sure. Since the Paradise Mound venture psychic hostility had been gradually mounting against both Bernard and myself.

Our return from Eastbourne during the morning of Monday, 8 August had been a dismal and bleak affair, with the only possible indication that others were conducting suspect ritual events that night coming from Charles Walker in Worthing. Traces of a magic circle inscribed in grass had been discovered the morning after between Clapham church and the entrance to the woods. Whether this was connected with the Black Alchemist in any way was impossible to say.

The other strange occurrence featuring the eighth day of August was the coincidental birth at 8.18pm of Princess Beatrice – the first child of Prince Andrew and the Duchess of York. Curiously enough, the next day's tabloid newspapers gave considerable space to the recurrence of the number eight in her time and date of birth. The *Sun* spoke of the 'Magic of the all-eight date', claiming it signified good fortune to the superstitious, Cantonese-speaking Chinese. The news story also spoke of doctors and nurses in Malaysia who had desperately tried to cope with the dozens of expectant mothers wanting their children born on the eighth, even if it meant inducing the birth.

None of this related directly to what the Black Alchemist may or may not have been trying to achieve on this date, but the whole general theme of good fortune and induced birth seemed pertinent to the wealth of psychic material concerning his alleged intentions.

The first apparent repercussions of our interference at the Paradise Mound came in the form of two psychic-attack-style nightmares experienced by Bernard during the night of Monday, 8 August. One involved him being thrown into a large pit in a wood (Clapham Woods again?) by four hooded figures, while in another he was hurled into a dark pool of water by the same four characters. Thankfully, these nocturnal intrusions did not continue.

Despite such unnerving incidents Bernard had remained optimistic. He was sure that the activities scheduled to have taken place on 7/8 August would still go ahead at some future date, and when they did he would accompany me to the location in question.

The astral airwaves had then remained silent for a whole week until, out of the blue, a group meditation on Sunday, 14 August had resulted in an assortment of Black Alchemist-style imagery and impressions suggesting that he and his colleagues were on the move again. These incidents culminated, without Bernard's involvement, in a car journey to a ruined chapel near Mereworth Woods in Kent, during the afternoon of Sunday, 21 August.

Our mob-handed expedition (about twelve of us went) resulted in nothing, but quite independently Bernard had contacted me the following morning to report a simple yet perplexing dream experienced overnight on Saturday, 20 August. In the darkness he could make out a group of six cowled figures sitting cross-legged around a small open fire, somewhere close to the edge of a wood. One figure identified as BSA knelt before the fire chanting barbarous names while tossing small squares of paper on to its glowing embers. As each piece burst into flame she uttered a name under her breath and the others responded by raising their hands.

With this imagery had come the distinct impression that BSA

was conducting a powerful ritual in which a demonic entity named 'Ca-ru' had been raised and despatched to Bernard. The magical act involved the use of numerology in association with his own name and colour vibration. The following day this apparent psychic attack had externalised as acute flu symptoms including giddiness, headache, nausea and a complete loss of vitality. Furthermore, he claimed his aura had become sickly yellow in colour! By mid-morning on the Monday, Bernard gave up on work and crawled back to bed after cancelling our meeting for that evening.

This brief, but vivid dream showing BSA inside a wood fitted the location in Kent visited by myself and the Earthquest team the very same day. I could understand the use of a personalised ritual involving Bernard's name and colour vibration, but the name 'Ca-ru' made only partial sense. According to Jules Garinet, a nineteenth-century French historian, Carreau was one of the many demons who plagued the afflicted nuns in the notorious 'Devils of Loudon' multiple possession case of the seventeenth century.[1] It was said that Carreau, in the absence of another demon named Baruch, had kept vigil over 'the drop of water' that bewitched the stomach of a Sister Seraphica in this most disturbing affair, which culminated in the execution of Urban Grandier, the convent's officiating priest, on 18 August 1634.[2] The date itself seemed important, for it was on the anniversary of Grandier's death in 1988 that Bernard first dreamt of BSA's invocation to Carreau; anniversaries such as this play a major role in questing lore.

Fired by Bernard's unfortunate plight, I devised an absent healing meditation in which the assumed link between Carreau and Bernard could be severed completely. With his approval, this simple exercise was conducted in the sanctity of my own home with the help of local psychic Carole Young and our mutual friend, the children's author Cara Trimarco.

Thankfully we were successful in our task and as the energies changed inside Bernard, he was 'shown' the demon Carreau. It turned out to be an unsightly entity consisting of maggot-like body sections, a round insect head, bulbous reptilian eyes, short forearms with sharp claws, and a long tail supporting powerful hind legs. He could see this hideous monster emerging from the murky depths of a mist-laden, tropical swamp filled with foul-smelling water. With this vile picture came the words: 'Carreau, bringer of grief and misery. Shows no mercy.'

Had this vision been a hallucinatory side effect of his high fever? At first I thought so, but later I was informed by London occultist Steve Wilson that he had come across a belief in Carreau among the French-speaking population in Minnesota, USA. In their folklore it was a parasitic swamp demon introduced into Indo-Chinese culture during the French occupation of Vietnam. Even more disturbing was the belief that it existed not just as an astral entity, but as an indigenous swamp monster. Carreau, Steve said, could also be found in fantasy novels by Lin Carter, who completed the best-selling Conan books after the death of their creator, Robert E. Howard.

There was too much evidence to deny the possibility that BSA had discovered Bernard's name and colour vibration and had used their antithesis to break down both his physical and psychic defences whilst invoking a parasitical swamp demon named Carreau to carry this disease to him, like a mosquito might carry malaria to its victim. Once at its target, the noxious entity attached itself to Bernard and began sucking away his life energy, a situation that eventually would have weakened him permanently.

The predominantly French nature of the Carreau manifestation had rekindled conversation concerning the possibility that BSA had roots across the English Channel in France. A previous meeting in The Griffin on Tuesday, 30 August had thrown up clear psychic impressions suggesting a link between her and a wine-producing château in the Loire Valley. All we could say with certainty was that the estate lay in a valley, close to the river, and was bordered by tall hedges and woodland. Apparently, the family in question still used a coat of arms and was linked with a small museum containing horse carriages.

Bernard regained his usual good health following the Carreau episode and life had returned to normal until early September when the roles were reversed and I suddenly found myself the focus of a strange series of events.

They began with a sequence of disconcerting dreams concerning the goddess Hekate and developed into an awareness of her growing presence *in my own home*. This situation increased to such a degree that at the stroke of midnight on Friday, 16 September I had actually conducted a magical working to invoke the favours of Hekate. For this ritual I used black and red candles, burnt an incense – made up of sickly smelling herbs, powdered human skull and droplets of my own blood – and played tracks from the second album by Gothic rock band Fields of the Nephilim! On completion I glimpsed the shadowy form of a mature woman in black, red and gold with tongues of fire lapping around her ethereal body.

Eleven o'clock that same evening Bernard had independently glimpsed an indoor ritual involving a black candle placed in a bowl of rose-coloured liquid. Next to it was a human doll – its neck, body and legs daubed in red ointment. The candle was unlit, suggesting more was to come, and accompanying this clairvoyant image was the impression that this ceremony would occur during the five dark days of the lunar cycle.

Bernard believed this dubious ritual was being directed at me by someone in the Black Alchemist camp. I tried to dismiss the thought of psychic attack, but by the time we next met on Monday, 19 September, my own aura had apparently changed from its usual golden yellow to a distinctive blood red. This signalled changes within me, he said, and probably accounted for my unprecedented Hekate invocation and the repeated acts of physical strength and uncharacteristic shows of aggression I developed during this period.[3]

Despite these disturbing incidents, my life soon returned to normal and I became totally mystified as to why I should have wanted to invoke Hekate. It was something I had never done before and will probably never do again. The possibility that I really did suffer some form of psychic attack could not be ruled out.

There the matter had rested until Bernard's dream of the derelict house and his encounter with 'Rachel Goodison'. In the wake of the apparent attempts at psychic attack, how the hell could he even think of trusting the woman?

'So you believe it could be a trick?' he asked, looking a little less confident now.

Could be! This was almost certainly a trap and unless he was careful he would fall right into it.

'Perhaps you're right,' he sighed, finishing his beer and placing down the empty glass. 'All right, I'll be careful, but I still say she will come to us in the future for some kind of help. And when she does what are we to do then?'

I shook my head and stared up at the mid-evening clientele who were now stubbing out their cigar butts and sliding off to the restaurant. He would have to promise me that he would never respond to any 'call' asking him to meet her at some lonely spot, certainly not without inviting me first!

'OK, I accept that,' he agreed.

For if he did go alone there was a very real chance that these people would make sure he was never seen alive again.

6
The Hosts of Hekate

Thursday, 10 November 1988. The keys jangled as I unlocked the flat and climbed the stairs, a tiring day of pushing copies of *The Black Alchemist* finished for a few hours at least.

Entering the kitchen, I dropped my pilot's bag on the floor and clicked on the kettle for a much needed cup of tea. 'Top of the Pops' and 'Eastenders' were on television later, so it would be an evening in, doing no more than entering a few recent invoices.

A knock at the hallway door took my attention. The thud of rising footsteps on the carpeted stairs announced the arrival of Fiona, the girl downstairs. She was a friend and had helped me to proof-read the finished manuscript in preparation for its final publication.

Fiona was also psychic and had ably shown this over the last two months with the odd snippet of information here and there. At the beginning of September she had begun to dream of Hekate, and this I had initially put down to the influences I had inadvertently drawn to the house, particularly as her bedroom was directly beneath the Black Room, my own place of meditation!

'I thought I'd come up and see you as something weird happened earlier on,' she mused in her broad Southend accent (a more abstract form of East End cockney). 'Yeah, I was watching the tele when suddenly I could see this image in me mind of a stone slab, and being chiselled into it were these words to do with Hekate.'

She handed me notepaper containing a page of her clear handwriting as she emptied the kettle.

I read her words and wondered, before reading them again.

Hellish, Earthly, and Heavenly . . . goddess of the crossroads,

> guiding light, Queen of Night. Enemy of the sun, friend and companion of darkness; you who rejoice . . . to see blood flow. You who wander amidst tombs in the hours of darkness, thirsty for blood and the terror of mortals; Gorgo, Mormo, moon of a thousand shifting forms.

And this she had seen being inscribed on to a stone slab? With nothing else in view at all?

'I could see a hand and a chisel, and there are a few words missing,' she admitted, pouring milk into mugs. 'But that was it; it was as if I could see them from above. They were just within eyesight on this stone slab set into the ground. I think it was connected with the statue I saw in September.'

On Saturday, 10 September she had experienced an extraordinary vision of Hekate in the form of a life-sized statue of the goddess. She had drawn what she could see adding: 'Queen of Underworld – 4 heads. 6 arms. One hand carries jet black puppy, headless. In another hand carries torch . . . Something burnt. Desecration. Sickle. Black Puppy. Desecration of an altar. Honour of Hekate.'

Although three heads – one a snake, one a dog and the third a horse – were more usual for Greco-Roman Hekate statues, I found that in the *Chaldean Oracles* of the second century AD, as well as in other classical sources, Hekate possesses four heads, representing the four elements and probably the four lunar phases.[1] Puppies, as Fiona had rightly suggested, were, with black ewe-lambs, the chief sacrifices offered in the name of Hekate.[2]

My neighbour's astounding insight into Hekate had mystified me, but there had been no further developments until today. Her statements concerning this carved stone inscription appeared to be a convenient means of conveying a simple, though poignant invocation to Hekate.

Gorgo and Mormo were decisive names, so I asked her what she could tell me about either of them.

Sitting down at the kitchen table, she looked pensive for a moment. 'I reckon Mormo is the name of a demon who is supposed to eat the souls of young children, while Gorgo has got something to do with Medusa.'

It was time to check this lot out. Without further ado I left the kitchen and ventured through to the front room where a selection of books are shelved.

A few minutes of searching revealed some potentially interesting facts. In a book on Greco-Roman magic entitled *Arcana Mundi* by Georg Luck it states that Gorgo and Mormo are demonic ghosts of classical tradition who were once believed to live in graveyard tombs.[3]

Elsewhere, I discovered that Gorgo and Mormo are considered to be Greco-Roman female demons who, along with several other similar so-called *lamaiai*, are collectively referred to as the 'Hosts of Hekate'.[4] These vampiric entities are believed to have kidnapped and devoured small children and to have accompanied Hekate on her spectral journeys through the midnight realms.

Gorgo almost certainly originated from earlier Greek accounts of the Gorgons – the three hideous sisters with serpents intertwined in their hair, teeth as long as boar's tusks and looks that could turn men to stone. Medusa was one of the three Gorgons, and after Perseus had slain her, the hero was carried back to safety aboard a ship named *Gorgo*.

Satisfied by the accuracy of her description of these two vampiric creatures, I reached for Toyne Newton's epic work *The Demonic Connection* and read again the chapter on Hekate. I was staggered by what I found. Page forty contained a significantly different variation of Fiona's invocation to Hekate showing the human mind's apparent ability to translate foreign texts into its own colloquial language. The text in question was of Greco-Roman origin, although Toyne had lifted it from a book written by occult historian Francis King.[5]

Returning to the kitchen I showed Fiona the entry, knowing she had not read *The Demonic Connection*.

'What? You're kidding!' She took the book from my hands and read the entry. 'Not the same as what I saw,' she admitted. 'But close.'

Whilst she browsed through its pages, I thought carefully about her new-found ability. 'Picking up' actual words such as Gorgo and Mormo could mean she was turning into what I describe as a direct information psychic – someone who can consistently produce psychic information containing verifiable names, dates and places. This is opposed to a symbolic information psychic, who experiences psychic communications in symbolic terms alone.

Perhaps we should try a meditation, here and now, see what happened; it could produce further direct information.

'If you want,' she mused, 'but I shouldn't think I'll get much.'

We would see.

Grabbing cups of tea, we entered the Black Room and sat on the purple carpet, amid the assortment of hard chairs used usually during meditations. I took her through a creative visualisation exercise to calm her mind and direct the senses, then left her to it; so, could she see anything?

She sat silently, waiting for images to form inside her head, a pen poised to paper. She shrugged her shoulders and opened her eyes. 'No, just a date – December 21.'

This was the date of the winter solstice, a point of great change in the seasonal cycle and a feast of great renown in many different cultures throughout the world. Fiona had no concept of the winter solstice and its importance to religious customs.

She closed her eyes once more and further moments of silence followed. 'Thomas', she said next.

Thomas? Thomas what? Then a thought occurred to me – maybe 21 December was the feast day of St Thomas. I told her to stay there as I got up to leave the room. Quickly finding my copy of *The Penguin Dictionary of Saints*, I searched through the feast-day listing. I was correct – 21 December was the feast of St Thomas Didymus the Apostle. This was brilliant, but what did it mean?

Deciding I would say nothing for the moment, I returned to the Black Room and sat back down.

I found her studiously scribbling on to notepaper. Five minutes later, she looked across and offered me the pad. 'That's all I get. It's probably all rubbish.'

Slowly, I read her words:

Calendar of witches? Festival. 6 celebrations. Thomas last. Gathering of people to celebrate. Gathering for a specific purpose. Big gathering. To pass. Bringing together of forces.

Not happy. Revenge. Destruction of a holy site. No damage. Involvement. BSA. Important. Has to be there. Not on time. Late. Does a small ritual. Celebrations begin. Dancing in circle. Bernard will have involvement. Not tell you straight away. He will attune to site. Large Place.

What was I to make of this? She obviously felt it was real enough, and she certainly appeared to be on to something. The calendar of the witches revolved around eight great sabbats, not six, but in olden times the feast of Thomas was considered to be the last sabbat of the year. What about this gathering? What could she tell me about that?

She looked bewildered. 'Don't know, all I see is a wooded clearing with people around a fire. Hekate is involved and so is BSA. However, she will fall out with these people and Bernard will see all this and keep his mouth shut for a while. I feel it's gonna happen soon.'

Would it occur on the feast of St Thomas, just six weeks away? I told her about the feast dates and asked if she could tell me where it would take place.

'I only see a large, ancient site that is to undergo some kind of ritual destruction,' she admitted, lighting a cigarette. 'It relates to this Thomas business, and this "calendar of the witches".'

Now I was stumped. It made no real sense to me, not yet at least. As to the gathering involving BSA, I only hoped to God that Bernard did tell me in good time. Visions of him receiving a call from Rachel Goodison and then shooting off to Sussex only to find a reception party waiting for him did not bear thinking about. I was going to have to re-emphasise my warning to him.

Fiona's new information appeared to confirm Bernard's feelings that Rachel was in trouble with her superiors, probably over the publication of *The Black Alchemist*. It would undoubtedly bring her and her associates considerable adverse publicity and attention in the coming months. Any site with even the vaguest link with the book would become the target of either occult vigilante groups or copy-cat Black Alchemists set on outdoing the real thing.

Should Fiona prove correct then it implied that the Black Alchemist scenario was opening up to reveal new pieces of the jigsaw, further players on the cosmic chessboard and a wider view of the scenes behind the activities of Rachel Goodison and her former associates in the Friends of Hekate. What's more, it seemed we should look towards the feast of St Thomas for further revelations about what exactly would happen next.

7
The Summoning

Saturday, 17 December 1988. '*Bernard, come to me,*' the powerful male voice ordered. '*Come to me, now.*'

The psychic twisted in his sleep, sweat pouring from his highly agitated body. He tossed and turned, fighting the unknown summoning. But it was too strong.

He must try to stay in the bedroom. Yes, do not go. Do not give in. But there was no fight. He found himself being pulled to the derelict house once more and in front of him loomed tall, dark figures.

He could sense their presence through the grey misty haze. Black figures; two or more of them in cowled robes.

He was no longer in bed, but in an empty room, kneeling with his forehead touching the wooden floor, back at that place, where *she* had met him . . . Rachel.

Rachel?

There was a chalk circle around him on the bare floorboards and strange symbols, like Chinese characters, inscribed within its wide circumference.

Beyond that was the vague recognition of blank walls, their wallpaper peeling, and low skirting boards, their paint chipped and dented. The foul setting was confirmed only by the noxious smell of dank decay stifling the remaining air.

He was within their circle, summoned to be here in front of *him* and one other.

Momentarily he regained his senses and tried to struggle, to look up, but he could not move; his body seemed paralysed.

Then came stern words. Not spoken but placed in his mind. He did not want to listen, but still they reverberated inside his head.

'*You will find in a wood a broken sword-stick,*' the mocking male voice began.

No, he would not listen.

'With this you will eliminate him, and then destroy yourself. You will know how. You will know when.'

No . . . no.

'The bodies will not be found . . .'

No . . . no, please.

'Your energies will then be in the power of the high priests,' the deranged voice said finally.

Get out of my head . . .

Writhing violently, Bernard fought wildly to regain consciousness, uttering a cry of relief as he hurled himself into a state of semi-consciousness.

The feel of the warm, soaked bedclothes became his anchor upon reality as he pushed open his bulging eyes and forced back the duvet cover.

Oblivious to the heinous invasion of her husband's inner privacy, his wife simply murmured her protest at the nearby turbulence and rolled on to her side.

The nausea rising up inside his throat made Bernard move swiftly. Fumbling for the closed door handle, he staggered into the darkness and found the bathroom, just in time to be violently sick.

Pumping out vomit, he purged his body of this abominable intrusion and then steadied himself on the cold wall.

He washed his face and went downstairs to the kitchen. The intensity of the overhead light made him squint, but it was a welcome sight, and one that confirmed the nightmare was really over.

Shaking his head, he lit a cigarette.

Never would he find that sword-stick. Never would he even think of where it might be, and never would he tell Andrew what had occurred tonight. The psychic researcher would only pester him until he finally gave in to making a search for this ritual object.

An awful dread welling up inside told him that his worst fears *would* become a reality *if* he allowed himself to recover that ritual weapon. This he could never do, for if he did he knew it could prove fatal for both of them.

THE SUMMONING

Monday, 19 December. From his office at work, Bernard dialled Andrew's telephone number and awaited a reply.

He wanted to cancel their meeting planned for that evening.

The familiar voice at the other end of the line sounded weary.

Without any introduction Bernard told his friend that he would be unable to meet him for their planned Christmas drink in The Griffin, due to illness.

'I don't feel too good myself,' the author confessed. 'I'm ill with flu. I've got a sore throat and a cold, so don't worry about it. Pushing the book has had to stop, I'm afraid. It's just made me ill.'

The psychic sympathised and rescheduled their get-together for early January.

'Anything new?' Andrew finally asked.

It was a cue for him to hint at any psychic developments in recent weeks. 'Not to speak of,' he replied, cutting short the conversation. He just could not tell him what had really occurred. Not for a while at least, not until it had all been long forgotten.

Winding up the difficult call, he replaced the telephone receiver.

Bernard felt bad about saying nothing to Andrew, but it was the only way. The living nightmare he had played out in the derelict house had completely unnerved him. It was the worst psychic experience he had ever been forced to endure in the name of questing. For not only did it disgust him, it clearly suggested that these people meant business and could easily influence his mind through the non-local bond forged between him and the Black Alchemist when he had first touched that wretched stone spearhead back in May 1985.

It was not a situation he relished, and if there was any way he could put out to these people that he wanted nothing more to do with their dealings at all, ever, then he would do so now, for this mental torment could only go on for so long . . .

Yet his inquisitive mind still wanted to rationalise and confirm the nature of what had occurred. The nightmare had taken place at the derelict house, the same setting as his earlier encounter with Rachel Goodison. His intuition told him this abandoned building existed in a physical sense. It was being used as some kind of makeshift temple by the Black Alchemist and his fellow apostates in the Great Work. He was sure the Black Alchemist had been present in the room, and thinking about this afterwards he had gained the overwhelming impression that this had been BA's final act against him before leaving the country; probably as a result of the book's publication the previous month.

Despite the Black Alchemist's apparent departure, the implications of the ritual summoning were that someone had visited a location close to his own home in Essex. Here they had concealed an artefact for him to find, almost as a parody of the questing concept of retrieving hidden objects by psychic means. Information had been planted in his head as to where this ritual weapon lay hidden. This he was to retrieve and use firstly against Andrew and then on himself.

What was meant by the words 'bodies will not be found. Energies will come under the control of the high priests,' he had no idea.

So, out there somewhere, most probably in the vicinity of Danbury, was a 'broken sword-stick' ready to be recovered. The choice of a sword-stick was yet another mocking parody of their past exploits. In November 1986 he had been intuitively led to find a magically potent sword-stick at a local antiques fair. At the time the old Indian mystic who had sold it to him had suggested that it would one day be used by Andrew to combat the rising might of a dark figure he instantly identified as the Black Alchemist. The discovery of the original sword-stick was graphically portrayed in Andrew's book, tending to suggest that the Black Alchemist was now aware of its contents.

Even though Bernard had not detected Rachel's presence in the derelict room, she must have known what was going on. Perhaps she did not agree with it?

He sighed in resignation. No, he could not allow his subjective feelings to cloud a blatantly obvious issue. Presumably he had been wrong in his earlier assumption that she was softening in her attitudes towards him, as this new menace was a sheer act of callous aggression.

Rising from his desk, he readied himself to leave.

For the moment, he would put the whole affair out of his mind, enjoy Christmas in the company of his family and worry about this loathsome business in 1989.

8
The Venus of Regret

Sunday, 29 January 1989. Bernard brought his beige Montego to a halt in the gravel-floored parking area on the edge of the deserted green. Flicking off the headlights, he peered out at the impenetrable darkness, its grip weakened only by the welcoming lights of The Cricketers Inn on the far side of Danbury Common.

Leaving the comfort of the warm car, he zipped up his leather jacket and braced himself against the bitterly cold January air as he began the long walk, a deep sense of foreboding rising from the pit of his stomach.

To the east was dense woodland and to the west were secluded lakes and pools shielded by further woodland. These lay inside the grounds of Danbury Country Park and it was here that he and Andrew had played cat and mouse with the Black Sorceress of Arundel during February the previous year, and it was here too that something told him he would find the 'broken sword-stick'.

He knew it was the only way; the only way to get this whole damn business out of his system completely. The meeting with Andrew in early January had inevitably led to him revealing details of the ritual summoning; he just could not keep it a secret from his friend. Yet despite Bernard being adamant that he could not be made to change his mind, the psychic researcher had suggested it was better to find the concealed artefact. They could handle whatever happened, and in this way the episode could be curtailed without causing further problems. Quite obviously he had flatly refused even to consider this option, but in the past few weeks he had begun to realise that Andrew was right. Unless this sword-stick, or whatever, was removed then he would constantly think about it, out there somewhere, just waiting to be discovered.

He was seeing Andrew again the following night, so he had finally made the decision to make at least a preliminary search for the ritual weapon. However, he would make the trip alone as he knew instinctively that, if Andrew were to accompany him, the whole situation would alter dramatically.

In the stillness of the early evening, Bernard followed the grass verge bordering the woodland country park. To locate the hidden object he would simply use his intuition and see where it led him. So far he had experienced nothing, only the feeling that he should carry on walking.

Occasionally, cars sped by on the quiet minor road, their headlights dimming only when Bernard was picked out just yards away. Where possible he kept to the overgrown verge and after some fifteen minutes came upon the exit drive to one of the small car-parks nestling just inside the country park. Its five-bar gate was padlocked, but a gap to one side allowed him entry.

The anxious psychic saw only the billowing shapes of stern trees surrounding him on all sides, their branches battling almost constantly in the seemingly ever-present wind at this isolated location.

Yes, it was here somewhere, he could sense it. But where exactly?

Flicking on the torch, he used its beam to search for a direction as he reached down and picked up a handful of cold dirt. Relaxing his mind, he stood for a moment, looking for subtle signs of any physical presences at this place of discontent.

Unexpectedly he heard a rustling sound behind him, a disturbance at ground level among the undergrowth. Swinging around, he was relieved to find it was only a fox, startled into movement by his close proximity.

But in this game you look for omens, meaningful signs that form part of the overall Web of Wyrd and show you where to turn next.

Bernard moved across to where the fox had been moments before and, with his mind alert, attuned as best he could. Yes, here somewhere. He must look around.

He surveyed the surrounding clumps of bramble and scanned beneath the low branches of small trees, searching for possible clues.

Then he saw something. On the ground was an out-of-place object – a natural flint nodule precariously balanced on top of the soft earth. It appeared shaped, and reaching down he realised it was a perfect representation of an earth mother, complete with obvious breasts, rounded hips and two blunt stubs for legs. It had no head, and was purely a natural flint, but it had the characteristics of the so-called Venus statues he had viewed the previous summer at the Ggantija megalithic temple complex on Gozo.

So, could it be connected with the concealed sword-stick? He held the heavy flint tightly and for a few brief moments focused his mind.

Yes, it was connected in some way; left here by the same people. Its energies did not feel threatening and it possessed a green auric field exuding fairly pleasant vibrations, although these could be properly assessed later. There was something else to find first.

Slipping the Venus into his jacket pocket, he moved on, shining the torch towards a larger open area some yards in front of him.

Suddenly he became aware of an encroachment, a shifting force, a feeling inside that sensed the previously calm atmosphere changing to one of tense expectancy.

Things were happening around him, he felt he should move faster. He also realised he needed some form of immediate protection.

Calling upon his personal guide, an Anglo-Saxon monk, he drew a cone of white light around his body and asked for further guidance. The response was an urge to return to where the Venus flint had been found. Relocating the spot, he knew there was something else here, something just below the mixture of dead brown leaves and soft earth. Pulling away a tentative handful, he was disconcerted to see a cylindrical object sunk deep into the ground.

This was it. This was the one.

It *was* an Indian sword-stick, no doubt about that.

Clearing away the muck from around the buried object allowed him to clasp hold of its end. He pulled upwards, but succeeded only in withdrawing its handle. Still left in the hard muddy earth was its metal blade, which necessitated one final tug before it loosened enough for him to remove it completely.

Bringing the two pieces back together, he noted the dilapidated condition of what remained of this reproduction Indian sword-stick, once sold to English tourists and now considered an illegal weapon in Britain.

Its lethal form glinted faintly in the torch-beam as he slowly turned it in his hand, just inches away from his face. Crude symbols stood out from among the scratches and scuff marks that littered the blunt, rusty blade which had been meant to cause death.

Beyond his line of sight now rose a dark swirling mist, a black vapour transforming rapidly into an amorphous figure of tangible darkness. His sense of foreboding erupted into a fit of utter hatred. He began thrusting out with the broken blade, stabbing violently at the abomination before him.

He plunged downwards, then twisted to slice upwards, venomously sinking the slim blade into his unwitting opponent again and again, as though acting out some bizarre dance of death.

And then it disappeared – the nebulous black mass had gone, leaving him alone with the would-be murder weapon poised maniacally in his limp hand. A total realisation of what he had just done, and what he knew could have happened, suddenly dawned upon him. He became dizzy with disgust. With one last look at the repulsive sword-stick, he let it drop to the ground.

He just wanted to get away from here; go home to his wife; leave this abhorrent place.

It was all too much for him.

Leaving the ritualistic weapon, he pushed his way out of the bleak woods as fast as was humanly possible, realising already that if Andrew had accompanied him on this nightmare journey, then he would have been on the receiving end of the broken sword-stick.

Monday, 30 January. Bernard drew on his cigarette. 'Anyway, I got back to the crossroads and realised that I was acting irrationally,' he revealed, as I listened in total disbelief.

'So I went back, found the sword-stick and dumped it in the

boot of the car along with the flint. That was last night and that's where they've stayed until now.'

The offending items lay together on the small wooden table amid the authentic Tudor decor inside St Anne's Castle, a well-known public house at Great Leighs in north Essex.

Studying the broken sword-stick, I saw it was a cheap imitation of the one found at the antiques fair by Bernard in November 1986. This particular example was in such bad condition that no one in their right mind would have sold it as a collectable antique. There seemed little doubt that it had been deliberately misused and broken – in a physical as well as a magical sense – to represent a total antithesis of the original item.

The remaining eight inches of its decaying blade displayed three badly executed symbols that were only just visible. One was a stylised S-shape linked by a trailing line to an indistinguishable magical sigil, beside which was a simple spiral. Spirals are symbols of energy gradually expanding and gaining momentum; the others I was not so sure about.

The weapon had obviously been in the earth for some while as the blade had begun to go rusty and a tiny black beetle had burrowed into one of the gaps in the floral leaf design on the hand-grip.

Bernard sipped low-alcohol Kaliber beer and looked satisfied. 'I reckon the idea was for the amorphous mass to attach itself to you. This would then have changed your appearance into someone else.'

Almost certainly the Black Alchemist, I suggested.

'You're probably right,' he admitted, sitting back in the wooden chair. 'The sword-stick would then have influenced me to lose control and stab out wildly, like last night. I don't suppose I would have been able to stop myself; it's too awful to even think about, isn't it?'

Well, thank God I didn't go!

He agreed with a brief smile.

Mulling over the situation, I assumed that those behind this little stunt had programmed the sword-stick with a manufactured thought form created through ritual processes. This condensed energy mass would then have been sealed into the weapon by inscribing its blade with sigils. To this incantation they would have added words to the effect of: 'You will only be released when the sword-stick is removed from the ground.'

So, having achieved manifestation, the amorphous mass would have been free to attach itself to me before transforming into a clairvoyant illusion of the Black Alchemist – the justification Bernard would have needed to stab out wildly as he became intoxicated by the entity's presence. Only afterwards would he have regained his senses and seen, to his horror, that his friend was now dead, a realisation it was hoped would induce his own suicide.

Magical operations such as this were like priming and programming a computerised bomb; yet instead of using keyboards and software, ritual magicians use visualisation and sigils with almost the same effect, or so it seemed.

'Anyway, that's all over,' he said next, wanting me to dispose of the artefacts and get on to more stimulating subjects of discussion.

And we did talk about other topics for an hour, but still I would not put away the offending items. They remained on display, visible to all who passed the table.

Accepting that Bernard was unlikely to psychometrise either object, I slipped the Venus flint into my hand and tried attuning to its past. Normally, I was as psychic as a brick, but just occasionally I had a few direct hits with psychometry – the art of clairvoyantly obtaining information concerning an object's history.

Loosely stroking its well-worn surface, I allowed my mind to relax and then simply said the first things that came into my head. Whether imagination or not, it seemed clear to me that the flint was wholly different from the feel of the broken sword-stick. Perhaps it had been left in place by Rachel Goodison, almost as an afterthought, and without BA's consent or knowledge. Maybe it came from her personal belongings and was placed in Danbury Country Park as a sign of her genuine regret over the intended outcome of Bernard's astral summoning to the derelict house. Furthermore, it could also be a sign that she was aware of his visit to the stone temples of Ggantija on Gozo the previous year. Here the Venus-style earth mother was worshipped in prehistoric times, raising the question of whether she chose to leave an appropriately shaped flint for this very reason.

'Well I had thought of that,' he mused, rubbing his chin and glancing down at the crude statue. 'But how would she know? Same way as we know about what she's up to, I suppose.'

By psychic means, of course.

'Anyway, I see it surrounded by a green aura and I also get a connection with flowers and the word "temptation".'

In occult tradition green is the colour attributed to the planetary influence of Venus. It symbolises the human emotion governing such matters as love, health and nature. The earth-mother flint was therefore a perfect representation of these Venusian qualities.

The reference to 'temptation' was a warning to show him that, although softening, Rachel Goodison was still a practising priestess of Hekate and had not changed her overall attitude towards ritual magic. Despite this there must have been a small part of her that dearly wanted to relinquish her involvement with warped figures such as the Black Alchemist, and it was the emotions governing these feelings that had made her leave this Venus statue. Something told me she actually wanted to meet Bernard and had used the goddess-shaped flint as a means for him to locate her whereabouts.

Now he looked confused. 'But why leave the statue and the sword-stick, together? Surely one cancels out the other.'

Perhaps she realised there was a very real possibility we could both be killed as a result of the sword-stick's programme, so she deposited the Venus statue in the knowledge that Bernard would find and pick this up *before* touching the concealed weapon. Planting the flint had been the only alternative, for if she had failed to conceal the sword-stick itself, then she would have betrayed BA's final instructions. Final? Had he really left the country?

'Oh, I think so, don't you?' Bernard confirmed, before searching inside his brain for a few moments. 'To Spain . . . yes, checking out Gnostic documents . . . old manuscripts . . . once belonging to an early Christian community such as the Essenes.'

Wait a minute. The Black Alchemist was in Spain, checking out Gnostic Christian material? This seemed like a nonsensical statement at first, but then I realised its possible significance. Most of the schismatic Gnostic sects, outlawed by the Early

Church, had been located in ancient Egypt, where the most important books on alchemy were written during the same period. In certain Christian traditions alchemy and the associated Hermetic mysteries (after Hermes, the Greek god of wisdom and knowledge) were accepted alongside canonical Church doctrines until well into medieval times. Alchemy is still seen today as forming part of the Orthodox Church's teachings by obscure monastic communities such as those at Mount Athos in eastern Greece.

This aside, Spain seemed a funny place to go in search of Gnostic documents. Perhaps he was combining his researches with a long holiday, lazing on a sun-kissed beach somewhere.

'With him out of the way and Rachel Goodison in some sort of trouble with her superiors, then that looks about it to me,' he declared, as if this closed the pages of the book's unwritten sequel.

'I reckon the sword-stick business was a last-ditch attempt at getting us out of the way, and now that's failed, I can't see them wasting their time any more. Can you?'

I shrugged my shoulders.

'No, that's it. Finish. We can all go home, which is where I'm going now.' Looking slightly more contented than when he had first walked in, he drained the contents of his glass and stood up.

What Bernard did not seem to realise, or failed to accept, was that Rachel Goodison and the Black Alchemist were key players in a much greater game. Tentative evidence of this had been alluded to in not just his psychic material, but in other people's information as well. To think we could just get up and walk away was naive in the extreme. The coming months and years were going to show us things we had never even dreamed possible, and whether he liked it or not, we were both implicated; the more tangible evidence we could gather to confirm the reality of these people, the easier it would be in the long run.

I needed to know more about the Friends of Hekate and anyone else connected with this disconcerting affair, and, one way or another, I was willing to take risks to find out.

One more point. To think we had the Black Alchemist on the run was ridiculous. He might be sunning himself on some Spanish beach, but one day he would be back, older and wiser and ready to kick arse on a massive scale; and guess who would be first in line?

'I'll cross that bridge when I come to it,' he replied, slipping his hands in his pockets. 'For the moment Armageddon can take place and it won't bother me. I'm finished with this business once and for all.'

PART TWO
The Dark Council

9
The Wheel of Destruction

Sunday, 26 February 1989. Ascending the concrete staircase enclosed by grimy glass, I reached the first-floor level and moved along the open balcony to the final flat. Pushing the door bell, I awaited a response.

Momentarily I leant over the brick wall and gazed down at the scruffy-looking kids noisily playing football in the small parking area reserved for residents and visitors.

I was back in south London and the *déjà vu* of my regular visits to this same address ten years before sent an unexpected shiver down my spine.

It was the long time home of a friend of mine named Helen, who might be described as a bubbly, robust Londoner. She had an extraordinary psychic talent I had first discovered back in 1979 when still a youthful investigator of the unexplained. Helen was ten years my senior and had telephoned to report a series of UFO sightings in January that year.

This same period had seen my sudden rise of interest in the occult, particularly the life and times of Britain's most notorious ritualist, Aleister Crowley. Sharing my interests with Helen had a profound effect upon her psychic 'gift'. Almost immediately she began receiving a wealth of names, dates and places concerning a past life we had supposedly shared as sixteenth-century witches in the French Pyrenees. Gradually this evolved into quite intricate information on all aspects of Aleister Crowley and his infamous occult career.

By July 1979 Crowley was appearing to Helen on a regular basis. Daily his spirit presence would dictate the chapters of a manuscript entitled *The Inner Book of the Law* – inspirational material meant to have been his canon for the forthcoming new aeon of mankind.

Helen and I became entangled in a web of Crowley magick (he spelt it with a *k*), and not unnaturally a large number of psychics connected with my sphere of influence began warning of a woman in my life who was being manipulated by corrupt psychic forces. They suggested I should have nothing more to do with her, and in August that year this was exactly what I did. When I last saw Helen she was about to embark upon an air journey to the site of Crowley's infamous Abbey of Thelema at Cefalu, near Palermo in Sicily. Here we were to have conducted a complex rite that would have supposedly allowed Crowley to enter my mind through some inexplicable process. Thankfully, this did not occur and I lived to fight another day; the whole thing being written up and published in 1987 under the title *Helen and the Beast*.

After 1979 I had received only spasmodic correspondence from Helen. Apparently, after I had left the scene she had become involved with a very questionable occult group based in Croydon, Surrey, who made offerings of cockerels during unholy rites.

Following a major row with a gentleman friend in March 1982, Helen had left behind both the occult and Crowley for good. I recall her writing to me around this time asking if I and anyone else who knew her would light a candle on a certain date in the hope that she could break free from her mental misery.

I heard no more from Helen and often wondered what had become of her; I found out just two weeks ago. Finding myself close to her London home, I had dropped a copy of *The Black Alchemist* through her letter box. Inside was a note asking her to ring me, and this had led to our first meeting in almost ten years. It took place on Friday, 10 February and, quite obviously, there had been much to talk about. For a while she had been the landlady of a pub in Sevenoaks, Kent, and for the past two years she had acted as housekeeper for a well-to-do family in Bexleyheath. She now lived with her teenage daughter, who spent very little time at home.

My reasons for recontacting Helen after all these years were quite mercenary. Knowing she was an uncannily accurate direct information psychic I wondered if she might be able to further my knowledge of the whole Black Alchemist affair.

Bernard had made it quite clear he wanted nothing more to do with the subject unless an inner voice forced him into action, which was unlikely. If this was his wish, then so be it, but I felt there were still many loose ends that needed explanations, so perhaps Helen was the one to help me. I knew this was a horrendous risk to take, especially as we had parted company under such drastic circumstances; I just hoped I had made the right decision.

I rang the door bell once more, having received no response the first time. It looked as if she was out. Turning to leave, I caught sight of her walking along the concrete balcony, heavy shopping in both hands.

'Sorry I wasn't here,' she called in her brash south London accent, which typified her happy-go-lucky outlook on life. Hearing that she had been the landlady of a public house had not surprised me.

Putting down the shopping, she found her key and unlocked the door. 'Come in, make yourself at home. I'll get rid of this lot and put the kettle on for a nice cup of tea.'

In the lounge, I sat down as Helen pottered about in the kitchen. Her sparsely filled bookcase, situated below the stereo system, showed what little interest she held in the mysteries of life. There was only one book on the occult among her handful of steamy novels, her set of encyclopaedias and her token cookery book, and this was *The Black Alchemist*. From our previous meeting I knew she had not pursued her interest in psychic matters during the intervening years, other than to arrange an occasional ladies' afternoon where she would get together with a handful of friends for a little fortune telling.

Helen entered the room clutching cups of tea and after passing the time of day we discussed the possibility of conducting a psychic session.

'You can if you want, but I probably won't get anything,' she mused, pulling across an armchair and stubbing out her cigarette in readiness (she, like Bernard, was a heavy smoker).

Helen drew the blinds before lighting a couple of candles and sitting down to face me. 'What do you want me to do?' she asked, not having done this sort of thing for so long.

Moving a dining-room seat to face her, I grabbed some notepaper and sat down in eager anticipation. When she was sufficiently relaxed, I took her through a simple visualisation exercise to help her focus on the matter at hand.

The room fell silent, leaving me to stare up at the closed blinds that all but blocked out the dull orange light emanating from the street lamps outside. Occasionally a dog barked or a child yelled, piercing the heightened atmosphere in the dim lounge.[1]

'Dulcimer,' she exclaimed out of the blue. 'A word, I don't know what it means.'

Dulcimer. I had a vague suspicion it was some kind of musical instrument.

'It might be a person,' she suggested, shifting in her chair. 'I can now see a clearing in a wood. There's a bonfire and I see lots of people standing around in black robes with hoods.'

I told her to carry on.

'I count sixteen. They're standing around looking into a hollow – a pit or something.'

Clapham Woods perhaps? I kept silent, just jotted down Helen's words before asking her to describe this pit.

'It's like a hollow area; it's as if they can stand on the edge and look down into it. The bonfire's inside this pit.'

I tried to picture the scene. It seemed she could see people standing on the rim of a raised area on the edge of a basin-like hollow located at a lower level.

'Yes, that's right. That's what I see,' she confirmed. 'And now five of these robed figures are approaching the fire. There's something on the ground,' she exclaimed enthusiastically. 'It's like a skull. Yes, it's like a massive goat's skull; and there's something being placed beneath it. In fact, two things – one long, curved and made of bone, the other larger and heavy.'

Where was this taking place?

'In the pit. In woods, near a big hill, a few weeks ago. Several weeks ago, in fact.'

The communication was becoming faster and more fluent.

'The goat's skull was there at the time. A man stands behind this skull and pours liquid over it, like some sort of offering. Libation. I get the word "libation". They did a libation.' She paused to watch more of the scene unravelling in her mind's eye. 'Closing in. I get something about "closing in".'

THE WHEEL OF DESTRUCTION

This was beginning to sound dangerously like the Hekate rite witnessed by Bernard and Richard in connection with Clapham Woods during early August the previous year. Helen knew nothing of these communications. There were, however, some quite obvious differences. The libation could be some sort of offering to Hekate, although goats were not an animal sacred to her in classical tradition.

I asked Helen why she was seeing this ritual. What had it to do with us?

'It's the same people, I suppose.'

Who? The Friends of Hekate?

'Yes, I suppose so. It's the next step. The next move. These artefacts are still there now.'

But where was this place? We could do nothing unless I knew where it was.

'C. Somewhere beginning with C.' She went quiet. 'A big hill. A centre. Winchester?'

Winchester in Hampshire?

'I think so, yes.'

This was bizarre. An anonymous letter sent to Toyne Newton in 1981 mentioning the Friends of Hekate spoke of groups or 'cells' based outside Clapham Woods in West Sussex. Of the three locations mentioned, one was Winchester. The other two were in London and Avebury in Wiltshire. Unfortunately, no tangible evidence had ever been forthcoming to support these possibly groundless claims. Furthermore, Helen had read *The Black Alchemist* where the letter appears in its entirety. Still, it was a promising start.

Could she see more?

'This large hill, it's very high up,' she declared. 'I can smell fresh air. I get the name St Cathirins, or Cathlin Saint.'[2]

Of course, St Catherine's Hill, a prominent Iron Age ditch and bank hill-fort lying just south-east of Winchester, close to the M3 motorway. Cut into the turf of its grass-topped plateau is a square-shaped maze known locally as the Miz-maze which was almost certainly linked to the Norman chapel built on the elevated summit under the patronage of Henry de Blois, the bishop of Winchester, *circa* 1140-50. The building's dedication to St Catherine had given the hill its present-day name.[3]

Again, I said nothing to Helen, lest it might influence her words. It was sufficient to merely confirm that her 'Cathrin's Hill' actually existed.

'Well, this place is important to them. It's like a centre, a hub of a wheel,' she explained, opening her eyes. Helen had decided she could take the matter no further tonight.

This was quite remarkable material. If she was prepared to, then I suggested we go to Winchester as soon as possible to check out her words. If we could find and retrieve a couple of ritual artefacts, then it would be a giant leap forward in our understanding of the shadowy groups operating in the south of England.

Helen thought about the possibility. 'I'll let you know. I don't even know where Winchester is . . . but I'll tell you one thing,' she said seriously, 'if you check with Bernard, I think you'll find he saw this ritual but decided to say nothing.'

Sunday, 12 March. Pulling into the muddy parking area below St Catherine's Hill, I brought the car to a halt and stepped into the open air. After two weeks of psychic material, some hesitation and even more reservations, we had finally arrived at the place of Helen's dreams.

The south London psychic emerged and slipped on her long beige raincoat. It was a fairly mild spring afternoon, but it was going to be windy up there on the hilltop so a little extra body warmth was essential.

So much had happened since we first got together for that psychic session at her home in February, it was difficult to know where to start. In the past two weeks I had received various letters from Helen containing a wealth of psychically gained information concerning the Winchester area. Most of it had checked out but appeared unconnected with our quest. On more than one occasion she had travelled in dream to St Catherine's Hill and the Miz-maze, and now believed she could identify the exact position where the goat's skull libation had taken place.

On Wednesday, 8 March I had visited Toyne Newton and his mother Joan at their home in Worthing, West Sussex. They had been intrigued to hear of Helen's extraordinary psychic material, for it now appeared that the anonymous letter had not been the only source to speak of Winchester as the new centre of operations for the former members of the Friends of Hekate. Some years ago Toyne had worked with an elderly psychic named Mary. She had described Winchester as the 'hub of the Roman wheel' for the Friends of Hekate, a reference it seemed to the alleged lines of force, or earth energies, that are believed to converge upon Winchester, like the spokes of an invisible wheel. The 'Roman wheel' pun had to be a masked reference to St Catherine's Hill, especially as St Catherine of Alexandria was a Greco-Roman martyr who, according to legend, was bound upon a spiked wheel – the so-called 'Catherine-wheel' – before being finally beheaded.

Mary had made the link with Winchester as early as 1984, but Toyne had deliberately kept this information to himself, hoping that one day it would be confirmed. Now this had happened.

More importantly, I had spoken to Bernard, following Helen's suggestion that he had known about the goat's skull libation in the clearing but had chosen to say nothing. Without giving too much away, I had put this to him and instantly he had filled in the missing details. Apparently, he had viewed the ceremony in a dream 'about two months ago', i.e. around late December or early January. Why, then, had he not mentioned this to me at the time? 'Well, it's just more of the same, isn't it?' had been his answer.

In other words, he had no intention of booking himself in for another round of worry, headaches and earache from his wife by putting this lot into the public domain.

I respected his decision, but wished he had told me. Still, it did confirm that Helen was on the right track and also confirmed the words of Fiona, my young psychic neighbour. In November she had sat in the Black Room and described an apparent Hekate ritual taking place in a wooded clearing at an undisclosed hill-top site. She had seen a bonfire burning and believed this event would occur on 21 December – the feast of St Thomas and the date of the winter solstice. She had said it would involve Rachel Goodison and a group associated with her former colleagues in the Friends of Hekate. She had also said that Bernard would see this ceremony but make no mention of it at the time.

Later Fiona received further psychic information on mostly

Hekate-related themes, all of which proved to be uncannily accurate. Sadly, her personal development in this field had come to an end in December when she left Leigh-on-Sea to move in with her boyfriend.

Now it was up to Helen to take the matter on to new heights, and with Bernard's blessing I had finally convinced her to accompany me to St Catherine's Hill. For the first time ever I would be able to see her abilities at work out in the open; who knew where it would lead us.

Following a cursory visit to the Miz-maze, where we walked its well-worn path to the centre, Helen had orientated herself properly and identified the woods she had seen in her dream. Returning to the steep drop marking the perimeter of the Iron Age earthwork, we descended below the treeline.

Almost immediately we recognised the earthen hollow first described during the initial psychic session of Sunday, 26 February. The earthen ridge was, in fact, the outer edge of the ancient ditch, beneath which was a semi-circular clearing.

'Over there,' she nodded as we slid down the dry bank to the lower level. 'Here, look!'

I followed her eyes to a position on the far corner of the clearing. Approaching the spot she became visibly unnerved. 'I don't like it here,' she exclaimed, stuffing her hands in her pockets. 'I see the colour red, like a fog rising up from the ground. I don't want to stay here.' She shivered in disgust.

Scanning the ground for visible clues of past rituals, my eyes caught sight of an old fire pit.

Helen saw it too and shivered again. 'This redness. It's all around the vicinity of the fire, and I can see the goat's skull here now on the ground, where it was placed. The objects are here, I sense their presence.'

Bending down, I grabbed a handful of charred earth. This was her bonfire all right, but it had certainly not been kindled in the past couple of months; shoots of grass and weeds were already pushing their way through the blackened earth.

Helen ambled across and looked painfully towards the ground. 'I see the whole ritual replaying itself, now as we stand here. The figures in dark robes, the fire, the libation and the placing of the objects. The libation was carried out using a curly horn,' she announced, staring into thin air. 'It was placed into the earth at this very spot.'

Taking this as a cue to dig, I picked up a sharp stick and began prodding the soft loamy earth, before enlarging the hole with my hands. A spoil heap steadily grew in size. Pausing for a moment, I rubbed my forehead and looked up at Helen; she seemed to be in some sort of distress.

Hyperventilating, she moved backwards. 'I see two blue eyes, in mid-air, staring at me.'

She began to panic, so I tried to calm her.

'I can't shake them out of my mind. And words. I hear words ... "Mazda", "Angra", "Ahriman"; something to do with a battle. And a shiny dagger, buried.'

I told her that Ahura Mazda and Ahriman were opposing forces in the dualistic Zoroastrian religion of ancient Persia. 'Angra' was a reference to Angra Mainyu, another form of the evil god Ahriman. Fire festivals played an integral part in the Zoroastrian faith.

She seemed unmoved, her gaze was still firmly fixed on the watching eyes.

I told her to visualise herself drawing a flaming pentagram between her and the eyes. See it pushing them away until they finally disappeared.

Concentrating her mind, she constructed the fiery pentagram. 'OK, it's worked,' she announced with a sigh. 'But hurry, Andrew, please.'

One last try at finding these concealed artefacts ...

'No, come on. I want to go. I'm beginning to feel sick and dizzy.' The psychic began to swoon.

It was time to leave; Helen was about to faint. Any ritual artefacts grounded here had now moved on, I was sure of it.

Abandoning the conspicuous piles of earth and unsightly holes, I put my arm around Helen and led her away. There was nothing more we could do today; her visions had been vindicated and that was all we needed to know.

10
Markus of the Miz-maze

The motorway journey from Winchester back to London passed easily enough, giving us the whole evening to sort out what was going on. Already Helen had consented to a further psychic session in an attempt to crystallise some of the confusing ideas going around in her head since our sudden departure from St Catherine's Hill.

Helen was preparing some food in the kitchen, leaving me lost in my thoughts in the comfort of an armchair. A glass of Liebfraumilch in my hand, I tried to work out what to do next.

When Bernard and I first confronted the deeds of the Black Alchemist in 1985, the psychic information clearly implied that he was a loner who lived in Eastbourne and worked a corrupt form of Greco-Roman alchemy and ritual magic. He was on some sort of total enlightenment kick which he believed would give him complete control over his own destiny. This apparently necessitated the utilisation of various energies appropriate to the different aspects of his magical workings, and these were to be found at places of ancient power – in other words sites of either a prehistoric or religious interest. Rituals would be sealed by the depositing of inscribed artefacts at such holy places, and it was the discovery of one of these so-called fixing markers in Lullington churchyard that had triggered our own involvement in the Black Alchemist affair.

By October 1986 Bernard had glimpsed scenes of the Black Alchemist working with at least four other people, all of whom were brought in to further his own magical operations. This small group included the woman we knew as Rachel Goodison, who appeared to be the former priestess with the Friends of Hekate.

There were further indications hinting at the Black Alchemist's involvement with other groups during the Paradise Mound episode the previous year. If you added to this the tentative evidence suggesting that the Friends of Hekate was merely a cell in a much larger concern, then it clearly implied that this whole affair possessed much wider implications than we had at first believed. Helen's Winchester material was not helping to alleviate these fears, so perhaps it was time to gain some insight into what these people were really trying to achieve.

Helen served a wholesome salad and, with the plates washed and dried, we darkened the lounge in readiness for our second psychic session. Candles were lit and Helen settled in an armchair as I sat poised with pen and paper in hand. My suggestion had been that we visualise ourselves returning to St Catherine's Hill and pick up where we left off that afternoon.

After raising the cone of power, Helen slipped deeper and deeper into a relaxed state until images and impressions began to appear in her receptive mind.

'A huge humming top,' she announced curiously after a minute or two of silence. 'I see a huge humming top of red energy focused upon the wood where the goat's skull ritual took place. I am being taken away from here to the Miz-maze, though.' She paused to study the new imagery. 'And I can now see a man in a black robe with a hood. He's not bad, but good. He swings an incense burner; I think he's a monk. He says his name is "Markus de Capelin".' She drew out the syllables of this unfamiliar name.

'Markus' is the Latin for Mark, an obvious scriptural name. 'Capelin' is a corruption of the French *chapelain*, meaning a chaplain. So who was Markus the chaplain? Some kind of personification of the sacred place in question, a so-called site guardian, perhaps?

'He says he walks the paths every day, but not those used by the Dark Council,' she said next.

The Dark Council? Who were they?

'The sixteen who conducted the ritual,' she replied casually.[1] 'That's the name I get.'

Markus's reference to the paths were presumably those of the turf-cut Miz-maze. There were only a handful of surviving examples left in Britain today and some of these were located close to former monastic settlements, strongly indicating not just a connection between the two, but construction dates before the dissolution of the monasteries from 1536 onwards. In one old woodcut monks navigate the earthen paths of a turf maze in a state of contemplation and prayer. Evidence such as this, along with folk customs connecting turf mazes with pennance and pilgrimage substitution, clearly confirms their links with medieval Christianity.[2]

In its current form Winchester's Miz-maze is thought to be no more than 300 years old. However, Jeff Saward, Britain's foremost maze historian, believes that an earlier example had existed on the spot since at least the thirteenth century.[3] The Norman chapel located on St Catherine's Hill until its suppression by Cardinal Wolsey in 1529, was closely affiliated with the bishop of Winchester and the cathedral monastery of St Swithun, so there were good grounds for associating both Markus de Capelin and the Miz-maze with this tradition.

'The maze has been there for a long time. He shows me it with herb gardens all around; these he refers to as "the tranquil gardens". He says they were used for meditation and contemplation.'

So why had she made contact with this man? What was going on at the Miz-maze?

There was another pause. 'I now see us digging in the clearing earlier today, and the goat's skull libation as well. The robed figures are marking four different directions into the ground. They represent lines of power which are to be sent out to other parts of the country,' she now revealed.

'Markus is showing me points further away from the hill – one in a field with cows and another in a valley. Four of them conduct the same ritual at each site before moving on to a new location even further away. The Dark Council are preparing St Catherine's Hill for a major event that will take place in the future. He's showing me hills – seven hills – high points, and another point linked with this network of sites. He shows me a whole load of like, concrete pillars with flat tops. They're all over the place in this field.'

A group of concrete pillars with flat tops? I shuffled in my seat. No, I certainly could not identify this site; there was nothing like that in the Winchester area.

'No, it's further out,' she corrected me. 'Lark-, Lark-, Larkhill,' she added, straining to hear the name.

Larkhill? No, it still made no sense. I would have to check the map.

'I see a speeded up version of the same ritual with the goat's skull here, amid these round pillars.'

This was getting intriguing, but still I had no idea what the purpose of these rituals was, so I asked Helen to explain.

'Markus is still here,' she confirmed. 'He's taking me down a long straight track that cuts through hills and valleys. He says the Dark Council are creating a network of ancient sites across England and Wales, 400 miles long and 200 miles wide.

'At each one they conduct ceremonies, leave objects, and ground their own ritual tools before moving them on to new locations. This network will give them control of their own destinies as well as an incredible power they will one day use to make changes in the world.'

Was this what the Black Alchemist and the Friends of Hekate were attempting to achieve – a network of ancient sites covering the entire energy matrix of Britain? If so, then how did St Catherine's Hill fit into this picture?

'It's a centre,' she replied. 'Markus has said: "Stay with the hills below and above the eight. Follow the path. Draw a map. Azimuth, do it."'[4]

OK, but where were we to start?

'He says: "Ide Hill".'

11
The Energy Matrix

Monday, 20 March 1989. A pint of Ruddles County bitter before me, I sat at a corner table in The Griffin. Bernard had not yet arrived, so I flicked lazily through the diary assessing the wealth of inspired material produced by Helen in just a few short weeks.

Helen's mention of Ide Hill in connection with the most recent psychic session had completely thrown me. Ide Hill, as any reader of *The Black Alchemist* would know, is located on the North Downs of Kent. Known as the Dome of Kent, owing to the hilltop's hemispherical appearance, the setting is dominated by the picturesque church of St Mary. It was here that Bernard and I had come in May 1986 following disturbing dreams suggesting that the Black Alchemist had conducted a suspect magical rite in the rear of the churchyard. Evidence pointed towards the fact that BA saw Ide Hill as playing an essential role in his alchemical workings, although exactly what had never been made clear.

Now Helen had referred to Ide Hill in connection with the Dark Council which, she believed, consisted of sixteen figures, both male and female. She felt these people belonged to other magical groups as well, but came together for the purpose of furthering a long-term plan to gain magical control of ancient and sacred sites of Britain. Like the Black Alchemist, the Dark Council's targets were seemingly the prehistoric monuments – such as stone circles, barrows, earthworks and mounds – as well as Christian sacred places such as holy hills, wells and churchyards. At each they would conduct some form of magical rite to contain and harness the inherent energies thought to be generated at such locations. The ultimate aims of the Dark Council were still hazy, but such a view of sacred and ancient places was by no means new.

THE ENERGY MATRIX

A practising occultist once told me that whosoever controls the key sacred sites of a kingdom will control the destiny of the people of that kingdom. Such key religious centres were to be found in every culture of every country of the world. They were generally looked upon as the points of creation where the heavens, earth and underworld were joined by a spiritual pivot or thread.

In classical tradition a sacred centre was known as an *omphalos* – *omphali* in the plural – after the Greek word meaning 'navel'. It embodied the concept that the *omphalos* lay in the dead centre of the world and provided the source of its life-blood, just as the navel lay in the middle of the human body and acted as the lifeline between mother and child. The most famous 'navel of the earth' was the Delphic Oracle in Greece. In Britain, prehistoric monuments such as Stonehenge and Glastonbury Tor in Somerset have been considered as *omphali*. On the other hand, St Paul's Cathedral in London is seen by Christian mystics as the sacred centre or heart of Christianity in Britain.

Sacred centres are considered by exponents of the earth mysteries to be epicentres and microcosms of landscape geometry on a local, regional or even a national level. From such hearts pulses the earth energy or holy spirit that sustains and nourishes the web or network of subtle energies regulating and controlling life on earth. Upset your sacred centre and you could upset the bio-rhythms of everything within its sphere of influence. The technicalities of such profound matters are complex to say the least, and earth mysteries' author John Michell has successfully tackled the subject of geomancy, as it is known, in his books *The View Over Atlantis*, *City of Revelation* and *Twelve Tribe Nations*.

It went without saying that Helen had no knowledge of such books and should not have had any conscious knowledge of the less than obvious aims of corrupt magical groups such as the Friends of Hekate or the Dark Council. Indeed, I was sure that the psychic material she had produced during the last meditation meant very little to her at all.

Markus de Capelin, the spirit guardian of St Catherine's Hill, had spoken of a national matrix of holy sites being utilised by the Dark Council. There was reference to an arrangement of locations in a huge figure of eight, with St Catherine's Hill acting as a hub of the wheel and Ide Hill forming some kind of starting point. So far there was insufficient information to plot such an arrangement of sites on a large-scale map, but some interesting facts had already emerged.

Helen had been shown a circular area of flat-topped concrete posts at a place named Larkhill, which I had assumed was near Winchester in Hampshire.

Unfortunately, the location in question could not be identified from the simple description she had given. If, however, she had used the site's more familiar name of Woodhenge, then its identification would have been instantaneous. Woodhenge is an earthen henge monument located one mile north of the town of Amesbury in Hampshire's neighbouring county of Wiltshire. The concrete pillars seen by Helen mark the positions of the sacred site's four concentric rings of post-holes that once supported the tall wooden posts of four ritualistic enclosures in use around 2000-1800 BC. Lastly, and most importantly, Woodhenge – Stonehenge's ceremonial companion – is perched upon raised ground close to the village of Larkhill, a fact previously unknown to either Helen or myself.[1]

St Catherine's Hill near Winchester, Woodhenge in Wiltshire and Ide Hill in Kent – what did such places have in common and what did they mean to the Dark Council? St Catherine's Hill was undoubtedly the 'Roman wheel', the Friends of Hekate's epicentre of activity according to Toyne Newton's elderly psychic friend. Like Helen, she had referred to Winchester as the convergence point of ley lines, a less than appropriate term describing the geomagnetic lines of force that criss-cross the earth's surface and act as an invisible framework for the natural energies permeating the landscape.

Often these lines of force appear to coincide with the siting of prehistoric and sacred monuments, showing that our distant ancestors were perhaps aware of the potency such locations held in their own seasonal life-cycles. This national web we refer to as the energy matrix, although each individual site possesses its own particular matrix which can be altered on a subtle level by many different factors, including human interaction. Occult rituals of the sort apparently conducted by the Black Alchemist and the

author Andrew Collins, who for fifteen years has worked with many talented psychics uncovering hidden artefacts and investigating landscape and historical enigmas (pic: John Horrigan).

Bernard and Helen seen here in Danbury churchyard. Their psychic information complemented each other's confrontations with the Friends of Hekate (author's pic).

The church of St John the Baptist, Danbury in Essex, seen here at night. It was in the churchyard that the Black Alchemist concealed an inscribed dagger spiked into a large animal's heart on 5 November 1987 (author's pic).

The ebony dagger spiked into an animal's heart found in Danbury churchyard on 5 November 1987. Its inscribed symbols celebrated the symbolic gestation of a magical entity connected with Lykaina, the she-wolf (author's pic).

The author stands upon the Paradise Mound outside the East Sussex town of Eastbourne. Here the Black Alchemist is believed to have conducted a series of occult rites during 1988 (author's pic).

Above: The 'broken' sword-stick discovered by Bernard in Danbury Country Park on 29 January 1989. Was it deposited as a mockery of the Black Alchemist story? (author's pic)

Below: The author's impression of Carreau, the Indo-Chinese swamp demon allegedly raised by Rachel Goodison and her colleagues in August 1988.

Right: St Catherine's Hill, Winchester in Hampshire, the Iron Age hill-fort named as a ritual centre used by the Friends of Hekate (author's pic).

Below right: Hekate, the three-headed Mistress of the Underworld, whose blood-sucking *lamaiai* became the vampires of East European tradition.

Left: The turf-cut Miz-maze on St Catherine's Hill, Winchester, where the alleged spirit guardian, Markus de Capelin, first spoke of the so-called 'Dark Council' (author's pic).

Below left: Bas-relief of St Catherine inside the Royston bee-hive cave in Hertfordshire. Did her medieval cult include devotion to the Midnight Sun, the full-moon eclipse? (author's pic)

Right: Night-time shot of St Mary's church, Ide Hill in Kent. Why did this peaceful hill-top location become so important to the activities of both the Black Alchemist and the Dark Council? (author's pic)

Below: The goat's head dagger concealed in Ide Hill churchyard and retrieved by Helen and the author on 24 March 1989. Was it left there by members of the Dark Council? (author's pic)

Illustration showing 'Hecate's Wheel', taken from a sixth-century BC stone disc from Ionia in Asia Minor. Was Hekate's wheel-like device later adopted by St Catherine?

The serpent bracelet and mother of pearl cosmetics box found by Bernard in Danbury Country Park on 16 January 1990. Was it left as a goodbye gesture by Rachel Goodison? (author's pic)

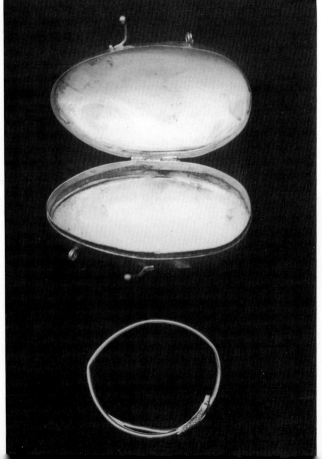

Dark Council are calculated to affect the localised energy matrix of a site.

Woodhenge made no real sense to me as yet (why not choose Stonehenge as a more obvious target?), but Ide Hill, we knew, had already been utilised by the Black Alchemist. Did Helen's words imply some kind of connection between his activities and those of the Dark Council? Already she had suggested that former members of the Friends of Hekate belonged to the Dark Council and, if true, then a link, whether direct or indirect, had to exist between these three separate pieces of the jigsaw.

Most of these thoughts I had so far kept from Helen as I did not wish to influence or taint her psychic information, even though her capacity to absorb this sort of factual material was relatively low. At the end of the day we needed clear evidence of her words, otherwise this whole scenario could be put down to an over-active imagination spiced with a little genuine inspiration.

Yet still Helen produced further snippets of information. Over the past week she had clairvoyantly seen more locations she felt were connected with the Dark Council's activities. These included the megalithic complex of standing stones at Avebury in Wiltshire, as well as the neighbouring Silbury Hill, Britain's largest man-made earthen mound. Avebury was one of the three sites named in the anonymous letter received by Toyne Newton as playing host to a group affiliated to the Friends of Hekate.

My concentration was broken by the approach of Bernard, dressed in a blue casual jacket and jeans. He ordered a pint of Guinness from the barmaid before sauntering across to join me at the table.

We spent an hour going over the whole Helen situation. From the outset he had taken a keen interest in her psychic material, making constructive comments where applicable. The afternoon Helen and I had visited St Catherine's Hill he experienced a potentially intriguing psychic vision. He had been working in the house when suddenly he gained the distinct impression of the same clearing he had seen in connection with the goat's skull libation. Into view had come a pack of huge, fearsome dogs, possibly Irish wolf-hounds. They proceeded to catch and tear apart a hawk-like bird of prey with a broken wing. This occurred at the exact position the goat's skull had been placed, and in

Bernard's mind the bird symbolised the process of calcination (the reduction of a substance into powder using fire) within the alchemical transmutation.

This curious vision had occurred around 2pm, the very time we had begun our search of the clearing in question. Had it therefore been a reaction to our presence at the location? Bernard seemed to think so.

In Greco-Roman tradition alchemy came under the influence of Hermes, the god of writing and knowledge; hence the term Hermetics or the Hermetic tradition. Hermes is equated in Roman mythology with Mercury, and both gods are generally depicted holding the so-called Caduceus wand. This is composed of a long shaft with two snakes curling around its stem to form the figure eight – a symbol denoting duality and eternity. Eight is undoubtedly the number intrinsically linked with both Mercury and alchemy, and it was probably for this reason that the Dark Council were supposedly using the number eight in association with their own magical interpretation of the British energy matrix.

A Mercurial connection made sense, especially as the feast day of the Christianised St Mercury – an alleged Roman martyr of supernatural origin – is 25 November, a date he shares with St Catherine of Alexandria. This gave us an indirect association between St Catherine's Hill, alchemy and the influence of the god Mercury, and in so doing strengthened Helen's belief in the importance of this hill-top location. Furthermore, it has been argued that the pavement maze of classical tradition was associated with the influence of Hermes or Mercury,[2] which, if correct, must have some bearing on the presence of the turf-cut Miz-maze on the summit of St Catherine's Hill, Winchester.

Even more obscure, but possibly relevant to these findings, was the word 'dulcimer' spoken by Helen during the initial psychic session at her home in February – the one which revealed details of the goat's skull libation at St Catherine's Hill. I had recently discovered that a dulcimer is a musical instrument first mentioned in the Bible (Dan. 3:5, 15). Despite this, it is not a known Jewish instrument and its original Hebrew name *sumphoniah* has been widely translated over the centuries – 'bagpipes', 'crooked trumpet', 'lute', 'lyre' and 'organ' being just some of its interpretations.[3] Another source spoke of a dulcimer as a stringed instrument played on with two sticks. This, however, was all I could find on the subject, and I still failed to see why her mind should have wanted to latch on to this particular instrument.

Turning to other matters, I spoke to Bernard about Woodhenge and the renewed interest in Ide Hill which, by coincidence, had been on the itinerary of sites visited during an Earthquest excursion to Kent and Surrey the previous afternoon. Oddly enough, some of the more sensitive members of the group had been drawn to search behind the organ inside the church, believing the Black Alchemist had recently returned to deposit an artefact here. Nothing was found, so they had given up with a shrug of the shoulders, and there the matter had rested.

Bernard seemed thoughtful and after a few moments of silence said: 'Is Woodhenge connected with music?'

I asked him why.

'It might be important to what Helen said about Ide Hill and the use of the figure eight.' He thought for a long moment. 'Something to do with the musical octave – eight notes to an octave, that sort of thing.'

Quite possibly, the music of the spheres as John Michell referred to it . . .

John Michell, *of course*. I'd completely forgotten about the importance he placed on Woodhenge. In his classic book *The View Over Atlantis* he had spoken of Woodhenge as the expression of a Mercurial influence, constructed to harness and amplify natural sound by means of stretching strings of varying lengths and heights between different wooden posts, just as the Pythagoreans had replicated the sonic patterns of the universe. Thus Woodhenge symbolised a tone, a stringed musical instrument laid out according to a plan of the universe – the outer earthen bank representing 'the crust of the firmament' and the inner moat matching the watery layer, which ancient astronomers saw as the lining behind the universe. Mercury was the traditional inventor of the lute – one of the stringed instruments compared with the dulcimer – and he was depicted as the god of music and wind instruments, thereby associating Woodhenge with this self-same influence.[4]

Michell had concluded that the various straight alignments of ancient places criss-crossing Britain had come under the control and influence of Mercury during Roman times. Furthermore, Caesar had cited the quicksilver god as the Druidic guide of pathways, who presided over journeys and marches. Mercury was also patron of boundaries and boundary markers or markstones. Mercury could justifiably be seen as a representative of the energy matrix of Britain, probably the reason why the Dark Council were using this musical influence for their own degenerate purposes.

'Well, the picture's gradually forming, isn't it?' Bernard mused, lazing back in his chair. 'I reckon you're right about what these people are trying to achieve, but I can't help thinking about the safety factor. Helen is very vulnerable living alone, and if you open up too many cans of worms it will be her that'll get hurt.'

This I realised. I would be careful, but still we needed hardcore evidence to back up her claims, and for the moment she seemed willing to co-operate in whatever way I thought necessary.

'Watch this weekend,' he unexpectedly announced. 'There's a lot of fire in the air and you don't want to get yourself burnt, do you?'

12
The First Doubt

Tuesday, 21 March 1989. In the gloomy darkness Helen ascended the tree-lined path towards the apex of a high hill. Ahead of her was the radiant image of a beautiful lady standing next to a sturdy stone bench, a place of comfort for hikers wanting to rest their weary legs.

The spirit woman looked young, but her eyes showed she was as old as time itself. She wore a plain white dress but the electric-blue splendour of her well-defined aura enlivened her earthly appearance. Although Helen did not recognise this devout holy lady, she seemed to belong to this sanctified place, yet appeared sad and concerned for some reason. Her hand pointed behind her to the black mass of thick undergrowth and towering trees as if there was some kind of urgency.

Intuitively Helen knew she must leave this guardian form and continue her journey along the earthen ridge, where she would eventually encounter the source of the lady's anxiety.

Brambles reached out to ensnare her as she gradually advanced towards a wide open space encircled by tall trees, beyond which loomed the slim spire of a small country church. She could sense movement now. People in black, shifting about in the shadows, silently executing a set of predetermined actions, a ceremony of some sort in the stillness of the open churchyard.

Only a hazy red fog illuminated this perpetual darkness. It rose slowly and engulfed the now familiar image of the huge goat's skull she had seen before. It was positioned on the ground close to trees, almost certainly upon the grave of some poor soul. A libation was in progress, the liquid being poured from the raised hand of a cowled figure on to the hollow eyes of the long-dead creature.

Another figure, a male, was now breaking away from the others and moving in her direction. Could she be seen? She prayed she was just a flitting will-o'-the-wisp in this fearful drama. With a floppy cowl hiding his face, the man came within six feet of her position and pulled out a shiny dagger from inside his full-length robe.

Her heart raced and her mind froze as he poised ready to strike. She breathed a sigh of relief when he thrust the ritual weapon into the holy earth and began uttering incomprehensible words of arcane power.

He couldn't see her. *He couldn't see her*.

Removing the sharp implement, he once again concealed it about his body as he turned away and rejoined the group of some seven or so silhouettes who chanted slowly while standing in a circle.

They *all* seemed oblivious to Helen's presence, giving her a chance to move in closer, see what they were doing, hear what they were chanting.

Helen followed in the footsteps of the shadowy individual, back to the circle. Still there was no response from the assembled party.

The master of ceremonies now stopped and held out his hands as if to increase his state of mental concentration, and slowly he turned towards Helen.

Sheer horror welled up inside as she realised he was now staring directly at her. Almost instantly her throat constricted and she began to cough and splutter. She could no longer breathe properly, and was rapidly losing her sense of balance.

Others broke free from the circle and began surrounding her, moving in, their eyes fixed upon this psychic intrusion.

In desperation she tried to recite the words of the Cabbalistic Cross, taught to her by Andrew at Winchester. 'Ateh . . . Ateh el Malkuth, ve-Geburah . . .' No, it was no good. Her mind was spinning in a black void with the images now just a blur of black faces silently weakening her every limb.

She called for Markus de Capelin, but this was no holy place under his guardianship. She called him again, but still no answer came as a sense of hopelessness reduced her to tears and submission.

THE FIRST DOUBT

Her ribs hurt and she knew she must break free, or there would be no return.

The woman in blue flashed into her mind. She was there, in the distance trying to help.

Her inner strength began to rise as she thought of Andrew and their work, and the plight of the holy lady who had called her here to witness this desecration. They must help her; must set her free by restoring the natural balance and tranquillity of this sacred place of God.

A new-found inner strength provided Helen with the sheer determination to push her way back to the surface, back to a point of reality.

Out of the suppressed depths of her inner mind rose new images – St Catherine's Hill, Silbury Hill and a dagger, its hilt made of bone. Then came words in a melodic female voice saying: 'This is evil. Do not touch it until protection is given. Cleansing must be done. You will find at Ide Hill. Used as part of ritual – an offering to the goat. Hekate.'

And then only silence.

Helen opened her eyes and found herself slouched on the lounge sofa in the pitch black. Only the diffuse light of the sodium lamps outside gave the room vague form.

There was an acute throbbing pain inside her chest and a strong sensation of nausea which was not alleviated when she lit a cigarette.

Getting up, she switched on the light and knew she should not have tried a meditation without Andrew. But she had wanted to find out more about the Dark Council and what they would do next, so she had simply relaxed her mind to see what would happen. Now she regretted it – all this was doing her brain in.

She thought of Bernard. She was not as strong as him; how did he cope with this sort of thing? Perhaps he could give her some advice on how to be stronger.

She wanted to help Andrew, she really did. She wanted to uncover artefacts and go on quests, but felt under pressure. The only items she had ever come across using her psychic talents were a couple of rings dug up on the Surrey Downs a few years back; the difference being that these had been found under her own steam and at her own pace.

She had given Andrew psychic information to the best of her capabilities, and this she did not mind; he was a good friend to her. Yet disappointment had followed their uneventful trip to St Catherine's Hill, and she now realised that unless her psychic material proved a little more fulfilling, then the growing anxiety that seemed to accompany the bad headaches would soon force her to withdraw completely.

13
The Ides of March

Friday, 24 March 1989. I listened with more than a little concern to Helen's doubts about her strength of commitment and her growing disillusionment with the recent psychic material. She had already aired her feelings in a letter written on Tuesday following her disturbing Ide Hill meditation of the night before.

Sitting at her kitchen table, she poured us both a cup of tea. It was Good Friday and we had decided to get together to discuss the whole situation; see where we would go from here.

I understood her sentiments and could only comply with her wishes. If she wanted to step down or slow the pace a little, then she had only to say the word.

'I don't mind going on, Andrew,' she continued, pulling across her current notepad full of scribbled information relating to her most recent psychic experiences. 'I just need to know how to handle it, that's all.'

I suggested that we see how it went over the next few weeks; things might settle down a little more. If not, then I was prepared to go along with whatever decision she made.

'Anyway, I've had more feelings about Ide Hill,' she revealed, picking up a pen. 'I keep seeing images of people out there in the churchyard.'

I asked her to tell me more.

'I saw it again in dream. But this time I approached the church from another direction. There's some kind of green in front of it, isn't there? And there's a crossroads with some old houses by the road and a funny little spire.'

That was it, just as Bernard had described the place back in 1986. What was new, however, was her description of the female spirit guardian encountered next to a stone seat. I had never come across any such bench at Ide Hill and presumed it must be located somewhere beyond the southern boundary of the churchyard.

'I reckon they're using Ide Hill to charge up their artefects,' Helen said next. 'I got something about two days in the church and then eight days in the ground.' She looked down at a crudely drawn sketch of a dagger. 'It could be they've buried this knife with the bone handle. I've also seen the symbol in your book. What is it?'

The *Monas Hieroglyphica* of Dr John Dee, the Elizabethan magus and astrologer, I reminded her, whom the Black Alchemist appeared to want to emulate.

'Yeah, I keep seeing it on something – the dagger, perhaps?' she added, going quiet for a moment. 'I'm not sure. I also see either the same dagger or another one with a goat's head carved into it.' She doodled a very basic sketch of a cross-piece incorporating this design, but did not push the matter, knowing she was already getting confused.

If Helen was correct and an object had been concealed in the church before being moved into the churchyard, then I wondered whether it might have been hidden in the vicinity of the organ – where the Earthquest members had felt compelled to explore the previous weekend. Without mentioning this information, I asked Helen if she had any idea where this object might have been located inside the church.

'I can point it out if you draw me a map,' she suggested, sliding across the pad.

I quickly sketched the church's ground-plan and passed it back to her. Picking up the pen, she dropped it down at the exact position of the organ, which stood against the north wall, just inside the chancel. 'But I reckon this dagger, or whatever, is now out in the churchyard,' she confirmed.

There was no mistaking her accuracy in this matter – inspiring me into immediate action. What about going to Ide Hill tonight? It was 8.30pm and we could be out there by ten o'clock.

'You are joking, aren't you?' she exclaimed, a look of disbelief on her face.

Rule one in questing is spontaneous action – respond to psychic information immediately, no matter how late or how far away the location might be. This creates a sense of urgency and expectation that has invariably proved to be a perfect environment for catalysing psychic events when out in the field. Leaving such trips until a convenient Sunday afternoon often leads to unsuccessful quests, as the enthusiasm and motivation caused by the initial psychic outburst will have waned considerably by that time.

'But it's dark, and it's a long way,' she protested, hardly believing her own ears. 'You're not serious, are you?'

Of course I was serious! I would make sure we had adequate protection before entering the churchyard.

Helen thought long and hard before rising from her seat. 'Well, if you want, but you'll have to give me a few minutes to get ready. You wash up the few things in the bowl and I'll try and find my old boots. It'll be muddy out there tonight.'

Bringing the car to a halt on the gravel track in front of the church, I killed the lights and sat back to take in the setting. Around the small green – not unlike the one at Danbury – were a few scattered houses, their interior lights muted by thick curtains.

Helen and I smoked cigarettes and watched the churchyard for over fifteen minutes before we even contemplated getting out of the car.

On the opposite side of the green were two fairly sedate pubs open for business, yet despite these obvious signs of life there was no one in sight anywhere. Ide Hill seemed unwelcoming, as if no one came out at night and no one visited here during the hours of darkness. It was a ghost village, like some New England homestead. One Victorian house, its front wall finished in white-painted slats, looked as if it had come straight out of the pages of a horror story by H. P. Lovecraft! This deserted, hilltop location certainly had a peculiar atmosphere at night.

'So what do we do?' she asked, looking apprehensively across at the thin church spire mounted upon a narrow stone tower, hidden among a billowing canopy of trees. 'At the moment all I get is bad feelings coming from the rear of the churchyard.'

Having already conducted the Cabbalistic Cross visualisation in a nearby pub car-park, we could do little more than play it by ear. We would slip quietly into the shadows of the graveyard and attempt to locate any source of negativity. After that, we would have to make it up as we went along!

Helen raised a smile, but I could see she was not happy. Her hands were shaking slightly and her eyes belied her usual happy-go-lucky personality.

Leaving the old Cortina, I locked the doors, tried to look inconspicuous and led Helen through the lychgate into the churchyard. Edging past the western wall we found ourselves inside the sombre cemetery, its erect crosses and leaning grave-slabs only just visible in the murky darkness.

We could go no further. Some sort of indication was needed of what we should do next. Reaching out, we held each other's hands and tried to concentrate on the location's etheric counterpart.

'Those trees over there,' she whispered, nodding to a thick clump of bushes on the eastern edge of the churchyard. 'I see a red mist in front of that cross.'

Out of the blackness I could just make out the source of her concern – a silhouetted stone cross mounted upon a rectangular pedestal some few feet short of the trees. Acknowledging her words, we walked cautiously towards the spot.

'There's something here. I'm sure of it, Andrew,' Helen said, her voice heightening. 'I see the red glow; it's here. Ol' my gawd, I see the goat's skull, suspended above the ground, in front of the cross.' She began breathing erratically and started to shuffle backwards.

I tried to tell her it was just a thought form, a memory of their presence in this churchyard; nothing more. Quickly I banished this unwanted residue by visualising and then throwing a flaming pentagram in its direction.

'It's gone,' she confirmed. 'But I can still see the red glow. It marks the spot, I'm sure it does.'

The two of us stood looking at the cross-shaft. The actual position of the grave had long since vanished, giving us no indication of where we might dig. From past experience I knew we had reached the most crucial stage in any psychic quest – the retrieval, or not, of an actual artefact. Furthermore, the success or not of our next move could make or break not just the immediate quest, but our whole future together.

I told her to remain still and use her inner eye to see if she could pinpoint the precise epicentre of the red glow, as this was almost certainly emanating from the concealed artefact.

Slowly she lowered her hand towards the ground as I watched her every move. 'There,' she declared with some conviction. 'It's there, and I can feel other things here as well, I'm sure of it. Perhaps as many as three, or four.'

The position indicated with her fingers lay at an angle some two feet from the cross. It seemed a random spot, without any obvious significance, so I only hoped she was correct as failure to find anything would induce instant despondency, and rule number two in questing is: despondency kills the conducive state necessary to produce accurate psychic information.

Her hand came into contact with the bare earth. 'There,' she said again. 'Try there.'

Switching on a tiny pocket torch, my fingertips became claws as I pulled away the wet but firm earth. No more than two inches below the ground, I touched upon the smooth metal surface of an object thrust vertically downwards. The dirt was rapidly cleared away.

I quickly identified it as the ornately cast handle of a dagger, its cross-piece fashioned into the likeness of a goat's head and a muddy black cord hanging from its pommel. Someone had pushed it into the earth to conceal its presence here.

With a look of complete horror on her face, Helen started to retch. 'Oh, Andrew, I've got pains in my throat and I feel sick,' she cried, reaching for her neck.

I told her to visualise white light entering her body as I quickly yanked out the ritual weapon and doused it with holy water, while reciting suitable words of Christian prayer. This would dampen its production of imbalanced energy which Helen had seen as a red mist at ground level. Slipping the dagger into my pocket, I looked around for Helen.

We would have to go. Placing an arm around her shoulder I led her away from the darkened churchyard, back to the safety of the car, where she could calm herself down and re-establish some sense of normality.

Helen regained her composure after a much-needed cigarette. 'I don't know what's going on, but I think that dagger was placed in the ground to charge it up,' she revealed. 'But there's other things in that churchyard as well.'

I asked her what she wanted to do, quite obviously not wishing to push the matter.

'I feel all right now,' she responded, staring back at the silhouetted image of the church. 'I just need a few more minutes to get my strength back and we can see what else is happening out there.'

Accepting her words, we rested, and then it was time for round two. Following another Cabbalistic Cross visualisation, we left the car and edged our way out into the churchyard. As before we were totally alone and therefore able to move freely among the gravestones towards the clump of trees where the dagger had been unearthed.

We needed a fresh fix on where to look; so, had she any ideas?

'In the trees, I see a red glow coming from within the trees,' she announced calmly.

Pushing our way through the thin layer of undergrowth we found ourselves entering a tiny clearing with only a couple of long-forgotten grave stones to keep us company.

'Here, over here,' she revealed, pointing down.

Helen indicated an area in the centre of the clearing. Crouching down I pulled away the soft, leafy earth. Almost immediately the tiny pocket torch picked out the tarnished surface of a chalice, crudely inscribed with magical symbols – including the *Monas Hieroglyphica*.

Again holy water was used to neutralise its magical influence, as I glanced nervously across at Helen. She seemed slightly anxious, but appeared to be handling the situation better this time.

She stood quietly, waiting for me to finish soaking the silver-plated cup.

Suddenly the church bell sounded the arrival of eleven o'clock. At that same moment Helen screamed at the sight of something unseen, something slithering into view from behind a gravestone.

'Ol' my gawd, *it's a snake*,' she yelled out as she frantically tried to break free of the undergrowth. Instead she merely became entangled in the thick brambles between her and the outside world, an unnerving situation that only made her scream out louder.

I told her to calm down. It was nothing, just a created thought form, probably a frightener left at the spot by whoever planted the artefacts. It did not exist.

'It does. It does,' she protested, as I leapt up and took hold of her arm, while trying to free her from the sharp thorns clinging tightly to her raincoat.

She began to cry, so with an arm as support, I guided her out into the open air. We were done here tonight. It was time to get away from this dreadful place, before it ended up destroying her completely.

Saturday, 25 March. 3am. Helen lay on the bed trying to forget the distressing events of that evening in the hope that she might snatch a few hours' sleep. Despite her wishes, the vivid memories of their disconcerting exploits at Ide Hill returned to haunt her again and again. Her mind regurgitated image after image of Andrew finding the goat's head dagger and of that cheap chalice inscribed with strange symbols.

She let these pictures pass through her mind, hoping they would return no more.

Gradually they did cease and very slowly she relaxed more and more until a stillness befell the bedroom. With her eyes fully open she now became aware of a mist entering the room and condensing into a solid mass just feet above her bed. As it slowly congealed she realised it was a huge goat's head – its horns long and curled and its eyes burning like coals of fire. So physically real was its grotesque face and long, angular snout, that she felt she could reach out and touch its matted grey hair.

Slowly its jaw dropped and from its demonic mouth emerged a crimson, forked tongue that flicked in and out.

Helen began shaking violently as she pushed herself back against the soft pillows and stared maniacally at this atrocious vision of hell.

Accompanying the vile manifestation was the overwhelming impression that those who had grounded these ritual items were now aware of their discovery – a realisation that so terrified Helen it forced her to emit one single, prolonged scream that broke the silence of the night.

14
Octavia's Hill

We needed independent evidence of what was happening to Helen as well as a stronger team to help combat any further psychic interference. For these reasons I had invited two close colleagues from Earthquest to join our efforts to uncover the shadowy activities of the Dark Council. One was Paul Weston, who had already accompanied me on the trek to the Paradise Mound the previous August. As a level-headed intellectual he could offer sensible advice on this sort of situation. The other was Alex Langstone, a friend who edited a pagan journal entitled *ASH*, short for Albion's Sacred Heritage; he had rendezvoused with the rest of us at Ide Hill around 6.30 that evening.

Following Helen's troubled night, which had brought with it the nauseous vision of the goat's head, she now believed that the Dark Council had returned to the churchyard and found that someone had unearthed their precious artefacts. Whether this was true or not was difficult to establish. Despite this, she felt sure they would return to Ide Hill around midnight tonight to complete their activities, regardless of our proximity. The whole thing had been arranged long ago to coincide with this Easter weekend and in no way would a small set-back like this force them to abandon their efforts.

The Easter connection made some sort of sense, as across Europe and the Near East bonfires have always been kindled on Easter Eve, a tradition that probably stemmed back to pre-Christian fire festivals. Ritual fires appeared to play an important role in the Dark Council's suspected work, something I realised after Helen had uttered the names of Persian deities from the ancient Zoroastrian faith during our visit to St Catherine's Hill earlier that month.

What might happen here tonight was beyond speculation, but having recovered from her ordeal Helen had agreed to return to Ide Hill. Before darkness fell we could hunt around for the stone seat she encountered in vision the previous Tuesday and then have a drink in one of the pubs across the green, before venturing back to the churchyard around 9.30pm. After that, well . . .

'The church is locked,' Alex exclaimed, slightly disappointed, rejoining Helen, Paul and myself as we stood where the dagger and chalice had been unearthed the previous evening.

Oh well, we would have to return another time. For the moment we should concentrate our efforts on locating the stone seat.

Leaving the churchyard, we joined the footpath that took us over the ridge of Ide Hill and offered a fine view of the flat Kentish landscape. It was strange, Ide Hill possessed a noticeably different ambience during daylight hours. The bleak Lovecraftian atmosphere experienced the previous night seemed almost unimaginable now.

A mature couple out hiking – both dressed in appropriate Arran jumpers and stout boots – came into view and went to nod a hesitant 'Good day'. Seizing the opportunity of possible assistance, I made reference to the stone seat. Had they seen it? Did it even exist?

The couple thought for a moment before turning to direct us further along the overgrown track. 'I think it's on the other side of the hill. A stone seat, let me think, yes, it was placed there as a memorial to Lady Octavia Hill, the inspiration behind the National Trust. She used to stand on the spot and wanted others to enjoy the same view.'

Lady Octavia Hill . . . The name was not familiar. Thanking them, the four of us journeyed on, pushing our way through the overgrown brambles and undergrowth towards our expected point of destination as the light seemed to fade by the minute.

At last a clearing appeared before us, just as the ridge sloped into a dense quagmire of woodland that stretched all the way down to the road. Before us stood a sturdy stone seat positioned so as to overlook a distant reservoir now only just visible beyond the rising treeline.

'That's it. That's what I saw,' Helen exclaimed, rushing up to the bench and touching its surface. 'I was standing on this side looking towards the direction of the church. The woman in blue stood on one side and pointed back along the path.'

'Here, look,' Paul said, now standing in front of the seat. 'It's got an inscription. It's badly worn but if you bring the torch over here we should be able to read it.'

All eyes now studied the sunken letters, half obscured by a thick crust of dirt and lichen. Gradually each one was cleared and word by word the inscription was unveiled.

> To the honoured memory of Octavia Hill who loving nature with a great love secured this view for the enjoyment of those who came after her.
> All thy works praise thee.

Exactly how Octavia Hill fitted into this story was not known. In spite of this her name posed some interesting synchronicities if nothing else. Octavia was not unlike the word *octave*. The number eight and the subject of music were both associated with the planetary influence of Mercury. Upon hearing of Woodhenge's unexpected introduction to this saga, Bernard had been inspired to link both this prehistoric monument *and* Ide Hill with music and the musical octave. These tentative clues had led me to recall John Michell's concept of ancient British trackways, sites and alignments being associated with the Mercurial current. All this appeared to make sense of Helen's psychic information suggesting that the Dark Council was staking out some kind of grid-like pattern of sacred places which when plotted on a large-scale map would form the figure eight. It was worth remembering that she had cited Ide Hill as the start of this national landscape geometry.

There was more. Helen believed that before being placed in the churchyard, the goat's head dagger, and possibly the chalice, had been hidden in the church. The precise spot she had indicated on a quickly scribbled map corresponded exactly with the position where, only days beforehand, members of the Earthquest group had been convinced an artefact lay concealed. What's more, they had searched in and around the organ, the musical instrument that accompanies the harmonic voices of the church choir. What better way to imbue an artefact with an energy reflecting a Mercurial influence?

Maybe all this was simply coincidence, but if the Black Alchemist and the Dark Council were both using Ide Hill, then it obviously held some kind of symbolic importance to them. Furthermore, Helen had seen the blue lady standing by the stone seat as if to emphasise its significance.

Another point which seemed relevant was that the footpath beyond the stone seat descended to the road below, meaning that anyone wishing to enter the churchyard surreptitiously could easily do so by using this pathway.

Helen agreed to place her hand on the cold stone to see if she could 'pick up' any psychic impressions. In response, she saw only the Madonna holding the Divine Child, which made sense as the church was dedicated to St Mary and its east window contained a majestic representation of Mary with the infant Christ.

As darkness had now encroached, it was time to venture back to the pub and wait there until we felt the time was right to re-enter the churchyard.

On the way back along the open track Helen distinctly heard the sound of hooves following in her footsteps. When she stopped, they came to a halt as well. When she recommenced, she heard them once more. Nothing was seen, and no psychic explanation was given.

The small, cosy pub contained only a handful of regulars. There were no other visitors and the general atmosphere was one of personal intrusion; almost as if we'd stepped into someone's front room. Still, it seemed a better choice than the busy pub a few hundred yards along the road which appeared to attract a clientele who prided themselves on frequenting the most rustic-looking ale houses in the Kentish countryside.

Sitting together at an old wooden table, I showed Paul and Alex the artefacts unearthed the previous night.

The goat's head dagger was unlike anything I had come across before. Cast in smooth yellow brass, it appeared to be a paper knife of Jacobean design. Both sides of the blade contained

Eliphas Levi's classic nineteenth-century illustration of the Goat of Mendes. Did the Dark Council utilise its Mercurial symbolism in their magical activities?

bas-relief scenes of naked men and women in the presence of wild animals and decorative foliage.

The smooth blade ended in a short cross-piece fashioned into a goat's head complete with large eyes, a hooked snout, long ears and curling horns that flowed into the handle. This had been carved into a slim tree trunk or branch, around which spiralled a snake or serpent with a ball or egg in its mouth. The pommel looped over as the head and neck of a griffin, its long tongue extending downwards to rejoin the top of the handle. Threaded through the hole, formed between the beast's head and its curled tongue, was a length of black bootlace some two feet in length. It was tied into a loop so that the dagger could be worn around someone's neck. This supposition was supported by the discovery of one single, curly black hair found caught in the space between the bootlace and the griffin's neck. There seemed little doubt that this had come from a man's chest.

The goat is considered to be a familiar symbol to practitioners of the black arts. It is the animal of the witches' sabbat and represents the horned deity, the so-called Black Man, worshipped in rural regions of Europe from medieval times through till the end of the seventeenth century. It is *not* an inherently evil symbol (no symbol is), neither is it an animal sacred to Hekate; indeed, in classical times it was usually associated with the frenzied rites conducted in honour of Dionysus-Bacchus. The only tentative link it has with Hermes and Mercury is through the Goat of Mendes, the animal venerated in the Nile Delta region of Egypt during Greco-Roman times.

In the nineteenth century, French occultist Eliphas Levi produced a line drawing of the Goat of Mendes for one of his books. So startling was the finished result that since then it has been constantly reproduced in coffee-table books on the occult, where it is invariably ill-described as the Sabbatic Goat. Levi's Goat of Mendes is much more than this – it is a composite creature with the head, horns and legs of a goat; the body of a man; the breasts of a woman, and the wings of a bird. On its head is an ignited torch, on its forehead is a pentagram, and it sits on a cube placed upon a globe; its left hand points down to a dark lunar crescent while its right hand points up to a waning moon.

The whole mesmeric image was originally meant to portray the hermaphroditic duality in nature and in the universe as a whole. Of importance to our debate, however, was the goat's phallus – it is a Caduceus wand complete with a pair of interlaced snakes, one black and the other white. Eliphas Levi undoubtedly saw the goat's duality in terms of the influence of Hermes and Mercury, so it was very possible that the Dark Council had incorporated this understanding of the Goat of Mendes into their own interpretation of the national energy matrix.

If so, then it did not diminish the role played by the Sabbatic Goat in the Dark Council's cycle of rituals. Like St Catherine of Alexandria, the eight great witches' sabbats are symbolised by an eight-spoked wheel. In November the previous year Fiona had suggested that the Friends of Hekate were utilising the 'calendar of [the] witches' in their rituals. Although she had only spoken of '6 celebrations', instead of eight, I was beginning to realise that she may have been correct, for Charles Walker had recently discovered a line drawing depicting 'Hecate's Wheel'. It was taken from a sixth-century BC stone disk from Ionia in Asia Minor and contains within its design a thick ring of looped folds, giving the basic impression of six coiled snakes around a central rimmed wheel containing six further snake-like curls. According to the caption accompanying the depiction, the symbol reflects the 'dark' side of 'the goddess of the moon'.[1]

The existence of this historical artefact implies that, like Fortuna and St Catherine, Hekate was once associated with a wheel-like device. In her case it appeared to symbolise six-fold divisions, perhaps an association with a yearly cycle of festivals, precisely as Fiona had suggested. Whatever the case, the wheel symbolism began to make sense of the Dark Council's interest in St Catherine's Hill, Winchester, as well as the goat and wheel symbolism attached to the witches' sabbat. These were my thoughts, although I made no mention of them to Helen.

The silver-plated chalice was almost an embarrassment. Standing some six inches high, it was the sort of item you could pick up as part of a set of six in your local department store. The outside of the bowl displayed a fairly well executed *Monas Hieroglyphica* – which is itself a complex variation of the planetary symbol for Mercury. To its left were lines radiating out of a simplistic eye. This could have been a crude form of the crayfish symbol found on certain Black Alchemist artefacts and derived from a magical formula composed in the fourth century AD by a Greco-Roman alchemist named Zosimos of Panopolis.

Completing the chalice's symbols was something quite peculiar. Hanging over the edge of the lip, on the face opposite the *Monas*, was a parallel line looped at the end to give the impression of a snake. The interesting feature here was that these parallel lines extended down *inside* the cup for a distance of some three-quarters of an inch before ending abruptly. This would mean that, when the chalice was full, the snake would look as if it was emerging out of the liquid and slithering over the edge of the rim.

Clearly there was a relationship between these items and the Black Alchemist material, but exactly what was difficult to say. Both Helen and I agreed that the Dark Council – the term first used by Markus de Capelin, the spirit guardian of St Catherine's Hill – did not just include former members of the Friends of Hekate, they were basically the *same* group reformed. We did, however, feel that it included several new figures from other groups who had each brought with them their own particular brand of ritualistic preference. I doubted very much whether they actually described themselves as 'the Dark Council'. However, as it seemed they were no longer known as 'the Friends of Hekate', we would use this new term until we knew otherwise.[2]

'So when do you think the dagger was placed in the ground, then?' Alex asked Helen, having carefully studied the two artefacts.

'Well, I feel they were left for two days in the church before being buried in the ground for a further eight days,' she explained. 'They would then have been moved on to a new location and the cycle repeated.'

'So when were they placed in the churchyard?' Paul asked next.

Helen nodded slowly as she lit another cigarette. 'Well, when I psychometrised the dagger last night I felt it had been in the ground since the seventeenth and would have been removed tonight. Before that it was inside the church somewhere near the organ, it seems.'

'That's where we were looking on Sunday,' Alex broke in. 'But Sunday was, what, the nineteenth? So we wouldn't have found anything as it had already been moved into the churchyard.'

Paul studied the brass dagger again before looking up at the handful of locals, who seemed to be dwindling considerably. 'You're right, Ide Hill has got a strange Lovecraftian, New England feel about it. It's like Innsmouth, the isolated community in Lovecraft stories where everyone is descended from fish people!'

It raised more than just a laugh and lightened the proceedings before our intended nocturnal exploits.

'I don't mind admitting, all this is blowing my mind,' Alex exclaimed, fumbling with the chalice. 'And where the hell will it go from here?'

Helen looked at him and shrugged her shoulders. 'I think you'll find they'll be back tonight. I've also seen Silbury again this week, so if they're not going to be here then they could be in the Avebury area, I suppose.'

Paul and Alex would return to Essex later that night, but Helen and I had decided to take a look at the megalithic complex of Avebury and nearby Silbury Hill the following day, Easter Sunday. She felt sure the Dark Council had been operative in this area, so we intended looking for evidence of her words. If nothing else, it would be a day out in a more spiritually uplifting environment.

One by one glasses were drained and finally the jovial group of four rose from their seats, shouted their thanks to the barman and ambled towards the deserted green.

'Still no one around,' Paul commented, leading the pace back across the green. 'This is absurd. I don't think we've seen anyone actually out in the open at all.' He paused momentarily, before adding: 'It's probably spawning time!'

The conspicuous-looking group chuckled to themselves as they marched briskly beneath the lychgate and edged along the western wall of St Mary's church to reach the disorderly array of crosses and graves filling the secluded churchyard. The night was clear, and quite bright, but a faint ground mist rose slowly into the still night air.

'What shall we do, then?' Paul asked, coming to a halt in the proximity of where the artefacts had been removed just twenty-four hours beforehand. 'Cabbalistic Cross?'

The four gathered together and conducted the familiar protection visualisation before linking hands and raising the cone of power. Rule three of psychic questing is to overcome embarrassment. Don't be afraid either to link hands with others of your own sex or to conduct meditations at times and places that may not seem convenient or even appropriate.

Recalling the troubled events of the previous night, we spent some time strengthening the wall of protective light as this would be our first line of defence against any stray energy forms lurking in the shadows. These things are like flu bugs. Once they get into your system they will bring you down; aura building is the best preventative measure against such extraneous psychic influences.

Completing the mental exercise, and with our hands still linked, we waited for some sort of response.

'I see them here last night,' Helen said in a low voice. 'Four of them, three men and a woman. It was at three o'clock, which was when I saw the goat's head. The dagger and chalice were offerings to him, and he was displeased at their removal.'

In other words we had drawn the goat influence to her home by removing the artefacts. Unfortunately for Helen, this made sense.

The London psychic fell silent for a moment only, then her hands began to tremble. 'Oh no. Ol' my gawd, I can see the goat's head here, now. And it's got a body this time. It's approaching us and moving closer. It's awful.'

I told her it was simply a thought form – a mass of energy collected together and imbued with only a base intelligence. It was not real and could not harm us, provided we remained strong and did not break the circle.

I felt no fear, but I could see by Helen's trembling hands that she was unconvinced of the thing's intangibility.

'Andrew, it's hideous,' she declared. 'It's about seven feet tall, with those same eyes like red coals.' Unexpectedly, she craned her neck to look over her shoulder. 'It's behind you, Andrew. It has a hairy human body covered in a white shroud, and it's got goat's hooves.'

Hooves? Of course, she had heard 'hooves' earlier, although I had interpreted this as implying she could hear *horses'* hooves, not the cloven feet of a goat-man.

Helen accepted the suggestion that the obscene supernatural entity had been around earlier, as she watched it move slowly around the circle, its long, red tongue flicking like a snake.

It was important for us not to take its presence seriously. Throw back anything it had to say and eventually this would act as a kind of self-destruct mechanism. Whatever happened, the circle was not to be broken and no one was to invoke fear, for fear would only increase its strength.

I asked Helen to find out its name. Gaining names was very important as in this game they can be used in a ritual banishment, like punching in a codename to delete a computer file.

'He calls me "Helena, the discoverer of the True Cross",' she revealed, unaware of what this meant.

It was mocking Helen by associating her with St Helena or St Helen, the mother of the fourth-century emperor Constantine the Great. In early Christian tradition she was said to have travelled to Jerusalem and discovered the remains of the Cross of Crucifixion on Golgotha Mount.

'He's approaching the circle again, between you, Andrew, and me. He says: "Just let me into the circle and I will show you more artefacts."'

I told her to ignore it. It was a trick. Once again I asked for its name.

'He won't tell me.'

'What is it, Mr Goat?' I said dryly.

Alex giggled, shaking the circle of linked hands. Helen and Paul joined the infectious laughter.

'He stamps around wildly now,' she revealed. 'I think he's getting angry.'

We laughed even more.

'He now says: "I am the Supreme."'

What sort of name was that! Supreme what?

This amused us even further. Good, if we could keep this up, it would eventually exhaust its accumulated energy and simply cease to exist.

'He says he is "Master of All",' she jokingly exclaimed, her tone rising by the minute.

It was certainly not giving us a sensible name so, as a purposely created energy form, perhaps it had never been presented with one in the first place.

Still our hands were linked. Periodically I told everyone to continue visualising the wall-like cone of light that divided our circle from the rest of the churchyard.

Helen relayed its messages. 'He says he wants us to kneel down before him.'

OK, provided it knelt down before us, first.

The spectral form persisted in wandering around the circle as if waiting for the moment when we would break our concentration, break our link, and that was not going to happen.

'He declines,' she responded.

Thought he might. I called his bluff and won. I asked Mr Goat what exactly he wanted.

She listened to his reply. 'Says: "You have taken a gift that was given to me."'

All right, it could have the dagger back, but it would not like what we had done to it. I was wearing it around my neck just as its previous owner had done.

The others giggled again, and this time we could not stop.

'Mr Goat seems to be fading in and out,' she suddenly declared in an excited voice. 'He seems to be breaking up.'

Good, it was working.

'He's not speaking any more and he's now climbing up the tree to the left of us. 'Ol' my gawd, he's going out on to the branch. *Do something*.' Helen started panicking again.

Some of the tree's branches hung over our circle and he was obviously attempting an entry from above. Again I told everyone to visualise the cone of power with as much conviction as possible. Thinking fast, I realised that now was probably the best moment to blast him, so I suggested we see the blinding white light from our circle radiating out like spokes of a wheel until it completely filled every crevice and dark corner of the churchyard. See it pushing through the tree, and see the goat-man evaporating like a vampire hit by the sun's rays.

'It's done it. He's disappeared,' Helen confirmed, sighing loudly. There was a moment of silence, before she added: 'The churchyard feels calmer now. I don't sense anything around at all. I think it's over, but I have the feeling of someone moving closer, a physical person this time.'

'Me too,' Alex confirmed. 'I'm sure I heard a rustling in the undergrowth.'

'I heard it as well,' Paul cut in. 'Come on, I think it's time to leave.'

Energy forms were easy to beat, but humans were quite another matter. Closing down the circle, we made a quick exit and headed back across the green towards the welcoming hospitality of the public house.

15

Cracking the Crucible

Sunday, 6 August 1989. The ringing of the doorbell announced the arrival of John Horrigan and his wife Kerry. Like the rest of the group already seated in the front room of my Leigh-on-Sea flat, they were members of the Earthquest team.

The couple climbed the stairs and joined the assembled party waiting patiently for the meeting to begin. Present were Paul Weston and Alex Langstone, who had both accompanied me on several occasions to see Helen over the past three months, and a young psychic named David. Over the past year he had supplied me with a wealth of disjointed but quite intriguing information concerning the apparent activities of the Black Alchemist, Rachel Goodison, and locations he believed to be associated with the Friends of Hekate/Dark Council.

All present had pledged their support to help counteract a dark ritualistic event that Helen felt would occur on or around Friday, 18 August – the feast day of St Helen in the Christian calendar.

After I had supplied everyone with tea, we turned our attention to Helen's continued contact with the Dark Council. The first couple of months had been quite intense for the south London psychic, with clear and accurate material produced almost every week. Since then, however, her mental link with their clandestine activities had become strained and much less defined, a pattern I had noted before with other direct information psychics. For those still relatively new to the story, I summed up the more intriguing incidents recorded in Helen's magical diary over the past four months.

On Thursday, 27 April, Paul and Alex were with Helen and myself in Ide Hill churchyard when we had chanced upon another silver-plated chalice and a tiny glass phial containing a strange pink liquid. The cup, identical to the one found at the same spot in March, had been daubed with red nail varnish and crudely inscribed with a number of undecipherable symbols. Although empty when picked up, the inside of the bowl exuded two quite distinct aromas, one like surgical spirit and the other similar to rotting meat. We had been unable to test the pink liquid as on Monday, 1 May the glass phial had unexpectedly burst in the breast pocket of my overcoat on arrival at the very spot where it had been discovered just four days before.

Strangely enough, various other incidents occurred at Ide Hill that same afternoon. Minutes before the pink liquid had filled my overcoat pocket we had decided to take a closer look at the grave in the vicinity of where all four artefacts had been unearthed. It belonged to Jane Boaks who died at the age of seventy-four on 15 March 1921. This I had found mighty coincidental as in Roman times 15 March was known as the *Ides* of March, immortalised in Shakespearian tradition. A coincidence perhaps, but 15 March also happened to be the date Helen believed the goat's head dagger had been concealed inside the church, before being transferred into the churchyard two days later.[1]

Another curious revelation on that May Bank Holiday Monday concerned the identity of the mysterious blue lady first seen by Helen standing next to Lady Octavia Hill's seat, during a meditation at her home on Tuesday, 21 March. Since then she had glimpsed this spirit guardian on further occasions, but after leaving Ide Hill on this particular afternoon Helen had referred to her as a 'saintly lady' named 'Edith' who 'did a lot for the Church'. Previously, she had only spoken of her as a nun who 'didn't look like one'; she apparently wore only a plain white robe and displayed no obvious signs of Christian devotion.

On hearing this in the car coming away from Ide Hill, I had squealed in delight as, unbeknown to Helen, I had recently discovered that the etymological derivation of the *ide* in Ide Hill came from the Anglo-Saxon female name *Eadgyth*, later Anglicised as Edith. So, in effect, the location would once have been known as Edith's Hill.

So who was this Edith? I felt I knew. Just six miles north-east of Ide Hill was the village of Kemsing where, according to Anglo-Saxon tradition, in AD 962 (AD 961 in some accounts) a daughter was born to King Edgar and his devout wife Wulfrida amid signs and portents of her future greatness. She was given the name Eadgyth, and after spending her youth in quiet seclusion at Kemsing she devoted herself to God and was taken by her mother to the monastery of Wilton in Wiltshire, where she spent the rest of her short life. She was honoured with the title of abbess and having turned down the throne of England – following the death of her half-brother, Edward the Martyr – Eadgyth predicted her own demise and sadly passed away on 16 September AD 984 at the age of just twenty-two. She was later canonised and became noted for her visitations in spirit form long after her physical death.

Helen's description of Ide Hill's spirit guardian as a 'saintly lady', a nun, who 'didn't look like one' fitted St Edith very well. Anglo-Saxon nuns would not have worn Norman-style wimples and black robes. They probably wore brown or white garments of simple design. St Edith also 'did a lot for the Church' as Helen aptly put it. She endowed the abbey with great wealth and provided enough money for the residents of Wilton to build a new church dedicated to the memory of St Denis.

Even today there is a holy well dedicated to St Edith of Wilton at Kemsing, so I saw no reason why the blue lady seen by Helen, as well as the Eadgyth behind Ide Hill's place-name, were both not allusions to this Anglo-Saxon saint. What the local historians had to say about such matters was not known; however, a St Edith connection with the psychic questing story was by no means new. In August 1988 Bernard had almost certainly encountered her radiant spirit in Danbury churchyard prior to the Paradise Mound episode, and as early as March 1980 my colleague Graham Phillips had begun receiving visions of her and a local holy well dedicated to her memory whilst living in Wolverhampton. He saw her as a very important woman and for some reason she appeared to be keeping a watchful eye on our questing activities even to this day. Helen, by the way, had no knowledge whatsoever of these earlier incidents concerning St Edith of Wilton.

The final anecdote concerning our involvement with Ide Hill was somewhat amusing; well, to us at least. For some months I had been corresponding with a young and very promising

Eastbourne psychic named Derek Prior. He had avidly followed the Black Alchemist story and on several occasions had been drawn to various East Sussex sites on the strength of his own psychic inspiration. He had never located any artefacts, but was optimistic about the possibilities of such psychic discoveries.

Quite independently, Derek began seeing Ide Hill in dreams and visions during late April, and grew to believe that the Black Alchemist or one of his associates had visited the churchyard in recent weeks. So strongly did he come to accept this view that two days after we had uncovered the second chalice and glass phial beneath a cast-iron celtic cross head, Derek journeyed to Ide Hill with some friends. Here he received the impression of an object buried beneath a cross and was led into the churchyard to the position where, unbeknown to him, we had made our own discoveries. Upon entering the undergrowth he had noticed the disturbed earth and suspected the worst. His fears were confirmed when, on entering the church, he looked in the visitor's book and found we had signed it just two days beforehand!

Derek Prior was undoubtedly the most unlucky person in psychic questing and all because he was pipped at the post by our own nocturnal exploits! Still, at the speed he was developing his own abilities, he would achieve success soon enough.

John fidgeted in his chair, looking over to where I sat in the midst of notes and papers scattered across the carpet. 'So what's all this about heavy stuff happening, then?' he asked in his broad Southend accent. He wanted to get on to the main meat of the day, but the story had still to be brought up to date.

Over the past couple of months Helen had been able to minimise her focus on the Dark Council's apparent activities by aiding Paul, Alex and myself with our interests in the Seven Swords of Meonia. These were eighteenth- and nineteenth-century ritual weapons I had been tracing the history and whereabouts of for nearly twelve years. So far six short steel swords, all identical to each other, had been unearthed under somewhat mysterious circumstances and we were now searching for the seventh and final sword.

Helen had put her mind to the subject at the beginning of May and had immediately provided us with invaluable clues concerning a Seven Swords connection with the town of Brighton in East Sussex. In the weeks and months that followed she had subsequently produced a veritable wealth of new material on the Victorian mystery and intrigue surrounding the Swords. Quite obviously, this had allowed Helen to focus her mind away from black questing – which could in no way be described as a healthy area of study – and on to more fulfilling questing pursuits.

Despite these new-found interests Helen had repeatedly been informed during psychic communications that Friday, 18 August would see a major Dark Council ritual somewhere in Britain. The significance of this date, as opposed to any other, seemed to lie in the fact that it was the feast day of St Helen and, by coincidence, the day before Helen's own birthday. Further information from the south London psychic in the past few weeks now indicated that this monumental event would take place in the vicinity of St Catherine's Hill, Winchester. What's more, it would apparently involve the transformation of a force associated with St Helen into some form of antithesis linked directly with Hel, the Norse goddess of the underworld.

To me this made complete sense. St Helen, or Helena, was more than just the mother of Constantine the Great and the discoverer of the True and Living Cross in early Christian tradition. In Britain and elsewhere in Europe St Helen became associated with an Iron Age goddess named Elen. In the Welsh *Mabinogion* tradition she presided over the roads and ancient trackways that criss-crossed the landscape, an attribution retained today in the remaining Sarn Elen roads of Wales. As Elen of the Hosts she was associated with the spirits of the dead who travelled the spirit paths in dead-straight lines as will-o'-the-wisps and flickering flames. Light and fire were the two most important symbols of Elen, whose name derives from *el* or *elle*, an Old English prefix denoting 'light' or 'bright', as in the *el* of *El*ves or *El*le folk, who were types of Little People said to appear as mysterious balls of light.

Elen, and therefore St Helen, was seen by some as the patron of the British energy matrix, controlling the lines of force denoted by the ancient and holy places, and marked out at night by the kindling of bonfires during ancient fire festivals. Back in March psychic information relayed to Helen by the spirit guardian Markus de Capelin had suggested that the Dark Council were utilising the Mercurial energies of the British energy matrix. Now it seemed they had turned their attentions to a female counterpart in the form of the goddess Elen, the life-giving light of the land.

To hijack and transform the national energy matrix into some kind of antithesis of Elen would require the use of an appropriate *omphalos* of great magical potency. Once chosen, the Dark Council, or whoever, would need to replace the goddess of light with some kind of dark counterpart, in this case the Norse Hel, using carefully planned ritualistic activity. If successful, they could then establish Hel as their own mistress of the energy matrix in the belief that through this relationship they could subtly influence the collective minds of the masses, thus allowing the tides to change in their favour.

As I had emphasised on many occasions before, whether such people could *really* achieve chilling results of this nature using occult practices was totally irrelevant. The sheer fact that groups such as the Dark Council appeared to believe in such power showed them to be very dangerous people indeed.

The problem here was that our Helen aligned with the subtle aspects and influence of St Helen through her name association and coincidental birth date – remember, the goat-man in Ide Hill churchyard had mockingly referred to her as 'Helena, the discoverer of the True Cross'. Helen was also linked in mind with the Dark Council, so if they conducted a heavy ritual involving Elen or St Helen it would almost certainly have a powerful effect upon her mind and body in more ways than one.

'OK, I can handle all this, but what's going to happen and how does it relate to St Catherine's Hill?' John was excited by the sheer prospect of encountering paid-up members of the Dark Council.

Most of these connections with St Helen and the goddess Elen I had worked out some while back, but now Helen believed this grand ceremony would take place at St Catherine's Hill, Winchester. On hearing this my stomach had churned, for I knew it made perfect sense of what we had learnt so far. Furthermore, David had independently cited St Catherine's Hill as the obvious location for this intended event, so I let him explain why.

From the carpet he nodded in anticipation. 'Right, well the way I see it is that St Catherine's Hill has been repeatedly charged with negative chaotic energy for a very long time. It has been prepared.'

The rest of the assembled group turned their heads to take in his information.

'On the night concerned this accumulated energy will be symbolically released as a blood red fire into the energy matrix, almost like cracking open a crucible of liquid flames and letting the contents flow away.'

'Why choose Winchester?' Paul queried, seated on the settee. 'Why not anywhere else?'

David swallowed before answering. 'Because it was the seat of power from where the Anglo-Saxon and Norman kings governed and controlled the kingdom; remember, it was thought to be King Arthur's Camelot during the Middle Ages. For some people it is still a sacred *omphalos*, concerned with national sovereignty and kingship. To the Dark Council it not only represents the seat of the old kingdom, it is the seat of a new magical domain – the hub of an enormous wheel of terrestrial power.'

I reminded everyone that Winchester had been referred to as a centre of operations for one of the three Friends of Hekate-linked groups mentioned in the anonymous letter received by Toyne Newton in 1981. Winchester had also been described by Mary, Toyne's elderly psychic friend, as 'the Roman wheel' – a clear allusion to the Catherine-wheel. When Helen and I had first visited the location on Sunday, 12 March she had spoken of an intensive series of chaotic rituals she believed had taken place there. These, she said, were corrupting the ancient site's inherent energies to such a degree that they were quite literally destroying St Catherine's Hill on an etheric level.

'Some form of counter-measure is going to be necessary,' David added, picking up the OS map containing the Winchester area.

'What about Helen?' Kerry asked from the armchair. 'Is she going, or what?'

Although there had been very little activity on the Dark Council front, she was unsure whether she wanted to go to St

Catherine's Hill or not. The two most important objectives for the night of 17/18 August were, first, Helen's safety and, second, preventing the Dark Council from aggravating St Catherine's Hill any further. To achieve these aims we would need to split into two groups – one to stay with Helen and the other to stake out St Catherine's Hill. For the moment, however, little more could be said or done until we had a clearer picture of what was to occur at Winchester on the feast of St Helen. There were twelve days at least before the big day and in that time anything could happen; anything at all.

16
Midnight Sun

Wednesday, 16 August 1989. Helen stared silently out at the dark countryside as the Cortina estate cruised towards Winchester. In the back seat was Paul and keeping pace behind were John and Kerry Horrigan with Alex in his red Ford Fiesta.

The next exit on the M3 motorway would take us on to the minor road leading to the base of St Catherine's Hill, and then the night would really begin.

Some decisive changes to the schedule had been made since our last get together to discuss the current venture, not least of all a last-minute change in dates. Matters had taken an unexpected turn on Wednesday, 9 August following an important telephone call from my friend and colleague Caroline Wise. That morning she had received a lengthy letter from Chesca Potter, a well-known artist and illustrator of mystical themes, with whom she had penned an informative booklet on the mysteries of the goddess Elen.

The letter spoke of an extraordinary dream Chesca had experienced during the night of 4/5 August. Without any knowledge of our interest in St Catherine, or of our planned assault on St Catherine's Hill, the visionary artist had become aware of a night-time setting featuring a small group of people including Caroline and myself. She could see a ruined church on a grassy hillock, beside which was a house built and designed to draw away the sacred site's inherent energies.

Around midnight she and Caroline moved forward to conduct a ritual invocation to the 'Sun of St Catherine'. Raising her head she had found the dark indigo sky illuminated by a mesmerising 'Midnight Sun' of fiery red. By summoning its burning flames they were invoking the power of St Catherine. Why exactly she had not been told, and on waking she knew only that the dream's contents should be conveyed to Caroline.

I had listened in awe to Caroline's words and had nearly dropped the telephone receiver when she casually mentioned that Chesca's dream was probably connected with the full moon eclipse scheduled for the early hours of Thursday, 17 August – the eve of the feast of St Helen.

My mind reeled with conflicting thoughts and new insights as I realised the implications of what she had just said. The full-moon eclipse, as well as Chesca's remarkable dream, had to be associated with the dark ritual we believed would take place at St Catherine's Hill later that same day.

Thanking Caroline, I had immediately rung Chesca at her home in Leeds. Attempting to keep calm, I asked her what she felt her dream implied, to which she had said: 'I think it means that St Catherine is linked with something in the air at this present time, and I am being drawn towards her influence for a specific reason.'

Chesca went on to reveal that in certain Christian traditions St Catherine of Alexandria was seen as the cousin of St Helen, and sometimes even as her *mother*. I could find no standard references to these legends, although I knew the two saints were certainly seen as contemporary figures. She also explained how St Catherine embodied the darker aspects of pagan dark goddesses such as Hekate – a conclusion I had drawn after realising that she possessed her own wheel symbolism. St Catherine's apparent link with the Midnight Sun, the full moon eclipse, was important I felt, as such baleful occasions have always been seen as moments of great magical potency in religious traditions across the world.

Also of possible relevance to the saint's darker virtues was a curious fact I had unearthed concerning Winchester's chapel of St Catherine, built in the mid-twelfth century on St Catherine's Hill by Henry de Blois, who also founded the nearby church and hospital of St Cross. One source spoke of the chapel as being founded by the bishop of Winchester at a time when the 'cult of St Catherine' was at its height. It did not elaborate on this intriguing statement, leaving the reader to presume that Henry de Blois was in some way influenced by the existence of this cult.

What, therefore, was the 'cult of St Catherine' and what bearing, if any, did it have on Chesca's dream concerning the 'Sun of St Catherine'?[1]

Turning to more immediate matters, I briefed Chesca on what we believed would take place at St Catherine's Hill and she promised to meditate on the subject and let me know the outcome. Her letter arrived two days later and unbelievably it echoed, almost word for word, what I already intended to set up on the hill using swords as fixing markers. She had also enclosed some holy water from a sacred well dedicated to St Helen at Eshton, in the West Riding of Yorkshire.

In the days that followed I conducted some tentative research into religious and magical traditions connected with lunar eclipses and managed to unearth some potentially important facts. In summary, it seemed that fire, menstruation and a complete negation, or reversal, of lunar forces were the main themes associated with such fearful occasions, leading me to conclude that the full-moon eclipse *had* to be connected with the dark ritualistic event Helen believed would occur on or around the feast of St Helen.

But now we had a dilemma. Would the Dark Council 'crack the crucible' during the full-moon eclipse, in other words during the early hours of Thursday, 17 August? Or would they wait until the night of 17/18 August, the commencement of the feast of St Helen? Whatever the true answer, we had chosen the night of the lunar eclipse for our own nocturnal vigil. If we were early, and nothing of an untoward nature occurred, then at least we could place the swords in position to counter any intended actions by the Dark Council. These we could always retrieve at some later date.

As the day had drawn ever nearer, preparations were made. Helen had finally decided to accompany us to Winchester, so Kerry and I would stay with her inside a circle of protection on the banks of the River Itchen, just west of the hill. This would act as a base camp from which she could attune to the proceedings and hopefully relay psychic information on the Dark Council's assumed movements, should they put in an appearance. These would then be conveyed to John, Paul and Alex, who were going to stake out the clearing armed with a mobile telephone and whatever else they deemed necessary for the long night ahead.

THE SECOND COMING

We had arrived at Helen's flat during the early afternoon and here we followed Chesca's specific instructions on ritual cleansing and protection and then the journey to Winchester had begun.

The car interior was silent as we crossed open stretches of rolling agricultural landscape between Basingstoke and Winchester. Helen continued to stare out in solitude at the passing countryside deeply embroiled in her own thoughts.

Through the windscreen I began to make out the faint shape of a rising ridge of silhouetted downs, ending in a prominent hill crest I recognised as St Catherine's Hill. Slowly the ominous, sculpted landmark became clearer and satisfied that it *was* our destination, I drew Paul and Helen's attention to it. Soon afterwards Junction 9 signalled our departure from the motorway.

'Stop the car. Stop the car,' Helen pleaded, bursting into tears. 'Can I get out, please?'

Pulling the Cortina on to the rising ramp, I brought it to a halt on the hard shoulder. Helen took no time in scrambling out and crying uncontrollably on the roadside.

'What's the matter?' Paul asked from the rear seat.

It was getting to her – the thought of the long night ahead and not knowing what might lie beyond the horizon. I told him that Helen had insisted on coming with us, despite my suggestion that we wait it out in the safety of her home, away from any possible danger.

'Just take it easy,' Paul replied. 'A lot is going on in her head, and if we're not careful she won't last the evening, never mind the whole night.'

Accepting his words, I stepped outside to comfort her.

Putting the finishing touches to our circle of protection, I lit a Marlboro. This was going to be a long, drawn-out vigil and cigarettes were the only things that would keep me occupied when we hit the early hours.

Helen sat chatting with Kerry inside our makeshift hideaway among the undergrowth on the banks of the River Itchen, near the church of St Cross, somewhere south of Winchester.

A ring of burning green candles marked the extent of our

temporary sanctuary. Beyond these were representations of the four elemental forces at each of the quarters as well as an unbroken circle of sea salt – the ancient recipe for defence against malign psychic influences.

Every so often we would glance towards the western horizon, where the silhouetted image of St Catherine's Hill dominated the skyline. It lay just three-quarters of a mile away, so any rocket flares sent up by John, Paul and Alex would be seen without problem. They had left us earlier to survey the entire perimeter of the Iron Age ramparts and conceal four imitation Indian Army swords inscribed with magical symbols to imbue them with enough power to affect the hill's own inherent energies.

Above us to the south-west was the full moon, whose radiant light would soon be robbed by the passage of the earth's shadow across its face, and between now and then all we could do was sit and wait.

Thursday, 17 August. Laughter and joviality dominated the rest of the evening as the three of us told stories, recounted cherished memories and chatted idly. No one disturbed us, although on more than one occasion late-night walkers came within earshot of our position, necessitating periods of complete silence as we made sure they passed out of our range.

By 12.20am the pleasant atmosphere was changing rapidly. Helen had just picked up the presence of someone or something near the Miz-maze and could see John and the others lying on their stomachs close by. Moments before we had heard the distinct sound of rustling in the undergrowth, amplifying the sudden shift in perspective over the previous few minutes.

For the first time that night I began to sense unseen psychic energies pulsing like beacons from the black crest of St Catherine's Hill; Helen could sense it as well.

'I can see a blue van coming to a halt in the parking area below the hill,' Helen announced at last. 'It's like a Mazda, I think, and there's another van now, white, and a red car – a small one.' She stopped to examine the disconcerting scenario now forming in her mind's eye. 'Eight people in the blue van. Four in the white one and four more in the car. Sixteen in all.'

Sixteen people? Heading for the hill? I thought of John, Paul and Alex staked out at the clearing. Our only contact with them was via the mobile telephone, but this still necessitated me having to leave our cosy circle and make a car journey in search of a public pay-phone. So, before I did this, I wanted to make sure what was going on out there.

'Two men have now left the large van and are on their way up to the hill,' Helen revealed after some minutes of silence. 'They're in black – black tops, black trousers.'

They were almost certainly a scouting party. Any news of the other van and car?

'I can't see them,' she responded, falling silent once more before adding: 'I think the red car's parked up somewhere and I reckon they've also got mobile phones. I see the two men again – they're making their way around the hill. However, they're not going to where we found the fire pit, but into the trees, off to the left of the track. I don't think they've made contact with the lads.'

Further minutes of silence passed as no fresh imagery came to Helen.

'The two men have now lit candles in a wooded clearing,' she said next. 'I only hope John, Alex and Paul can see it. I think they're going to go for it now.'

What? The rest of them?

'Yes, they're going to make an approach from a different direction,' Helen confirmed, staring into the dark depths of the River Itchen. 'And I can now see charcoal grey sparks above St Catherine's Hill. Something's definitely happening up there.'

This stuff was getting heavy. It was approaching two o'clock and I realised it was time to find that telephone box and let John know the bad news.

Leaping to my feet, I visualised an opening within the ritual circle and made my exit back along the river bank towards the car.

Emerging from the undergrowth on to the deserted road, I saw something that unnerved me. Parked next to my Cortina was a red Metro, its windows wound down and no sign of the occupants, anywhere. Was this the red car Helen had seen park up somewhere?

The loud ring of the mobile telephone nearly scared the living daylights out of John, seated on open grass some fifty yards from the wooded clearing where the ritual libation had apparently taken place. Frantically, he fumbled with the device to locate the SEND button. Depressing it he said: 'Yeah, hello.'

Paul and Alex looked on with mild trepidation, wondering what the hell was happening down by the River Itchen to have prompted this eagerly awaited communication.

John – dressed for the occasion in a camouflage jacket and army boots – repeated Andrew's words. 'What was that? One blue van with eight people. One white van with four people and a red car with four people. All in black and coming up the hill. Heading towards us from more than one direction. Right. OK.'

Alex added up the total. 'That's sixteen people,' he announced quietly before smiling at Paul, who was returning equally amusing facial gestures.

'Nope. No scouts as yet, or candlelight. But we'll keep looking,' John was saying. 'Right, speak to you later.'

The rubber digits illuminated momentarily as John depressed the END button and dropped their only means of communication into his rucksack. 'Well, I don't know about you guys, but I'm getting inside that undergrowth, like now!'

No further words were necessary. The three blacked-out figures scurried silently into the nearby clump of bushes and lay motionless on their stomachs, awaiting the imminent arrival of sixteen members of the Dark Council ready to draw down the powers of the Midnight Sun.

Tense minutes passed before Alex noticed that one of John's legs was shaking almost uncontrollably. He nudged him and nodded.

'Oh, it's just my leg. It's gone dead. It often does that,' John mumbled, casually.

'Not worried, then, John?' Paul asked dryly.

This received a chuckle from Alex which became infectious.

The sudden rustle and flight of a large flock of pheasants cut short their humour. It had come from the vicinity of the footpath leading up to the hill, where they had earlier disturbed the very same birds when approaching the hill-fort. Someone or something had caused them to take flight and if they waited long enough they were going to find out what.

THE SECOND COMING

*

'They know there are people on the hill,' Helen unexpectedly exclaimed. 'I see two groups – one of nine and another group carrying staffs. I feel they've got the goat's skull with them.'

I recorded Helen's words on a pocket cassette and stared up at the gradually disappearing moon. Already the earth's shadow had eaten away a crescent-shaped lump of the lunar landscape, and more was vanishing by the minute.

In spite of the beautiful clear sky a low cloud-like mist had slowly engulfed St Catherine's Hill, making it impossible to see any more. It gave the hill crest an eerie quality, almost as if the fog had been drawn down to mask the tracks of those wishing to hide their clandestine actions.

Minutes passed as all eyes gazed skywards and watched awestruck as the moon was gradually eclipsed. Three-quarters of its pitted face was now no longer visible.

'I see spike-like energies over the top of the hill,' she said next. 'They're like arrows, jutting upwards and then coming back down. They're in red, dark green and black. I also see glimpses of other things as well – a large bird in concrete, a crown on a pillow and a huge mirror.'

Finally the soft lunar orb was robbed of its last light and in its place was a diffuse pinky glow as if someone had pulled a great cosmic filter across the face of the moon. Total darkness engulfed everywhere, giving the night a peculiar ambience.

'I see them all together, kneeling in a circle, their heads bowed with six daggers laid out in front of them,' Helen continued unabated. 'Very clever.'

What was clever?

'They're elsewhere in the lower approach field while the candles are still burning not far away from where I can see John and the others. The whole group are drawing down the moon. It's a "waxing"; that's the word I get: "waxing". They're capturing the complete darkness and sealing it at St Catherine's Hill by drawing it through themselves. One is saying something and there's . . .' she paused to listen, ' . . . like chanting.' She attempted to replicate this rhythmic moaning before giving up and going on to describe what she could see next.

Still I recorded Helen's words as the total eclipse produced a magnificent corona of blood-red light. It was reaching its final stage and all around us the atmosphere was decidedly strange. Some birds had started to chatter, believing it to be dawn, and from out of the darkness came the growing sensation of encroachment and intrusion. Helen had even seen a white wraith moving swiftly across the river. Then came a loud splosh as a heavy object descended forcibly into the water just feet away.

'What the hell was that? A fish jumping?' Kerry exclaimed in amazement.

It certainly did not sound like one. The incident combined with the extraordinary environment to unnerve me slightly. I told Helen and Kerry to re-enforce the cone of power even though the green candles were now no more than burning wicks in pools of molten wax.

Still the private party continued across at St Catherine's Hill. 'I can see them bringing their wand-like sticks down to touch the ground, but that's all. Now they're just kneeling there in meditation, doing nothing.'

Glancing upwards, the night looked unlike anything I had ever seen before. The moon had reached its ultimate moment of eclipse as only a bright orange disc, like a renegade setting sun, hung in the night sky. This was exactly what Chesca had seen. This was her Midnight Sun, the Sun of St Catherine, utilised since the dawn of time for archaic sorcery of a dark, sinister nature. This was why we were here tonight, and I just hoped to God that what Helen could see in her mind's eye was actually taking place in the real world, not in some parallel universe or in some astral domain beyond the physical.

I hoped to God she was right, for if this was just her imagination then the resulting despondency might force her to withdraw from the scene completely.

5am. Weariness was overcoming the three of us. Light was beginning to fill the cold, grey air and the dawn chorus of birds had begun to ring out for the second time that morning.

I yawned loudly and lit one more cigarette to occupy my brain. The Pro-plus tablets helping to keep us awake had all gone and only a few mushy sandwiches were left in the collection of plastic bags filled with discarded cling film, crisp wrappers and empty cans.

The night was drawing to a close and the lunar eclipse had long since passed. Only one tiny chunk of the orb's upper curved edge had still not been retaken, and now its faint light was being rivalled by the approach of the pre-dawn sun.

Stern movement on the path was greeted with some nervousness which lessened the moment we heard the sound of familiar voices and laughter.

It was John, Paul and Alex returning from their night vigil, still perky and seemingly in good humour.

I called out to alert them of our hidden camp deep within the murky undergrowth.

There were smiles on their faces as the three young men approached the now depleted circle of protection, the candles having given up the ghost long ago.

Joviality of this order was not expected. Something had to be wrong. Looking up at John, I awaited some comment on the long night vigil.

Pulling off his rucksack, he shook his head and frowned. 'No, sorry. We saw nothing – nothing at all.'

17
Brave Faces

In the semi-darkness, Kerry, John and Alex slouched in armchairs as Paul and Helen sat on the lounge floor, staring through the open curtains at the shimmering image of the full moon raining down its mesmeric light upon their adoring faces. The abstract setting was heightened still further by the ambient sounds of the German electronic band Tangerine Dream emanating from the two carefully positioned speakers.

'Doesn't it make you want to scream out,' Paul exclaimed, transfixed by the hypnotic power of this silent satellite of the night sky. 'It's as if you could lose yourself in its gaze. I could watch the moon for hours.'

Not particularly interested in their devotional observations, I cracked open a can of Guinness and took a gulp. It did not seem as if anyone was particularly interested in finding out what had really happened at St Catherine's Hill the night before.

Helen was holding out well under the strain of the situation, putting a brave face on the unquestionable fact that what she had seen and described during the full-moon eclipse had not come to pass. No evidence of van loads of black magicians conducting suspect rituals had been recorded by John, Paul and Alex in any way, shape or form. As dawn approached we had returned to St Catherine's Hill to see if we could find any trace of the Dark Council's presence there overnight. This had brought only further disillusionment.

Without much to say we had journeyed back to south London, catching the rush-hour traffic in the process. I was not a happy man when we finally pulled into the parking area below Helen's flat around eight o'clock that morning.

Some tried to get some sleep, others larked around whilst

Helen and Kerry went for a stroll in a local park. The rest of the day had been low key so far.

Dozens of times already I had attempted to re-evaluate not just Helen's alleged psychic imagery of the previous night, but our whole understanding of the so-called Dark Council. Did they even exist? In Helen's mind I firmly believed they did, and the various physical artefacts appeared to support this assumption. Remember too, it had been *me* who had asked *her* to try and gain psychic information on the activities of the Black Alchemist and the Friends of Hekate, not the other way around. Furthermore, so much of her material did make sense, and was entirely beyond the scope of her conscious mind, it would have been foolish simply to dismiss the whole affair out of hand.

Perhaps she really was under too much pressure. Having realised that the Dark Council material was engulfing her life, Paul, Alex and I had attempted to steer her towards other areas of interest and this was beginning to pay dividends. Her psychic material concerning the history of the Seven Swords of Meonia was sheer dynamite. In recent months we had made encouraging journeys to Brighton and Cardiff Castle in South Wales. These quite separate communications had even allowed Helen to acquire a psychic guide in the shape of William Burges, the nineteenth-century Gothic architect, Freemason and Rosicrucian who was seemingly behind the manufacture of the Victorian copies of the original Meonia Swords.

The Dark Council material had been on the decline since June, and before this week the only outstanding date had been the dark ritualistic event scheduled to take place on the feast of St Helen. This ill-fated episode had been predicted as long ago as April, and yet it had only been in the past few weeks that its apparent links with St Catherine's Hill and the full-moon eclipse had become apparent.

Despite the outcome, in no way could I accept that we had been entirely wrong in our assessment of the situation. Too much made sense for us to simply throw out the whole venture as purely the product of over-active imaginations. Chesca's quite remarkable dream had appeared to amplify the importance of St Catherine and the Midnight Sun, and David had independently confirmed the alleged threat posed to St Catherine's Hill.

Perhaps we had chosen the wrong night and everything Helen had viewed was yet to come – she *had* specified the night of 17/18 August, not the night before. On the other hand, maybe what she saw actually took place elsewhere. Either way, something had not been right. There was an important lesson to be learnt here, and this was not to put your whole trust in psychic material, not without good reason at least. Ignore this warning and, in the wake of such misadventure, you could end up throwing the baby out with the bath water. In other words, the real significance of what occurred would probably be cast aside.

Still, it did not really matter any more. As long as we stayed with Helen until her birthday in two days' time then no harm could come to her, whatever the reality of her presupposed psychic material.

'I feel I'm drawing the moon into me,' Helen declared, kneeling on the floor and talking out aloud. 'I wonder if the Dark Council are picking up on what I'm doing. Perhaps they're doing the same.'

I said I doubted it very much (not after the previous night's non-event).

Only silence followed from Helen.

'So, what's happening, then?' I asked, wondering where the evening was going from here.

Standing up, Helen walked across the room before turning to give me a filthy look. She slammed the door behind her and made for the stairs.

The assembled party broke away from their private thoughts to stare at each other and shrug their shoulders in dismay at Helen's unexpected reaction to my words.

What was wrong? What did I say?

Everyone listened as Helen could be heard padding around upstairs. Moments later the front door slammed as she left the house.

'What happened?' Alex was asking. 'What did you say?'

I just felt it was not a good idea drawing down the moon. Surely this should not have provoked such a sharp response.

'Err, I think you'd better go after her,' John suggested, leaning on the edge of his seat.

I gave it five minutes and then sent out a search party. Kerry went one way and Alex and I descended the concrete stairs down to ground level. Weaving in and out of the building's support pillars we looked everywhere, before splitting up and going in different directions.

Giving up I climbed back to the first floor, and then saw her, on the steps, trying to avoid discovery. She ran down the staircase with me in pursuit. I asked her to stop and eventually she did so, coming to rest on a low brick wall in the centre of the flagstoned courtyard.

In the darkness, I tried to console her as she wept uncontrollably. 'I feel under so much pressure, as if I should be coming up with the goods all the time,' she admitted, her face in her hands. 'I feel so trapped. Whatever changes are going on at St Catherine's Hill are happening inside me as well. I'm changing, Andrew.'

She accepted a hanky and blew her nose. 'I really do want to know about the whole Dark Council business; my curiosity wants me to carry on, but I just feel I can't. I feel they're taking me over. I just want to be on my own. I just want to be myself.'

She wiped her eyes. 'Oh, I know you mean well; all of you. It's not your fault. I just feel so ill inside. It began on the way down to Winchester and it's still there now.'

I tried to sympathise with her; tell her she was not under any obligation to produce psychic information on any level. We were all her friends and cared about her greatly. I hated to see her like this, and as for the Dark Council material of the previous night, it could be forgotten.

'I'm so mixed up, Andrew. I just don't know what to think,' she admitted, before lowering her head in defeat. '*I just don't know what to think any more.*'

Sunday, 20 August. Pushing open the wrought-iron gate I stepped inside the extensive grounds of Hadleigh Castle, southeast Essex's only real ancient monument. Perched high above the Thames estuary, facing out towards the Kent Downs, it is an ideal spot to spend a relaxing few hours away from residential Leigh-on-Sea, and this is what we had decided to do on this hot August afternoon.

With me was David, the young psychic, eager to find out what had occurred at St Catherine's Hill during the full-moon eclipse.

Navigating the knee-high castle foundations, delineating the positions of individual rooms marked with an appropriate nameplate, we found a cool area on the grassy bank overlooking the Thames and dropped to the ground.

I went over what had happened and how Helen had run out into the street on our return from Winchester. Somehow this incident had seemed to act like some kind of release for her – it had broken the spell – as the following day she had seemed as right as rain. We travelled to Ide Hill and spent the whole lunchtime outside a pub laughing and joking, then whiled away the evening in the conservatory of a south London bar trying to guess each other's past lives! Having got back to Helen's flat, John, Kerry, Paul and Alex had returned to south-east Essex, allowing me to spend an extra day alone in her company.

The following day – Saturday, 19 August and Helen's birthday – we had strolled around the bookshops and antique emporiums of nearby Greenwich, before driving across to Orpington hospital during the late afternoon; her mother was quite unwell and Helen appreciated the lift. I had then made my way back to Essex, all the time mulling over the whole four days, wondering where the hell it would go from here.

'You'll find she may now drop out of the limelight,' David suggested, picking at the grass. 'And if she does, I shouldn't worry about it. She needs a rest from it all, but she'll be back.'

All the indications were that Helen would indeed depart from the scene; and I could not blame her, really. She had continually gone on about changes taking place inside her body and her mind. The day before yesterday she had even dreamt about shattering the mirrors she saw as caging her into a self-made void.

'OK, so you didn't get a result out of Winchester,' he continued, 'but I still reckon you tipped the balance of something that was occurring down there. You prevented them from cracking the crucible and I think you'll find there is now some sort of internal struggle taking place within the ranks of the Dark Council.'

Maybe so. However, the most important thing now was to

abide by whatever decision Helen made, for only she knew what she really wanted to do with her life.

Tuesday, 29 August. Climbing the stairs I opened and read Helen's letter, dated the previous day. Its contents were not unexpected. She said she was 'doing things' now she would never have dreamt of three weeks ago. Her daughter was leaving home, she was moving house and her entire life was about to change completely. It continued:

> I have shut myself off from my psychic work. I am stopping it coming through as it's making me very depressed as I was last week when you were all here. The psychic side of things plays a big part in my life. I get great satisfaction out of it . . . Parts of it are very uplifting and to share them with you and the others makes it all worthwhile.
>
> But then there is the other side, the dark side. It comes on like a bat out of hell, does my head in, drains me, makes me feel ill and makes me want to run away. It makes me think bad things of you and then when you come over with the others and want me to tune into this and get more information, I go into a blind panic . . . I know how deeply this drains me and this is why I have shut down. I can't take any more of it . . .
>
> I have known you a long time Andrew . . . and hopefully you will understand how I feel . . .

She said she did not want to push her psychic abilities to one side forever, as no psychic can. She just wanted a complete break for a while. Having promised to stay in touch, she ended the letter by saying that in the future perhaps the circumstances might be different and we could all work together on more spiritually uplifting quests.

For the moment all I hoped was that she could find some contentment in her life.

18
Rachel's Anguish

Monday, 18 September 1989. Dozing in an advanced hypnagogic state, Bernard became aware of a subtle shift of consciousness. Just for a brief moment he glimpsed his body lying beneath the bed covers before finding he was suddenly elsewhere.

The Essex psychic was passing through a wooden gate marking the entrance into a place of Christian sanctity. In the darkness, broken only by the diffuse light of nearby street lamps, he climbed the gravel path, past an assortment of ageing headstones and box-tombs on towards the porch of Arundel's medieval church of St Nicholas. Creeping up behind him was a small crowd of gargoylian creatures, elementals, given life by the thoughts of God-fearing parishioners in a bygone age. They were the size of dogs, with spindly legs, long arms, sharpened claws and gruesome snouts, and yet they were not hostile in any way; they being more afraid of him than he was of them. Seeing they posed no threat, he simply ignored their presence and completed his journey.

Leaving the path, he crossed the grass towards the foot of the stone buttress where he had encountered *her* astral form before in dream, when she had tried in vain to draw him here. There had been danger in doing so; he had always sensed it in the air, but not tonight.

Here she was again, standing calmly beneath the great stone wall awaiting his arrival, dressed in her black cowled cloak, with brown trousers and black boots visible below the knee-line. She exuded no feelings of malice or hatred, only fear and desperation. He had to know why she had pulled him here tonight after such a long absence.

Instinctively he reached out to greet her. Rachel was an old adversary who was now turning to him for comfort and help. Without hesitation he clenched her outstretched hand, allowing the two minds to join together in mutual submission.

Suddenly she began to show signs of instant revolt and unexpected concern. She tried to pull away, but his hand grip was too strong and he would not let go.

Believing he was the stronger of the two souls, Bernard simply held on to her palm, preventing her from breaking free. She wriggled frantically, but still he held on, and with her inner power waning Rachel's troubled image started to lose its potency.

To his complete surprise her astral body slowly rose from the ground like a helium balloon in a child's hand. It reached as far as it could climb and still he held on without budging an inch. All of a sudden the woman's feather-like form began to pivot on Bernard's hand until it was upside down. Unable to go any further, Rachel Goodison calmly reverted to an upright position and floated back down to earth.

Totally perplexed, he watched the setting gradually dissolve, like a television screen losing its signal. Utter darkness followed, and with it came the sensation of rapid movement, allowing Bernard to regain consciousness once more.

Aware of his predicament, he fluttered open his eyelids and smiled to himself. For several moments vivid flashes of the extraordinary dream filtered through to his waking memory. Scenes of the peculiar gargoylian creatures and of Rachel Goodison standing in front of the church buttress, and then finally of the handgrip that had forced her astral image to float like a balloon.

What the hell was going on? Why had this happened? She seemed to be much weaker than ever before and, as in his astral encounters with her the previous year, he had the gut feeling that she was in some kind of trouble; at least, she wanted to get out of trouble. But who was she running from and why should she attempt this unorthodox form of communication which had clearly not gone the way she'd planned? These thoughts mystified him.

He considered getting out of bed and scribbling down a few notes, but plumped instead for turning over and going back to sleep.

Tuesday, 19 September. Leaving the house, Bernard found his keys and climbed into the Montego parked on the driveway. Switching on the ignition, he reversed the vehicle on to the road and found first gear.

Danbury was his destination, to see Andrew for a drink and a chat about their mutual interests. The last time they had met about a month ago they had discussed the latest developments in the Seven Swords story. No doubt Andrew would be bubbling over with new discoveries when they took their places in The Griffin.

Leaving the quiet residential area, Bernard turned into the main road and quickly reached the dual carriageway that would bring him in sight of Danbury's conspicuous church tower. Jutting skywards from its rural hill-top setting, it served as a familiar local landmark for many miles around.

It was a mild evening and provided there were no traffic hold ups he would reach Danbury in a matter of minutes. Increasing his speed to 70mph he cruised along in the slow lane and found very little traffic on the open road.

For some reason his thoughts kept returning to the strange dream, well, out-of-the-body experience, of the previous night. Still he could not make out why it had happened, despite the fact that its memory had played on his mind throughout the day. Perhaps Andrew could throw some light on the matter.

In the rear-view mirror Bernard clocked the presence of a silver Ford Capri gradually gaining pace in the same lane. He thought no more of the matter, until it reached a distance of around fifty yards behind him, before noticeably reducing speed to keep pace with his own vehicle.

Curious, he thought. Must be kids messing about. It looked to be a fast model, possibly a 2.8 injection[1], so they were probably speed merchants; nothing more.

He used this reasonable deduction to quell the concern mounting inside him. The sheer fact that they had not pulled into the overtaking lane seemed to suggest some direct interest in his car.

No, he had to be wrong.

The silver Capri then moved closer and closer until at just twenty yards from the Montego's rear bumper, it promptly swerved into the outside lane and accelerated with ease until it drew level.

In between keeping his eyes on the road ahead, Bernard turned his head to find out what was going on. What he saw greatly disturbed him. In the front two seats of the other vehicle were hard-nuts, men in their twenties, with aggressive cropped hair that matched their looks of malice and cool contempt. The driver wore dark glasses and he could see that the passenger sported a dark casual jacket. They glanced across at Bernard, unnerving him more.

It was then that he noticed, low in the back seat, a third man wearing a trilby hat as if deliberately to hide his features. Whoever this was, he seemed strangely different to the other two men, slightly older and quite obviously superior in position; he was their 'boss' and they were his minders. He could get no real idea of the figure's size or general appearance, but realised there was something eerie, something almost *familiar* about him.

For too long, perhaps thirty seconds or more, the Capri continued to keep pace before it accelerated rapidly and pulled back into the nearside lane, some way ahead of Bernard's car. All he managed to catch was the 'C' in front of the registration number, showing that the vehicle was licensed either in 1985 or 1986. He then watched as it moved on to the slip road and climbed the ramp towards the roundabout above the flyover. The vehicle's swift manoeuvring on to the A414 left him in no doubt that they were heading into Danbury.

He too now moved on to the slip road to follow in their tracks. Reaching the roundabout he saw that the Capri had now squeezed in behind a slow-moving vehicle some 300 yards further along the road.

Intent on establishing the car's licence plate, Bernard put his foot on the accelerator and attempted to catch it up. But it was no use, he became lodged behind a line of slow-moving cars and the Capri was last glimpsed turning a corner some half a mile outside Danbury.

He had lost them, and in addition to the frustration of not knowing who these people were and why they should want to tail him, he had failed to get their licence plate. What a stupid idiot. Still, other than his gut feelings inside, he had no real reason to cast suspicion upon them. They were probably just joyriders out taunting gullible motorists like him.

He wanted to believe this answer, but something told him he was fooling himself, for when he looked at the wheel he realised his hands were trembling uncontrollably.

Relaxing at a table, I saw Bernard enter The Griffin and stroll across to the bar. The barman listened to his words, nodded and commenced the slow process of pouring a pint of Guinness. The Essex psychic looked across and smiled warmly as a sign of welcome.

I waved casually and awaited his arrival.

He looked noticeably anxious tonight. Never before had I seen such agitation in him. Perhaps I was just unobservant and he was often this tense. Maybe he had a lot on his plate at the moment. As the managing director of a local business he worked long and often unsocial hours, particularly when his partner was away.

Collecting his pint of black liquid, topped with a thick, creamy head, he carried it across and took a seat.

Was he well?

'Fine, thank you,' he nodded, taking out his cigarettes. 'Well, no, not really. Some funny things are happening at the moment. I've just had a run-in with some skinhead types in a Capri, on the way up here.'

Skinheads?

'Eh, no, not skinheads as such, but the whole thing has shaken me up a bit.' He held out a hand as proof of his words; it was still shaking.

Frowning, I waited for the worst.

Bernard recounted the incident involving the C-registration, silver Capri and how it had stayed alongside his own vehicle for far too long before turning on to the Danbury road.

'I mean it could just have been kids out for the evening, but I don't think so,' he admitted, uttering a little nervous laugh. 'Maybe I'm wrong, I really don't know.'

He was regaining some colour now, but it seemed the incident still perplexed him. How about this character in the rear seat, this Mr Big, who the hell was he?

He shrugged and glanced from left to right. 'Not sure. This might just be connected with a strange sort of semi-conscious dream I had last night involving *her*, Rachel Goodison.' He drew out the syllables of the name as if forbidden to speak it in public.

I asked him to tell me more.

Bernard explained how he had encountered Rachel Goodison, the apparent priestess of Hekate, at the foot of a buttress in Arundel churchyard, and how her astral form had manoeuvred around like some kind of helium-filled balloon. 'It's certainly not the sort of thing that happens to you every night!' he concluded with a slight grin.

The Arundel connection was interesting. It was Bernard's psychometry of the so-called ape dagger found speared into a blood-soaked heart in Danbury churchyard during November 1987 that had led us to realise the woman's apparent association with this fortified West Sussex town. He had seen her standing at the foot of the great stone wall that surrounds Arundel's famous castle. Nestling just inside this imposing wall is the ancient church of St Nicholas, which Bernard had also described.

'She was where I've seen her before, in the churchyard,' he revealed cryptically.

In the churchyard? This was news to me.

'Yes, I'm afraid so. On more than one occasion I saw her standing by the buttress calling out to me in dream. I fought it and eventually it just stopped. I knew you would want me to tune in to see what else I could get,' he said, a note of humour in his voice, 'so I said nothing.'

When did this occur?

'When we first got on to this Arundel connection.'

That was around the end of 1987.

'Must have been, yes.' He looked around at the clientele engaged in their own conversations, either standing at the bar or sitting at tables.

In 1988 I had spent some time trying to find the woman we had referred to as BSA, the Black Sorceress of Arundel. All I knew was that she had some sort of active interest in antiques, and that the ape dagger found in Danbury churchyard bore a distinctive female handwriting which suggested it had been inscribed by her, and not by the Black Alchemist himself. There was also a vague hint that she was connected with Arundel Castle and had attended a well-known girls' school such as Roedean in East Sussex. Strangely enough, Toyne Newton's elderly psychic friend had also suggested a connection between Arundel Castle and the priestess with the Friends of Hekate; it was on hearing this that I had become convinced the two women were one and the same person.

'So, was there a connection between the dream and what happened this evening?' he asked, not quite knowing whether he should press the matter or not.

I would have thought the answer was definitely yes. But what did it all mean?

Perhaps the solution lay in understanding what he had said following the first derelict house dream the previous autumn; the occasion when he had encountered and then kissed Rachel Goodison.

At the time he had sensed her feelings towards him changing and had come to believe that in the future she would call upon him to bail her out of trouble. We had concluded then that she had fallen foul of her superiors over the publication of *The Black Alchemist*.

We had also decided that she was a weak link in somebody else's chain – her human failings would eventually lead her to expose even more of what was happening in her sordid life. All the indications were that Rachel Goodison, once the sinister Black Sorceress of Arundel, was going soft – an opinion made clear by the Venus flint left alongside the broken sword-stick in Danbury Country Park at the beginning of the year. In spite of these tantalising pieces of the cosmic jigsaw, extreme caution had been advised by all, and consequently no further incidents had occurred – until today.

There was still an outside possibility that the encounter with the silver Capri was just an unrelated incident. We already had the Black Alchemist, the Friends of Hekate and Helen's Dark Council, so how on earth would Mr Big and his minders fit into the picture?

Bernard looked at me and pulled a face as he shrugged once more. 'See what happens, I suppose.'

For the moment, the topic was dropped in favour of buying a round of drinks.

Telling him about the latest developments in the Seven Swords mystery took us through till nine o'clock when, without prompting, Bernard began to look somewhat distant, as if his mind was now on other, more immediate matters. He started sniffing the air. 'Can you smell incense at all?'

I said no, although obviously he could.

He posed the same question five minutes later and this time I depressed the record button on the pocket cassette and questioned him further about what he thought was occurring in our midst.

'The air's heavy, isn't it?' he mused, beginning to look more than a little agitated as he shuffled in his seat. 'It's probably nothing. Just forget it.'

Then, momentarily, I too received a waft of incense; the distinct smell of incense. Perhaps it was emanating from the pub's kitchen! No, there seemed to be an unusual atmosphere building in the bar around us. It had happened on many occasions before, and each time it generally indicated that some sort of psychic turbulence was in the air, so to speak. The noise steadily rising in the bar was slightly distracting, so I suggested it might be an idea if we moved into the open air.

Bernard nodded in agreement, so we downed the remainder of our drinks and stepped outside. Reaching the packed car-park he sniffed the air once more. 'Can't you smell it?' he asked again, looking towards me and frowning in complete bewilderment. 'You don't think they could have been out here earlier on, d'you? Staying in their car, perhaps, but conducting some kind of brief ritual?'

When Bernard makes statements such as this, it is usually a pretty good indication of what has really occurred. If this was so, then the cars should be checked, just in case they actually got out of the Capri.

Having looked over my own car, we turned our attentions to Bernard's Montego, surveying the bodywork, tyres and engine.

'Nothing as yet,' he sighed, standing back to view the vehicle. 'Maybe I'm wrong.'

I suggested he touch the bodywork and try using his mind. Nodding in agreement, he quickly found himself being drawn to the water well between the bonnet and windscreen. I joined the search, sliding my fingers along the length of the gap. Unexpectedly, I felt and pulled out something – pieces of paper folded into a small package. There were three in all and these I quickly studied in the diffuse light cast by the overhead lamps illuminating the car-park.

The first displayed Egyptian hieroglyphs printed in black and sandwiched top and tail between the words: 'To the memory of' and 'Priestess of the Hidden One'.

To the Memory of

Priestess of the Hidden One

By a lucky coincidence I recognised this text as the dedication plate of a book entitled *The Arts of the Alchemists* by C. A. Burland. Someone had obviously snipped out the wording on the page and used it for their own purposes.

The second piece bore printed words cut out of the same book to highlight the lines: 'She was buried, not through famine, nor iron sword, nor poison, but through all. Neither in heaven nor earth, nor in water does she lie, but EVERYWHERE she rests.'

The third piece of paper was slightly larger and on this in large, aggressive letters styled to look like Norse runes, with arrows for the serifs and strokes, was the message:

DONT THINK YOU
CAN CHANGE HER
MIND

Bernard did not look amused. 'Yeah, well, you can keep them,' he stated, striding back towards the pub entrance.

Hold on, this was going to need sorting out. Some guys virtually follow him into Danbury and then leave cryptic messages on his car – there was no way he could just walk away from this one.

Back inside The Griffin our seats at the usual corner table had now been taken, so we stood at the bar and ordered further drinks.

I attempted to assess the situation, hoping Bernard would fill in the missing details. The Capri's appearance had, we could now assume, been a firm frightener directed at Bernard; a clear case of 'We know who you are and where you live'. It had been followed up by the message left on the car bonnet warning him not to interfere in what appeared to be the fate of Rachel Goodison. However, it also implied that she had already made a decision that was favourable to them.

The dedication to the Egyptian priestess and the accompanying verse concerning the death and burial of an unnamed woman were further riddles hinting that Rachel would soon be dead. Whether this meant a physical or a symbolic death was difficult to determine. Was it possible that because she was now unreliable she had agreed to hand over her occult power to someone else? The runic-style message appeared to imply that if Bernard could get through to her, he might end up changing her mind.

So, was the figure slouched low in the back seat of the silver Capri her boss, the Mr Big of some sinister operation? Or was he someone else – someone more familiar?

'I don't even want to think about it,' he responded, shaking his head slowly.

So where did they come from? And why tonight?

A little reluctantly, Bernard finally agreed to psychometrise the folded-up pieces of paper, but after only a minute or so of concentration he placed them on the bar and looked baffled. 'No, all I get is the impression of a fast return to London.'

This was all too bizarre. Not only did there seem a likelihood of even more players in this strange game, it now appeared as if we were becoming entangled in someone else's internal politics.

19
The Dark Pool

Friday, 6 October 1989. Beneath his feet the snapping of twigs broke the midnight silence. Bernard merely continued walking, knowing he was nearing the end of his weary journey and would learn the truth soon enough.

Clawing branches brushed past as he wove through the matted web of tree trunks, until he saw the edge of the thick mesh of undergrowth. Beyond this was a dark open space, a small clearing dimly lit by the diffuse moonlight straining to break free of the low clouds passing overhead.

He could vaguely make out something peculiar in the midst of the unnatural glade, and not until he entered this discordant arena did his eyes allow the crystallisation of the wretched sight before him.

There was an ancient gnarled tree, its mangled bough split in such a way as to mimic the True and Living Cross of Calvary Mount. Barely could its dark form be seen, but clearer was the hideousness of its appointed task, for hanging limply from a thick noose, strung from the ugly cross-bough, was the lifeless body of a woman dressed in a long cowled cloak. Around the terrible roots of the monstrous trunk was a seemingly never-ending black viper of immense proportions, coiling itself tighter and tighter, like hands strangling the life out of a helpless victim.

Rejecting the purpose of these vile symbols, he stepped backwards as a veil of moving darkness cocooned the whole sickening spectacle, leaving nothing as a substitute.

Bernard pushed his way out of the dreadful nightmare until he reached a state of consciousness. He found himself shaking his head in disgust as he forced his senses to break free of this unruly dream. No, he did not want to return to that place any more.

Sitting up, he regained his composure and adjusted his eyes to the darkened bedroom. It seemed infinitely more comforting than the grisly scenario he had just been forced to witness.

It was that same nightmare. Twice that week he had awoken after being made to absorb its revolting content. Whether symbolic or not, there was little doubt in his mind that it signified the death of the former Black Sorceress of Arundel.

Monday, 16 October. Resting in the comfort of the front room Bernard heard the telephone ring out. Although there was more than one extension, he shouted, 'I'll get it,' to his wife, who was somewhere upstairs. Moving swiftly through to the dining room, he picked up the receiver with some trepidation.

At first nothing, only an open line. But then a silky female voice suddenly proclaimed: 'It will be the Dark Pool,' before a click signalled a return to the dialling tone.

Replacing the receiver, he sat down, a little unnerved. It was the second time this woman had given him the same message in as many days. Prior to this he had received another call where the voice had simply said 'Hello' in response to his own use of the word. So stunned had he been that after some three to four seconds of silence the caller had hung up.

And even before this he had received some five separate calls when, on answering the telephone, only the hiss of an open line greeted him before that too gave way to the dialling tone.

He had not told Andrew about the first calls as there was no real way of knowing who they were from. In spite of this, Andrew had experienced a vivid dream in which this same sequence of events had gradually unfolded. What's more, Andrew said the dream sequence had culminated in a series of brief telephone calls from a woman speaking on behalf of Rachel Goodison; possibly a trusted friend acting as a go-between. The upshot of all this would be a meeting between himself and Rachel to discuss her current predicament with the midnight mobsters in the silver Capri, whom he'd also had a chance to think about a little more clearly.

Although he had said nothing at the time, something now

wanted to tell him that the character Andrew had deemed to be the 'Mr Big' in Rachel Goodison's twilight world was already known to him. He had tried to throw out such a notion, but no, it would not go away – the figure slouched in the rear seat of the Capri, wearing a trilby hat to obscure his features, was in fact the Black Alchemist. This disconcerting realisation did little for him, probably because he had not wanted to think about the implications and, at the back of his mind, he still hoped there was an outside possibility that he was wrong. Yet if he was correct, then it meant that the man had returned to Britain from Spain, almost certainly to deal directly with Rachel Goodison.

Around the same time that the calls had begun he had also started to experience recurring nightmares – one showing the black cowled woman hanging from a gnarled tree and the other featuring a secluded whirlpool in the middle of a wood. In this one he had fought to stop himself from being sucked down into the hellish black waters. It was almost identical to one of the dreams he had experienced in the wake of the Paradise Mound episode the previous year. Somehow these nightmares were linked in with the mysterious telephone calls; how exactly he could not be sure.

In his mind there was a turbulence in the air, and for some reason this was affecting his own vitality. If this was true, then it might account for the recurring headaches and nausea he had been experiencing lately. He had tried to close his mind to these matters, and it appeared to be doing the trick, but there was no way he could prevent people from telephoning his home.

He played with his cigarette packet and pulled across a notepad (he was logging each call, just in case). 'It will be the Dark Pool.' What sort of message was that? Why didn't she just say something sensible? Why the cryptic clues? Presumably the Dark Pool was where he would meet Rachel Goodison. Perhaps it was also the site of the black whirlpool seen in his dreams.

The Dark Pool had to be local, somewhere known to them both, so the most obvious choice would be one of the three landscaped lakes in Danbury Country Park. If so, then when was the meeting to take place? Sooner, or later?

He thought about the silky-voiced woman on the other end of the line. Both he and Andrew agreed that it was not Rachel, but her 'contact'. His brief mental link with the tone of her voice told him she was ringing from London and was connected with some kind of agency, possibly one dealing with actors and actresses.

He felt confident that this almost fatalistic get-together was being arranged for the near future, and all he hoped was that he did not end up bottling out of the situation. On the other hand, if he did decide to let her down, he might be doing himself a very great favour.

A December evening. Outside in the hallway the telephone rang out. In the kitchen fixing a cupboard, Bernard listened as his wife responded to the caller with a polite, 'Hold on, I'll give him a shout.' There was a pause before: 'Bernard. It's for you.'

'Right, thanks,' he replied, laying down his tools and leaving the room. Assuming it to be a business call, or Andrew perhaps, he ambled into the hall and answered it in the dining room.

'Hello?' he enquired, waiting for a response.

A stern male voice delivered his abrupt message: 'Ignore any calls you may receive from a certain female.' The sound of the dialling tone signalled the termination of the disconcerting call.

Bernard dropped down the receiver in anger as he wondered what the hell was going on. Frowning, he left the room and ventured back into the kitchen.

Picking up the screwdriver, he forced it on to the screw and thought again about the telephone message. The caller must have asked for Bernard, otherwise his wife would not have passed it on to him.

'Ignore any calls you may receive from a certain female', undoubtedly suggested that someone, somewhere had decided he knew far more than he actually did, which was frustrating in itself as he really wished he did know more!

Moving across to the table, he picked up a rawl-plug and turned it over in his fingers.

It had been the first nuisance call, in fact the first odd incident of any kind, since the 'Dark Pool' messages from the silky-voiced woman during October. At the time he had assumed that, for better or worse, some form of clandestine meeting between him and Rachel Goodison was imminent. But nothing else had happened, nothing at all.

As it stood at the moment, he seemed to be in the middle of other people's feuds and power struggles; people he had never even met before! Why couldn't they sort out their own problems and leave him in peace? In this way he would be none the wiser, which suited him just fine.

20
The Serpent's Egg

Wednesday, 3 January 1990. The gentle fall of letters on the doormat in the hallway caught Bernard's attention. Approaching the front door, he bent his knees to retrieve the scattered mail.

Among the manila-coloured window envelopes containing bills and the odd letter was a late Christmas card with the brand-name Athena printed across its triangular lip. It bore the postmark BEDFORD 3.45pm 2 JANUARY 1990 and was addressed to him alone.

Tearing open the flap with his index finger, he withdrew the glossy card. It showed an evocative image of distant trees silhouetted against a background of intense orange fire, probably the burning of wheat stubble. Above this was a tranquil sky of royal blue, broken only by rippling cloud formations.

Inside the card he found no printed greeting, just a curious typed message which read:

```
B.

By the time you receive this, posted by a friend, I will
have been out of the country for several weeks.
I will not be returning until personal events have calmed
down.
I trust the 'gate' was strong enough.

R.
```

His heart raced as he studied every inch of the card to see if it held any further clues as to its place of origin. Finding none, he took a deep breath and strolled into the dining room, where he sat down and read the message again.

There seemed little doubt that it was some kind of telegram from the woman he knew as Rachel Goodison. The initial 'R' at the base of the message went some way to confirm the reality of not just the name, but also her very existence and the fact that she was leaving the country for a specific reason.

There was no malice intended with this card, it was simply an offer of information in the same way that anyone might extend a hand of friendship by sending a seasonal greetings card. Such a transformation in attitude was both extraordinary and would have been quite unthinkable just a year before.

Glancing from the envelope to the card, he attempted to re-evaluate his understanding of her predicament. Owing to the problems caused to her associates through the publication of *The Black Alchemist*, along with her own conflicting feelings about suspect ritual magic, she had fallen foul of the Black Alchemist. This had resulted in her relinquishing her occult power as a priestess of Hekate, a decision she believed could result in more than just a symbolic death. For this reason she had decided to consult him as an objective third party who understood her predicament and might even be able to help her escape.

Anticipating the massive problems this unnecessary interference would cause to the clandestine activities of her associates, the Black Alchemist and his henchmen had made it blatantly clear that any involvement in their own internal struggles would not be looked upon very favourably. In the end Rachel Goodison had submitted to their wishes and, as a result, had now left the country, probably to start a new life abroad.

Almost certainly she was now residing in a French château on the River Loire, under the wing of her own ancestral family. For weeks now he had felt that something of this nature was taking place, some sort of shifting around of personnel, so to speak. OK, so her problems were over, but what about the Black Alchemist – what was he up to now? Instinctively, Bernard seemed to know that he had left the country again – gone back to Spain, perhaps, to complete his study of Christian Gnostic documents.

One final facet of this saga still needed clearing up and this was Rachel's final words: 'I trust the "gate" was strong enough.' He felt he knew what this meant.

Recently he had become dimly aware of an encroachment, female in nature, somewhere in the Danbury area. He suspected it concerned Danbury Country Park, where he and Andrew had decided they would find the Dark Pool referred to in the cryptic telephone messages. Nothing had come of these thoughts, but the mention of a 'gate' implied one of three things – a mental bridge or gate linking his mind with hers, some kind of astral gateway set up using ritualistic activity, or simply a physical gate being used as a marker for some purpose.

He thought about these alternatives for a moment. Yes, it had to be a reference to the exit gate leading out of one of the small car-parks on the edge of the lakes. It was here that certain items had been left in his unlocked car when he and Andrew had encountered Rachel's spectral form during gale-force winds in February 1988. It was also close to this same exit gate that he had retrieved the broken sword-stick and Venus flint a year ago that very month. Had she returned to leave an item in the same vicinity? Was it some sort of final goodbye gesture?

There was only one way to find out. The next time he met Andrew at The Griffin perhaps they could take a short detour to Danbury Country Park and see if his intuition was correct.

Tuesday, 16 January. Pulling up to the car-park's exit gate, the car's headlights illuminated the dense mass of billowing undergrowth and tall trees, swaying and hissing in harmony with the fierce gales that had pounded Britain all day.

Bernard killed the lights, plunging the gravel track into darkness. The night-time setting was all too familiar, and even the weather had favoured us with violent, gusting winds, conjuring fond memories of past clandestine activities at this very spot.

I sat in the passenger seat next to Bernard, and sitting in the rear of the Montego was a 21-year-old girl named Debbie Benstead. She shared our active interest in questing pursuits, but perhaps more importantly she was an astute and highly accurate psychic who had joined the gang following an open-air all-dayer at Brentwood in Essex during May the previous year. Since September she had been producing vast quantities of raw, untainted psychic material on everything from our quest to find the seventh and final Meonia Sword to contact with elemental spirits of the landscape.

Debbie was becoming a close friend, and at the last moment I had decided to invite her along to meet Bernard for our regular get-together at The Griffin.

Around ten o'clock we had agreed to venture out to Danbury Country Park to see if he had been correct in his interpretation of Rachel Goodison's typed message.

Even though Ms Goodison had apparently changed her auric colours, I advised great caution about how we treated this situation, as it could still be a trap. Bernard did not seem to think so, but just in case we conducted the Cabbalistic Cross before going any further.

The gusting winds forcibly shook the car and produced a resounding roar among the vast expanse of woodland stretched out before us. Somehow such weather typified the backdrop necessary for black quests of this sort.

I suggested that he attempt to attune to the dense mass of trees and see if he could clairvoyantly picture any intruding imagery out there in the country park. Helen would see a red fog emanating from locations where a suspect ritualistic item lay concealed, while Bernard would either see a dark shadow resting at ground level or a mist-like vortex over the position in question. Both psychics would feel intense heat in the fingers when within a few inches of their chosen target.

Discarding a burning cigarette butt, Bernard slithered back into the seat and attempted to relax his mind.

Debbie bowed her head, allowing her long blonde hair to fall forward. She did not really expect to gain any psychic information this evening, but would try anyway.

With my finger poised on the record button of the pocket cassette, like someone about to pull the trigger of a gun, I waited for the sound of the perpetual winds to be interrupted by Bernard's calm voice.

'Three figures – one female, two male – in the car-park,' he revealed, quite casually. 'Not in robes, I would say.' He paused before adding: 'Only the woman came over to the gate.'

He was referring to the gate-post beyond and to the left of the car. Further silence followed giving me enough time to wonder whether I should switch off the cassette or not.

'What d'you reckon, then?' he finally said to Debbie as a fellow psychic.

'I'm not sure,' she admitted openly.

'I think she's left something.' He thought carefully about the implications of what he had just said before making a decision: 'I'm going for a little walk, are you going to stay in the car?'

Not on your life! If there was any artefact out there then I wanted to be by his side at the moment of retrieval.

The car doors opened just as a violent gust of wind whipped up the Athena card left on the dashboard and sent it sailing out into the night. Groping around on the ground, we quickly recovered Rachel's card, leaving us with the task of locating her final gift.

In the darkness, the three of us squeezed past the locked wooden gate and edged along the gravel track, trying to gain some kind of bearing. 'The gate-post,' he at last confirmed, looking around for Debbie. We reversed our steps and moved back towards the parked car.

'I get a pulling towards the gate-post,' he said again, as if by saying the words he could home in on the whereabouts of this concealed artefact.

He looked intently towards the grassy earth at the base of the right-hand post, around which a thick, heavy chain held the five-bar gate in position.

Frantic gusts whistled impatiently across the car-park, making it almost unbearable to be out in the open on this bleak, January night.

In virtual slow motion, Bernard bent his knees and dipped his right hand into the soft muddy dirt. It felt bitterly cold to the touch, but his careful concentration told him there was something down here, something to be found.

Just inches beneath the ground, his warm fingertips made contact with a smooth, unnatural surface, which he clenched and pulled upwards before off-loading it on to me. I showed it to Debbie.

'It's a cosmetics box,' she said, receiving the concealed treasure into her hand.

We needed the interior light of the car to see more, so returned jubilant to the other side of the locked gate. The car doors opened and once inside, Bernard switched on the overhead light.

'So, what have we got?' he asked, turning his head to face Debbie.

She passed the artefact over the seat and into my hands. It was an egg-shaped mother of pearl cosmetics box some three and a half inches in length and about two inches in depth and width. The two halves were held together by a clasp and clip soldered on to a thick silver band.

Opening it, we found a rather squashed silver snake bangle, with the head of a cobra and a cut red stone, possibly a garnet, set into its neck.

I passed it across to Bernard for first impressions.

'Very nice,' he quipped, not quite knowing what to do or say. 'A serpent in an egg!'

Strange . . .

Only in the past few weeks Debbie and I had been involved in a psychic quest featuring this self-same symbolism. Dragons' eggs had cropped up in our continued search for the Seventh Sword of Meonia, which had taken us to Cornwall over the New Year period. Among the ancient graves outside the cliff-top church of St Materiana in Tintagel – King Arthur's traditional place of birth – Debbie had been confronted by a full-blown manifestation of a Dark Age king named Vortigern. He had spoken of a quest to find the 'three eggs of the basilisk', each of which would have to be gained before we could be given the Seventh Sword itself.

This was all highly symbolic material and yet Rachel's gift appeared to pre-empt, or even mimic, aspects of a psychic quest totally unknown to anyone outside our immediate group. Even Bernard had only learnt of the Vortigern material earlier that evening.

It was another bizarre synchronicity, and yet why leave an item such as this for Bernard to discover? Should it mean something to him? Or to us?

'Some kind of parting gesture? A peace offering perhaps?' he mused in response to my ramblings. 'Anyway, that's it then. I can only assume that she's now in France somewhere and we've seen the last of her.'

This seemed to be wishful thinking on his account. For although she may have departed the scene, something told me that our paths were intrinsically linked and that sooner or later Rachel Goodison and the Black Alchemist would return to add even further chapters to this extraordinary saga. No, this business was not over yet; not for any of us.

PART THREE
Hexe

21
The Bygone Village

Saturday, 17 March 1990. John Horrigan shone the bright, laser-like spotlight into the open field and swivelled it slowly from left to right. 'There's your church.'

He was right. Picked out by the bright light some 300 yards away was an ominous church tower, starkly exposed above the tops of trees grouped together around its ruinous foundations. This was our destination.

Debbie was coaxed out of the car with the ultimatum that unless she accompanied us, then nothing was going to be found. No way could we discover the whereabouts of any concealed object without her assistance.

She sighed, reluctantly accepting her fate now that we had arrived at this accursed place.

It had started on Thursday, 25 January – the day that hurricane-force winds had devastated the whole of Britain. Something untoward was brewing in the Norfolk landscape and Debbie had psychically traced the root of the problem to a ruined bell-tower jutting out from a jumble of low-key monastic ruins she could see in her mind's eye. From her description of this location I recognised it as the abbey remains of St Benet of Holm, near Wroxham on the Norfolk Broads.

During the fierce winds certain individuals had, so Debbie believed, conducted a highly questionable ritual inside the bell-tower. Its intention had been to raise a magical force associated with a legendary Irish race known as the Fomorians, probably because the violent gales had originated in Ireland before moving across to the British mainland.

The Fomorians were hideous half-men, half-serpents who fought a constant struggle with the Irish hero gods known as the

Tuatha de Danann. Utilising such a magical power source only made sense after we discovered that the brick bell-tower of St Benet's – which was in fact the remains of a windmill grafted upon the earlier monastic ruins during the eighteenth century – featured in a local legend involving a fearsome dragon. It was said that the monks sealed the entrance to its earthen lair at nearby Ludham, forcing the mythical beast to seek revenge at the abbey. Upon its approach the monks were able to trick it into the crypts over which the bell-tower was built, and here the dragon of Ludham remains entombed to this day.

The bottom line of Debbie's psychic information was that St Benet's Abbey needed assistance on a psychic level, and so a date was chosen – Saturday, 17 March, St Patrick's Day, being the most obvious choice. Before our journey to Norfolk that morning we had suspected that a sinister group known to Debbie as the People of Hexe might have some involvement in this affair. Several times she had seen them in dreams and visions conducting rites at ancient and sacred sites across the country, and knew that one day our paths would cross. In spite of this clear information we had still tried to dismiss the possibility of their involvement, even after we had conducted a suitable healing meditation inside the abbey grounds at sunset that evening. Deciding that we should return at dawn to complete our task, we had retired to a hostelry named The Ferry Inn on the banks of the River Bure, at nearby Horning, realising we had a long night ahead of us.

Whilst staring aimlessly into the huge open fire blazing in the pub's stone hearth, Debbie had become convinced of the presence of fire elementals – fire sprites, flickering about in the flames. They spoke of a ruined church outside a village called Bygone, where a ritual fire had been kindled in recent times. Alex found the site on his OS map and, almost half-heartedly, we had decided to venture out here to establish the truth. Although Debbie did not want to admit it openly, the implications were clear – somewhere out there in the murky darkness we were going to find tangible evidence of a potent magical rite conducted by the People of Hexe.

One by one the eight-strong team readied themselves for the final assault on the abandoned church. Present were Paul Weston, Alex Langstone, John and Kerry Horrigan, Kerry's sister Lisa Mundy, and Lisa's partner, the headstrong Karl Dawkins.

At last we began the long and very muddy trek across the ploughed field, sown already with summer crop. The silhouetted church tower loomed ever nearer, but before we got any closer it was time to find out what the hell was happening here. Bringing the assembled party to a halt, we conducted the Cabbalistic Cross in unison and then visualised a radiant fire emerging from the heavens and cleansing the holy site in the name of the archangel Michael. It would disperse any unwanted influences resulting from its presupposed misuse in recent times.

Debbie still looked worried. 'It's cleared the church all right, but there's some sort of guardian here which we have only pushed to one side. It's still around, somewhere. If we want to do anything, we will have to work fast.'

Acknowledging her words, we advanced towards the unwelcoming edifice and soon reached the dark circle of trees surrounding the ruins. An entrance over the barbed-wire fence was pointed out by John and one by one we entered the once-hallowed ground.

There were certainly no feelings of sanctity here, even though the empty shell of this neglected house of God was still more or less whole. Only the roof was missing, leaving the medieval nave exposed to the elements. The solid stone tower, however, was the object of our curiosity this evening.

Karl scanned the ground and led the cautious questers into the earthen-floored west tower in pursuit of confirmatory evidence.

The searching torchlight picked out the black charred remains of a recent bonfire. Chunks of half-burnt wood and ashen cinders lay strewn across the dusty dirt, which did not look as if it had been touched by rain for many a year.

So the elemental spirits Debbie had found and spoken to in the blazing fire at The Ferry Inn had been correct. They had said we would find evidence of a recent fire and now this had been located. So far, so good. It was time to see whether the rest of their poignant message about dangerous rituals and deposited artefacts could be verified as well.

Debbie stood transfixed. 'There's something here. I can feel it

– it's alive. I can hear a rasping breath and the whole ground is slowly pulsing up and down, up and down. I'm not sure where it's coming from, it may be outside.'

Following her words the intrepid band moved out into the nave and passed beneath its open archway. Gradually we found the northern edge of the dark, crumbling tower.

'It's here, somewhere,' she confirmed, looking down at the undisturbed earth. 'I can still hear it. It's like a pounding heartbeat and it's coming from below the ground.'

I yanked out soft dirt with my hands as Debbie tried desperately to pinpoint the epicentre of her anxiety.

Nothing was found.

'It must be coming from the *other* side of the wall, then,' she reasoned, having paused to evaluate the situation. 'C'mon. Let's go back inside.'

Alex and Karl tailed Debbie and myself into the unholy church whilst the others continued to dig at the base of the tower. On the other side of the same wall Alex flashed the torchlight across the black-charred earth. 'Any ideas, Deb?'

'Just be quiet for a moment,' she pleaded, standing still and listening to what was in her ears only. 'I need a bearing, or we're not going to find anything.' She slowly turned to face the northern wall and then crouched down to study the ground. The light-beam from Alex's torch spotlighted her movements.

I knelt next to her and studied the loose earth, which was choked with a mixture of small rocks, broken glass and pieces of half-burnt wood.

She leaned forward and lowered her head. 'There's something here, I can still hear it. It's pulsing, breathing.'

I began to scavenge about in the dry dirt. Karl fell to the ground by my side as Alex continued to lean across Debbie, supplying the only source of illumination.

'Stop,' she yelled, pointing towards a tiny heap of dirt I had created with my hands. 'It's louder. You've unearthed it. Listen.'

We fell silent at the same moment that the rest of the group edged their way back into the tower, having given up their own search outside.

She looked down and saw a rock or stone caked with a hardened shell of dirt. 'What's that?' she queried, slowly recoiling.

I clutched it with my fingers. It was a fairly large uncut quartz crystal, about an inch long and three-quarters of an inch in width.

'Oh my God,' Alex exclaimed as the torchlight picked out the crystal's geometric shape.

'Shit,' Karl responded, rising from a kneeling position.

'Keep it away from me,' Debbie said, inching backwards before spinning around. 'Right, I'm going,' she declared, quickly leaving the tower.

Kerry grabbed her shoulder. 'Are you all right? What's the matter?'

'We've got to get away, *please*,' Debbie yelled, desperate not to stay any longer than necessary. 'We've triggered off the guardian. It's coming back across the fields, *now!*'

Pulling out the plastic bottle of holy water, I rapidly doused the offending crystal before scooping it back into my hand and placing it in my overcoat. It was time to leave.

The others responded instantly to her frantic departure and were already speeding across the muddy field as I reached the barbed-wire fence marking the boundary of this God-forsaken place.

Moving into the open, I saw that Karl had already caught up with Debbie, who was sprinting toward the cars.

Christ Almighty. What sort of night was this? I shouted for everyone to stop running, but no one took any notice.

Seconds later the final stragglers reached the edge of the open field and the comparative safety of the parked vehicles.

'OK, let's move it,' John shouted, before leaping into his car. Alex pulled open the driver's door as I jumped into the rear seat and Debbie joined me from the other side.

Engines and headlights burst into life. Doors slammed, and without even discussing where we were going next, the cars launched back on the empty road and screeched out of Bygone village.

Debbie stared vacantly at the passing grass verge as Alex made his way towards the abbey ruins of St Benet of Holm on the flat plains between the village of Ludham and the curving banks of the River Bure.

'Where's that thing?' she asked at last.

'That thing' was the quartz crystal we had found. I told her it was in the boot. In fact, it was still in the pocket of my overcoat which lay strewn across the back shelf.

She seemed concerned. 'It's a spider's egg,' she revealed unexpectedly. 'The fire was lit to incubate a baby spider, which would eventually have hatched and been used for ritual purposes and, what's more, it's still alive. I can hear it clicking. We will have to freeze it to kill what it contains.'

Placing it in ice made from holy water would be pretty mean. So who had put it there?

It was a little while before the question was answered. 'It was laid there by a woman, the midwife, and two male attendants. I felt earlier that villagers may have been involved, but now I'm not so sure.'

She fell silent for a minute or two before completing the story. 'Local people were visiting the site, yes, but I feel it has been hijacked by the People of Hexe, who have been using it as an incubator for their own thought forms. They see Norfolk as important due in part to its associations with Boudicca, queen of the Celtic Iceni tribe, who lived around here in Roman times. But can we just drop the subject? It's making me feel ill just thinking about it.'

I respected her feelings and left the subject for several minutes before asking her about the nature of the astral guardian we nearly came face to face with out there at the church.

'Well, when you picked up the crystal I suddenly became aware of a Minotaur thought form, half-bull and half-man, raised at the site by the midwife. It was moving in, closer and closer, from the open field where it had been since we used the Fire of Michael. The concept of the classical Labyrinth and its associations with the Minotaur are important to the Hexe group.'

This may have been so, but running away was not the best response under such circumstances. When running, the mind produces and releases an excess of emotionally charged energy that can be traced by other psychics and will increase the power of any thought form present at a site.

'I know,' she sighed, closing her eyes. 'I just had to get away from that place.'

'What happens now, then, Deb?' Alex asked, twisting his head to put the question directly to her.

'Well, that's it,' she stated in a defeatist manner. 'We've been avoiding confrontations with Hexe for a long time, but now it's happened there's no going back, is there?'

22
The People of Hexe

Friday, 23 March 1990. Debbie stepped into the Black Room, my place of meditation in the Leigh-on-Sea flat, and sat herself down on one of the old wooden chairs arranged in a wide circle around the walls.

In the ruined tower of Bygone church Debbie had used her psychic abilities to retrieve an artefact, the large quartz crystal left there by the People of Hexe. It had been deposited, she said, as an incubator for weak and unstable thought energies. We needed to establish the known facts, so it was time to record what she knew about the so-called People of Hexe – their background, their aims and what their intentions were for the prehistoric and sacred places of Britain.

Debbie's contact with this shadowy organisation had begun the previous November[1] when she experienced a rather disturbing dream involving a deep ritual pit. She found herself descending into its depths, passing prehistoric items, such as broken swords, amber beads, even traces of human flesh and blood. Accompanying these vivid images was the overwhelming impression that it had been a sacrificial shaft of great magical containment for the Druids, the Iron Age priest magicians of Europe. 'Into here they would cast their dishonoured warriors,' she had said. More disconcerting, however, was her suggestion that the site was being utilised today by the group of corrupt individuals she referred to as the People of Hexe. They saw it in terms of an astral gateway into a conceptual void they spoke of as 'the line that runs deep'.

Debbie had been 'given' the place-name 'Normanton Gorse' in connection with the sacrificial shaft, and for a while this had thrown us completely off the scent. There was more than one location in England bearing the name Normanton, but none boasted a ritual pit fitting the description given by Debbie. Only one appeared to possess the right associations, and this was Normanton, near Amesbury in Wiltshire. Here, three-quarters of a mile south-south-west of Stonehenge, was a vast Bronze Age barrow cemetery. During February this year Debbie had picked up further information about 'the line that runs deep'. It was, she felt, an alignment of ancient sites connecting Stonehenge in the north with Old Sarum camp, Salisbury Cathedral and Clearbury Ring in the south.

I recognised this alignment as the so-called Old Sarum ley first discovered in the 1920s by ley-hunting pioneer Alfred Watkins (it had also been noted by astronomer Sir Norman Lockyer during the early years of the century). It is wellknown to purveyors of the so-called earth mysteries through the published works of authors such as Paul Devereux, John Michell and Nigel Pennick. It runs in a south-south-easterly direction from Stonehenge and passes through each of the sites described by Debbie, before continuing on past Clearbury Ring to link with another hill-top earthwork named Frankenbury Camp.[2] Of more immediate importance, however, was the fact that the Old Sarum ley brushed past the eastern edge of the Normanton barrow cemetery between Stonehenge and Old Sarum camp.

With renewed vigour, I had rechecked different archaeological sources and finally located Debbie's sacrificial pit. It was not to be found in the Normanton Bronze Age cemetery, but a mile further south in the Wilsford barrow group. Referred to as the Wilsford Pit, it was discovered by chance during the excavation of a pond barrow between 1960 and 1962. Beneath the centre of the large concave depression archaeologists found the usual grave goods, but below this they had unearthed a conical-shaped recess of disturbed soil. This narrowed to form a vertical shaft six feet wide and over a hundred feet deep; it finally produced various Bronze Age finds including an ox skull, bone pins and several amber beads.[3]

Leaning against the base of the pit was an oak post which had once stood erect. Speculation as to its purpose has not been resolved, although similar posts in other ritual pits have yielded traces of congealed blood, flesh and fat, clearly showing their use as sacrificial shafts.[4] This knowledge went some way to support Debbie's belief that 'Normanton Gorse' was once used as a sacrificial pit for dishonoured warriors.

There was, however, no reference to bent or broken swords being found in the Wilsford Pit, even though surrounding barrows had yielded up despoiled ritual weapons of this nature; a weapon was usually broken or 'killed' to release its fighting spirit following the death of its owner.[5]

The Wilsford Pit fitted the general description of the site Debbie had visited in her dream, but still there was no explanation as to why she was 'given' the place-name 'Normanton Gorse'. Why not refer to it as 'the Wilsford Pit'? Further enquires revealed the truth, for although the shaft is technically in Wilsford, one source I discovered spoke of the pit as being located 'on Normanton Gorse'.[6] Since this name did not appear on the standard OS maps of the area, I accepted that Debbie had accurately described an important ritual site previously unknown to either of us.

Inspired by this tentative confirmation of her psychic information, Debbie had been insistent that this Bronze Age pit was being used today for questionable purposes by the People of Hexe. However, I had seen Bernard and Helen physically and mentally tormented day and night by black questing pursuits and there was no way that I, or any other member of the group, wished to see Debbie suffer a similar fate, so we had chosen to ignore the activities of the People of Hexe; that was until the previous weekend's little escapade at Bygone church.

Any group calling themselves the People of Hexe[7] undoubtedly took their name from the *hex* marks daubed or inscribed on the fixing markers – usually slivers of bone or crystals – they apparently deposited at locations utilised for ritual reasons. The word *hex* has a Germanic root and denotes a type of mark that when drawn invokes a magical action in a process known as cathexis. Hex marks are similar to the Germanic and later Norse language of the runes. Yet instead of using a combination of different signs representing different letters, lone hex marks – generally incorporated within a hexagonal framework – were employed for the same overall purpose.

Debbie nodded at this assessment as she poured a glass of

wine. 'Well, the first thing I want to make clear is that the term "People of Hexe" is purely a name my brain has decided to give them. I now realise they don't have a fixed name, although their signature always includes a hex mark,' she revealed. 'All I know is that these people are high adepts of the magical arts and that the three prime movers are all of foreign origin.'

Foreign?

'One – a man – is from Sardinia, I think.'

So what were they up to, these People of Hexe?

She took in a long breath. 'The resurrection of everything from forgotten deities to the ghosts of warriors and the spirits of legend. In fact, anything they can get their hands on, the darker and bloodier the better,' she declared, raising her glass. 'Hexe seek out these energy forms either through local legends or psychic means. They are then raised using ritual processes, and once manifested they are either contained at the site itself or transferred into purposely made fixing markers so that they can be taken away and planted elsewhere.'

So a bit like the boxes that suck in and contain ghosts and poltergeists in the film *Ghostbusters*!

'Well, not quite,' she replied with a smile. 'But similar. Sometimes they will introduce the resurrected energy form into the mind of a psychic, who will become its host until it is downloaded at a place of their choosing at some later date.

'At Bygone church, for instance, the charged crystal deposited in the tower was meant to ensure the rapid growth and stabilisation of the site's inherent energies in the form of a baby spider. Eventually this would have taken its place within the energy matrix, which they see in terms of a symbolic spider's web as well as the Labyrinth of Cretan tradition.'

OK, I could accept their actions, but what was the purpose of all this messing about? What were they trying to achieve?

'I believe they want to gain control of the spiritual mind of the people, in and around the power sites involved. Very slowly they are reconstructing a warped version of Britain's energy matrix using different configurations of power sites, including the Old Sarum ley. Alignments are very important to them as they are the paths of the ancient shamans, and provided these age-old astral entities still haunt the lines of power, they can be ensnared and controlled by Hexe.'

So how does the Hexe group operate?

She nodded in anticipation of her response. 'There is only a small core of permanent members, but they employ the services of many other people for specific purposes.

'Like us they work extensively with psychics, using them to track down supernatural forms, find hidden artefacts and manipulate intelligences and energies of the landscape.

'But these people are not in it for kicks, not for self-glorification or for the money, although it *is* their livelihood. No, they're just in it for ultimate control.'

Who pays these people?

'As I've said before Hexe are, I believe, involved with a much larger concern, a multi-national business conglomerate with companies in Britain. They fund their "explorations", shall we say. Such companies not only want complete control of both economic and energy resources on a materialistic level, they also realise that cultures, both past and present, have known of the importance of occult control and manipulation.'

I understood her words. Adolf Hitler had been obsessed with the occult and felt that to ensure world domination he should possess power objects he believed to have carved out the destiny of the world. These included the Spear of Destiny, or the Spear of Longinus, which allegedly pierced Christ's side during the Crucifixion. There is an example of a 'Heilige Lance' housed at the Hofburg Museum in Vienna, and when Hitler came to power he made sure this was sequestered into his ownership and removed, along with the rest of the Hapsburg treasures, to St Katherine's church, Nuremberg; the choice of location being revealed to him in trance, it was claimed.[8] The Nazis also instigated searches for many other power objects and believed that Hitler's diabolic mission was divinely inspired by the gods and heroes of the Norse pantheon. There is some evidence to suggest that the Allies actually believed in Hitler's use of occult powers and, as a result, employed their own occultists, witches and revivalist druids to counteract the Nazis' utilisation of such psychic forces.

At the end of the day, as I had said before in association with the Black Alchemist affair and Helen's Dark Council material, conviction in this sort of belief is very dangerous indeed.

THE PEOPLE OF HEXE

So who was this multi-national conglomerate?

'Their names are of little consequence as we cannot alter the position they hold in this matter. However, I believe they are the main spokes of the Wheel's influence in Britain.'

The Wheel was a term first coined by my colleague Graham Phillips in 1981. He understood them to be a sinister worldwide organisation claiming descent from the medieval Knights Templar. Before its brutal suppression at the beginning of the fourteenth century, this immensely powerful military order owned lands, riches and wealth across Christendom and controlled European banking, commerce and finance on a massive scale.

Graham and I had investigated his own psychic information concerning the Wheel's alleged influence in Britain. However, other than crossing paths with a few dodgy individuals here and there, we found no hardcore evidence to prove the organisation's modern-day existence.

She shook her head. 'No, I'm sorry. The Wheel *exists* as a brotherhood outside of the brotherhood, and the People of Hexe are conducting their occult affairs in Britain today.'

Well, it could always be checked out. So what about the Dark Council, the Friends of Hekate and the Black Alchemist, how did they fit into the scheme of things?

'Wheel-linked companies use magical groups as another guarantee of continued success and control, like consulting the stars on a much grander scale, or reading your horoscope, but ten thousand times more extreme.

'As for Helen's Dark Council, I believe they are simply a reformed version of the Friends of Hekate. The term "Dark Council" given by Markus de Capelin relates to something from his own time, some kind of secretive coven of high churchmen connected with Winchester during the Middle Ages.[9] The spirit guardian used this term simply because he could only relate to intruders conducting heretical acts in terms already familiar to him,' she tried to explain. 'To poor old Markus there was no difference between what was happening in his own lifetime and what was happening at St Catherine's Hill in 1989.

'The revitalised Friends of Hekate – the Dark Council, if you like – are almost certainly linked into this set-up. Instructional briefs, similar to those given to Hexe, are handed out through some kind of hierarchical process. These will then be acted on by individual groups employed as part of the greater whole, with many being none the wiser.'

Bernard had suggested something similar during the Paradise Mound sketch in 1988. And the Black Alchemist?

'Through his associates in the Friends of Hekate he came into contact with figures involved in much greater projects and, due to both his utter conviction and his tangible results, I reckon they have taken him under their wing.'

We would see. Perhaps the whole subject should be put to one side until such times as we gained fresh evidence of the People of Hexe – the name we would continue to use in reference to their activities. Naturally, this would necessitate further investigations which we had unanimously decided against in the foreseeable future.

23
The Doom of the Gods

Wednesday, 30 May 1990, 11.35am. 'Right, I think I'll get ready to go to lunch,' Nikki announced to Debbie, who was leaning against one of the two Canon copiers that acted as back-ups to the shop's huge Rank Xerox machine. 'I'm just going upstairs for a few minutes. Give me a shout if you get busy.'

'OK,' Debbie responded, moving across to the wire tray containing the outstanding printing orders. 'I'll just finish the job I'm on and I'll see if I can do any of these.' She held up a bunch of plastic files as evidence of her intent.

Debbie had worked at the copying centre in Leigh-on-Sea since moving into Andrew's flat the previous month. They had struck up a relationship at the beginning of the year and had eventually decided to live together. Andrew knew the partners in the photocopying centre who by coincidence were looking for a sales supervisor with previous experience, and following a couple of interviews they had taken her on.

Flicking back her long fair hair, Debbie returned to the smaller Canon copier and exchanged the original artwork on the glass plate before continuing the run.

Lazy minutes passed as an unexpected lull in business meant that her only company was the deep, continuous drone of the Rank Xerox machine usually only noticed on such blissfully quiet occasions.

Then came an unexpected dizziness and a sudden loss of momentum. She put her right hand to her brow and reached out with the other hand to support herself. Her head thumped badly and she realised she was fast losing consciousness. The room spun as the glare from the overhead lights suddenly increased and the perpetual hum began to rise in frequency until it gradually transformed into the rhythmic sound of low chanting.

THE SECOND COMING

'*Ravastack. Ravastack. Ravastack,*' was being sung in unison.

Fresh air accompanied these resonating sounds as she saw before her a large group of plainly dressed country folk with thick dark hair, hardened faces and deeply tanned skin. Among them moved others, with more familiar faces of a West European origin. These outsiders were dressed in bright red ski-jackets, thick dark trousers and stout walking boots.

'*Ravastack. Ravastack. Ravastack.*'

They were within a huge grassy clearing situated between vast coniferous forests located in a wide valley basin at the foot of enormous, snow-laden mountains.

The temperature was not freezing, but there was a crisp chill in the air that made her shudder and catch her breath.

'*Ravastack. Ravastack.*'

The local people were East Europeans, Romanian peasants, at some power site of great supernatural strength, close to the Russian border. They were performing an archaic rite to awaken a primeval force of immense power held in awe by those present. It was the fulfilling of a prophecy spoken of by their forefathers and their forefathers before them. Others not of this ancient race were egging them on to near hysteria – individuals who had penetrated their age-old web of superstitious intrigue and found the very heart of its potent ancestral lineage. Only they were now privileged to witness this great event.

Hexe. Yes, the familiar faces were those she had seen before in dream, connected with the British Isles. Now they were abroad, in Romania, working with indigenous shamans of an ancient tribe.

'*Ravastack.*'

What was Ravastack? They appeared to be awaiting the arrival of something or somebody.

Almost too suddenly, the ground beneath their feet shuddered violently before ceasing abruptly. Instant silence befell the gathered crowd; even the birds became hushed and still.

Debbie glanced about, wondering what had occurred. The trees then trembled unnaturally as a low ululating vibration welled up from deep beneath them.

Earth tremors now shook the ground, forcing people to stumble about and drop to their knees in shock. Others began staring expectantly towards the heavens as if the earthquake was a portent of a much greater doom.

In another instant the ground shifted dramatically, making the floor of the clearing undulate uncontrollably in the midst of the assembled party. Like some vast earthen jaw, the forest carpet ripped open to reveal a bottomless chasm, from which emanated a thunderous roar, resembling the sound of hot, billowing steam escaping from a vast underground geyser.

The atrocious cacophony accelerated to an unbearable crescendo until out of the gaping fissure emerged a hideous beast of colossal proportions – an abominable demon wolf with matted, ochre-red hair, its bulbous head containing a mouth full of foul-stinking, saliva-infested teeth and eyes of hot, molten fire.

Steadily it forced itself upwards, away from the fractured earth, pounding against the elements to reach the freedom of the open sky – the ferocity of its fight feeding the efficiency of the trap already set for it.

Its great size was totally unimaginable – not tens of feet long, but hundreds of feet from its gaping jowls to the very end of its abhorrent, trailing tail.

The Romanians looked on in marvelling disbelief as the underground shockwaves ceased and the enormity of this stupendous beast from the bowels of hell became apparent. They watched it climb like an ethereal airship riding an invisible storm until it dwarfed the blue sky, saturating it with a blood-red hue and transforming the terrain below into an imitation of some lurid Martian landscape.

It was their time. The time of Ravastack, long awaited and now upon them and the world for all to see.

'Debbie. Debbie, are you all right?' Nikki asked her friend, who was tilting dangerously towards the edge of the photocopier as if she was about to collapse.

The more familiar drone of the Xerox machine returned as Debbie became aware of her colleague's proximity. She looked up and tried to respond normally; her employers were not yet aware of her acute psychic abilities. 'Yes, I'm all right. I'm fine,' she lied. Her head pounded, she felt dizzy and nauseous, and she wanted only to lie down and go to sleep.

Nikki, holding her coat and handbag, placed an arm around her friend, not quite knowing whether she was unwell or not.

'I'll be fine, I promise.' Debbie assured her again.

1.20pm. Placing the tea bags in the pot, Debbie concluded her story as she made a quick salad sandwich. 'So that's when Nikki came in and found me. I don't know what she must have thought and I'm not sure what to say when I get back, either.'

And she believed the People of Hexe were in some way connected with this earthquake? I dealt with the boiling kettle and readied the mugs.

'Seems so, but although the whole thing looked really vivid, perhaps it's some sort of a portent of future events.'

Her disturbing vision made no immediate sense to me, and I couldn't see why Hexe, an apparently British-based magical group, might want to get involved with indigenous Romanian peasants. And the word 'Ravastack', the chant used to invoke this demonic wolf, rang no bells whatsoever. So unless we could equate her waking vision with an actual seismic event, there was nothing more we could do.

'I guess you're right,' she sighed. 'Oh well, just see what happens, I suppose.'

5.40pm. Having changed out of her work clothes, Debbie settled in the front room to try and catch some of the television soap 'Neighbours', leaving me to pack books in the kitchen. Orders for *The Black Alchemist* were still coming in thick and fast, and it was now a full-time occupation keeping up with the weekly demands.

Minutes passed before I suddenly heard her frantic calls. 'Andrew, come here, quickly. Look at this,' she was yelling loudly. 'Quickly. You'll miss it.'

Dropping everything, I ran through to the other room and found Debbie on her feet, pointing down at the television screen which showed camera shots of half-collapsed, pre-fabricated buildings, someone comforting an elderly woman in a head scarf, and scenes of men helping to clear away piles of concrete and rubble.

'There's been an earthquake,' she announced, a look of startled horror on her face. ' . . . *in Romania.*'

The scene switched back to the television studio in London where a smartly dressed newscaster sat poised to deliver the main story of the evening, a written script before him on the desk.

Dumbstruck, I stood with Debbie, gazing at the screen in tense expectation of his words.

'*Good evening. A major earthquake has struck towns and cities across Romania. So far estimates put the casualties as low, although there have been some deaths. Extensive damage is reported over a wide area, with the east of the country being the worst hit. There have also been reports of fatalities and structural damage across the border in the neighbouring Soviet republic of Moldavia, close to the epicentre of the tremors which struck without warning this lunchtime. From Bucharest we have this report . . .* '

Scenes followed of the quake-struck capital. One showed ill-equipped local men gesticulating wildly with their arms, obviously attempting to co-ordinate the clearance of mountains of debris now littering the streets. Another shot showed grieving women crying out for those they had lost. Still another captured people sifting about in the ruins, trying to find personal effects among the collapsed masonry, some still clearly in a state of shock. They were pathetic scenes that my mind was not yet ready to equate with Debbie's vivid description of her waking vision of an earthquake in Romania.

'Oh my God, this is . . . awful,' she said at last, shaking her head, almost unable to accept the reality of what she had seen in her mind just hours beforehand. 'What the hell's going on, Andrew? Why should I pick up on an earthquake so far away?'

I had been listening to the radio all day and had heard no mention of an earthquake before this television report. What's more, its epicentre appeared to have been in a remote region of Romania, close to the Soviet border, just as Debbie had suggested. Could she really have glimpsed this earthquake as it took place? The times of both occurrences would need to be checked and if the answer was yes, then I would have to take seriously her account of a massive ritualistic event co-ordinated by the People of Hexe.

Newspaper cuttings relating to the Romanian earthquake of 30 May 1990. Did this natural occurrence signal the commencement of the age of Ragnarok, the Doom of the gods, in the minds of the Romanian people? (cuttings courtesy: *Daily Mail*, *Evening Standard* and *The Independent*)

Thursday, 31 May. Gathering up the scattered daily newspapers I tore away the front-page lead stories concerning the Romanian earthquake of the previous day.

Placing them on the kitchen table I scribbled down a few notes for future reference. It seemed the earthquake had struck at 10.40 GMT, that was 11.40am British summer time, which meant that Debbie's disturbing vision had occurred at the same time.

According to seismologist David Redmayne of the British Geological Survey in Edinburgh[1], the earthquake had registered a magnitude of 6.7 Mb on the Richter scale, bigger than the Armenian earthquake of 1988 and the San Francisco quake of the previous year, which only reached 6.5 Mb on the Richter scale. Its epicentre was in the remote Romanian county of Vrancea, at the foot of the Carpathian mountains, some 150 miles north-east of Bucharest (45° 841′ north, 26° 668′ east); this latest quake being the fifth such tremor of its size to hit the region this century.

The main tremor had lasted for up to forty-five seconds and the areas worst hit were the towns of Braila, in the extreme east of the country; Brasov, a town in Transylvania, and the capital itself. There was extensive damage over a large area, but miraculously there had been comparatively few fatalities. Nine Romanians were known to have died with another 700 injured – some when people had jumped to freedom fearing the imminent collapse of the building they were in, a memory perhaps of the scale of devastation that had accompanied the earthquake of 1977.

Over the border in the Soviet republic of Moldavia there were reports of four people killed and, once again, extensive damage over a wide area, with the worst hit being the town of Kishinev. President Mikhail Gorbachev, who had flown out to Washington for a superpower summit with American President George Bush only the previous day, was now considering whether he should return to Moscow in an effort to co-ordinate relief supplies and foreign aid destined for the disaster-hit region. Tremors had also been felt in Bulgaria, and even as far away as Istanbul in Turkey and Vienna in Austria.

Peculiarly enough this had not been the only earthquake in the international news that day. At 02.34 GMT on Wednesday, 30

May tremors registering a magnitude of 6.1 Mb on the Richter scale in the remote forest region of Moyo Bamba-Rioja in Peru, had caused severe damage over a wide area leaving 135 dead, 800 injured and thousands homeless. There had also been an earthquake in Yugoslavia at 19.19 GMT on the 30th and another at Guerrero, Mexico, at 07.35 GMT that very morning. What's more, another major tremor had been reported overnight in Romania causing further structural damage to many buildings.

I poured tea and pondered deeply on the relevance of Debbie's dramatic vision of the Romanian earthquake. It made more sense now, but I had still to understand the actions of the local people, the appearance of the demoniac-like wolf and the presence of the Hexe group.

Perhaps the key was Romania's deeply held belief in superstitious folklore and arcane magical practices. Centuries of isolation and forty-five years of Communist rule had ensured that the country's belief in vampirism, werewolves, witchcraft and devilry had never died out. Strange therefore that the violent Ceauşescu dictatorship that had ruled the country with an iron fist for so long had been overturned just five months beforehand. Indeed, a reporter with the *Daily Mail* named Bob Graham had been covering the trial of Nicolae Ceauşescu's son, Nicu, in the Romanian town of Sibiu, when the earthquake struck.

The fall of Communist Romania was just the latest in a long line of similar political changes sweeping across Central and Eastern Europe in the wake of President Gorbachev's *Glasnost*, or new openness, policy that had made him a hero of Western democracy in recent years. The fall of the Berlin Wall, the imminent re-unification of Germany and the break up of the Soviet Communist government were bringing in new tides that would irreversibly change the course of world history forever.

The superpower summit in Washington would further ratify these immense global alterations, with talks on the place of NATO in Eastern Europe and the role of Germany after re-unification being top of the packed agenda. Rumours of President Gorbachev pulling out of the summit because of the earthquake were disconcerting to say the least.

With these world affairs in mind, perhaps the Romanian people had seen the earthquake in some superstitious capacity.

THE DOOM OF THE GODS

Maybe it had been a portent, an omen, of coming global changes. There was ample evidence to suggest that cultures across the world had often viewed natural disasters such as hurricanes, typhoons and earthquakes as the wrath of supernatural forces. Was it possible therefore that the people of Transylvania saw this latest natural cataclysm as the stirrings of some slumbering wolf demon dwelling deep within their ancestral past?

Was it equally possible that indigenous shamans or witches had deliberately released the caged beast by conducting some form of ritualistic practice in a remote forest region, close to the epicentre of the earthquake? There were no real answers to these questions; not yet at least. All I knew was that the tremors could not have split the earth open in a physical sense, as the rock fault responsible for the quake was a staggering 89km below the earth's surface. This meant that the tremors were unlikely to have caused the sort of damage described by Debbie. In consequence it seemed as if this aspect of Debbie's vision had to be viewed as symbolic imagery representing the release of some force or entity previously contained beneath the earth.

So what was the identity of the wolf?

The name 'Ravastack' still meant nothing to me. It could, of course, be the name of some localised deity or demon. More likely, however, was that the monstrous wolf was none other than Fenris (or *Fenrir* in some primary sources), an ogre of great renown who portends the end of the world and the doom of the gods of Asgard in Norse and Icelandic mythology.

According to the ancient sagas Fenris is the offspring of the sly and cunning trickster god Loki, who took on the form of a woman to mate with a frost giant. The gods of Asgard had been forewarned that this savage demon wolf would one day be their most lethal enemy. To make sure it did not fulfil its destiny the demon was tricked into the underworld and tethered with magic cords.

Yet then came the death of the god Balder, an event signalling the commencement of Ragnarok, the Doom of the Divine Powers in Germanic and Norse mythology. It was then said that in 'a distant forest in the East [of Europe] an aged giantess brought into the world a whole brood of young wolves whose father was Fenrir.'[2] One of these monsters chased, reached and finally swallowed the sun, which took on a blood-red hue before disappearing completely. For several years a hideous winter engulfed the entire world as snow storms came from every direction and violent war waged across the earth.

Fenris then broke free of his bonds with such force that the whole earth trembled and shook, while mountains crumbled and split. The mighty wolf afterwards accompanied the god Loki on a boat made of dead men's nails with a host of underworld demons and monsters in tow. Hot fire issued from its eyes and nostrils, and its gaping jowls dripped with the blood of men.

A monstrous battle then ensued between gods, demons and giants in which all but a few perished horribly. Stars came adrift and fell into a void and every living creature was swept away as the seas and rivers overflowed. Finally, the earth sank so that Ragnarok's place of commencement was lost beneath the huge tidal waves.

The end had come, but slowly the world re-emerged, as in the biblical story of Noah, and a new sun shone. With it came a new generation of gods. Balder, the fairest and best loved, was resurrected. New life sprang from the earth and the last surviving man and woman resurfaced from their hiding place within the wood and bark of the world tree, for that could never perish.

This was the story of Ragnarok, the Doom of the Divine Powers. It happened once and according to ancient prophecy it could happen again if the Fenris-wolf once again breaks free of its supernatural bondage in the underworld.

Although principally of Norse roots, the concept of Fenris and the age of Ragnarok emerged from a much earlier Germanic tradition. This was perhaps an important statement as the Dark Age Germanic peoples are known to have migrated as far east as Hungary, Russia and Romania.[3]

I was pretty sure that Debbie had witnessed a form of Fenris emerge from the earth and climb into the sky during the Romanian earthquake. She saw the gargantuan wolf reach the sun and watched as the blue sky turned blood red as in the tale of Ragnarok.

So much for an identification of the wolf, but why did this ritualistic event occur in Romania? Debbie saw a remote, forested area which, at a stretch, could well be described as the 'distant forest in the East' where the wolf offspring of the giantess rises to catch the sun, a role sometimes attributed to Fenris, whose own release causes the earth to tremble and shake – an apt description of an earthquake.

Wolves play a major role in the indigenous folklore of Hungary and Romania and not, as some might expect, just in Transylvania, the traditional home of the vampire and werewolf. In Romanian gypsy lore, great white wolves are said to haunt cemeteries and churchyards, where they wait to destroy the vampires and restless souls that lurk within. Their presence keeps away these demonic spectres, which would otherwise be free to inhabit the world of the living.[4] Other superstitions speak of vampires shape-shifting into wolves to stalk their prey; indeed, there were far more accounts linking vampires with wolves than there were with any other animal, including the blood-sucking bat![5]

This integral association of wolf and vampire stemmed back to the ancient belief in the power of the classical goddess Hekate. She was said to have been accompanied on her nocturnal journeys by a host of wolfish hounds and hideous blood-sucking demonesses, such as Gorgo and Mormo. These vampiric entities known as *lamaiai* were said to rise from their graveyard tombs to steal and devour human babies in a sanguine hell-feast of the type popularised in *Dracula*, Bram Stoker's classic tale of Gothic horror.

The Romanian wolf connection strengthened the case in favour of Debbie having witnessed the symbolic release of the Fenris-wolf from some dark Germanic underworld. Yet if this was so, did it therefore signal the commencement of Ragnarok – a new end to the gods of Asgard and a final Judgement Day for mankind?

Probably not, but there was disturbing food for thought in the events of the past two days and in no way did I feel it was over yet.

24
The First Seal

Tuesday, 21 August 1990. The muggy heat brought on lethargic tendencies, but still the job had to be done before the end of the working day. There was paperwork spread across the desk and Bernard, as managing director, could not allow the English summer to get the better of him.

Loosening his shirt and tie, he scribbled out the necessary forms then dropped his pen to take a breather. When he got home he would need to wash, change, then grab a bite to eat before heading out to Danbury for his scheduled get-together with Andrew and Debbie. It had been a month or so since their last meeting and there would be much to talk about. He got on really well with Debbie; they had much in common and her psychic information complemented what little he came out with these days.

Pouring a glass of spring water he turned his attentions back to the work at hand and wrote more. Several moments later he wiped sweat from his forehead and gave in; something was interfering with his concentration.

Not here, please. Not at work.

The stifling heat appeared to increase sharply making him take further gulps of cool water. It was bloaty stuff, this, but it was easier than buying cans of drink.

Again, he rubbed his forehead. The humid atmosphere seemed to be lifting, but in its place came a much stronger heat, broken by a cool breeze blowing in from an expanse of water beyond a sizzling hot terrain.

In the dry air was the taste of dust and dirt emanating from the steep scree slopes, and the only shelter from the blistering overhead sun seemed to be the shaded recesses beneath the glaring white cliffs towering upwards on all sides.

Here you could seek out religious treasures hidden beyond the reach of sunlight, yet accessible still to those who searched hard enough – archaeologists, opportunists and paid treasure finders.

And now another find. Unexpected. Found where no one else would have thought to look, not any more.

In a spoil-heap, perhaps?

A round disc of clay, hanging on a frail rope cord, twisting, spinning in the hot breeze. It was around two inches in length and about one and a half wide, and seemed to be made of baked clay. Stamped into its flat surface was a curious geometric design – a binding force of unspeakable power.

Ak-bou-id.

The seal of Akboud would be returned to the waking world.

He gazed at the forgotten seal trying to memorise its angular symbols. Set inside a rectangular framework were two equilateral triangles, interlocked into a single grid, with one further line passing from the centre of the rectangle's base to the tip of the inverted triangle. An interpretation eluded him; never had he seen anything like this before.

In his mind he attempted to trace the unseen hand grasping the end of the fragile cord, swinging the Middle Eastern artefact like a pendulum, but found only mist and darkness, as if the new owner was deliberately goading him.

The snatched vision soon faded, bringing Bernard back to the more stable reality of his place of work, but left in his mind was the grim realisation that the invisible hand belonged to the Black Alchemist.

Sunday, 9 September. Seating himself in his usual dining-room chair, Bernard decided he would attempt something he had said he would not do again. For two weeks the unwanted vision of the baked clay seal had remained fixed in his mind, haunting his thoughts and acting like a carrot dangled before a reluctant donkey.

He had fought to rid himself of any interest in knowing why he should have glimpsed such an obscure mental image, but finally he had given in to curiosity. He would conduct a meditation, see what else he could discover about this curious artefact.

Having stalled the inevitable for one final cigarette, he used his elbows to prop up his chin and allowed his mind to drift away from his home, from Essex, and finally from the shores of Britain.

He headed towards a hot climate, somewhere close to where past archaeological excavations had proved greatly rewarding to the Western world – excavations that had changed the face of religious understanding in the twentieth century.

Where exactly did not matter, he was not after a location, only the source of the discovery. For this he needed to search out the vision of the baked seal, the binding force of Akboud.

As before, the hot, rocky terrain was almost too much to bear. Only the mild breeze blowing inland cooled the bleak landscape of soaring cliffs that loomed skywards everywhere he looked.

Where was he; did he know? Scree slopes and caves, perhaps, but no further information given.

The oval-shaped disc twisted and turned upon the rough cord held, not by a hand this time, but by an object just out of view – a much larger item to which the cord had originally been attached.

Gradually its shape formed in his mind's eye – a long green triangle. Yes, he could see it more clearly now, a piece of copper scroll discoloured with age, its structure preserved by the hot sands for nearly 2,000 years. It formed part of a cylindrical roll, its short flat edge bordered by a fine rim; the rest having either vanished or been discovered elsewhere.

It appeared to be six inches in depth and around four in width, and punched into its corroded surface were angular characters in a language unknown to him.

This extraordinary artefact had been retrieved in this dangerous, desolate place under the guidance of corrupt figures who knew precisely where to begin their search, in exchange for a fat fee from the most corrupt bidder.

Frantic digging in loose rocks below a steep white cliff-face took place before its final discovery, and then a sense of glee, as if it was a find of paramount importance, a credit card to unlimited funds from unscrupulous individuals and questionable companies. People with links in high places and money flowing from no-questions-asked banks such as those in, say, Luxembourg?

The Black Alchemist had moved on considerably since his days of petty cat-and-mouse confrontations. His undiminished faith in the Great Work had won him respect from some very powerful sources indeed; people who were prepared to offer monetary support to those who believed they could fulfil individual aspects of a much greater plan.

The clay seal and the copper scroll were the Black Alchemist's first major finds. Their retrieval had come through both psychic processes and the culmination of painstaking research into Gnostic heretics of the early Christian Church.

When the Black Alchemist left the United Kingdom at the end of 1988 Bernard knew only that he was heading for Spain to research Gnostic Christianity. At the time such a move had seemed almost ludicrous for a corrupt figure who had spent many years studying and actively pursuing the often degenerate Greco-Roman alchemy and magic of classical Egypt. The psychic had believed that one day this desolation magic would be the alchemist's downfall; it would destroy him completely. Now he had shifted into uncharted territories conjuring new possible outcomes to this dualistic mind game.

An impression now told him where the man had gone to study his Gnostic Christianity – it was Santiago de Compostela in north-west Spain, the home of a major cathedral and a shrine to St James that had once rivalled Rome in popularity as a place of holy pilgrimage.

It was not, however, as a pilgrim that the Black Alchemist had arrived in this Spanish city. There were early Gnostic documents here; keys to unlocking a mystery hidden since the foundation of Christianity.

If he could discover what interest Santiago de Compostela held for the Black Alchemist, then he might understand why he had travelled to the Middle East and unearthed these magical artefacts. Perhaps then his mind would be haunted no more by the seal of Akboud.

Tuesday, 11 September. On a wooden bench beneath a fluttering parasol erected in The Griffin's fair-sized garden, Bernard finished his story concerning the Black Alchemist's new-found interest in archaeology.

Our long-time adversary's extended vacation in Santiago de

Compostela made complete sense. Aside from being the traditional burial place of St James the Just, this ancient pilgrim centre was also considered to be the final resting place of Priscillian of Avila. He was the founder of a heretical Gnostic movement which had spread like wildfire across Spain – and even into parts of France – during the fourth century AD. In an attempt to gain a full knowledge of the extensive writings of the Early Church, Priscillian had gone out of his way to recover lost gospels and forbidden treatises outlawed by the Roman authorities. Followers were regularly sent as far away as the Middle East to secure and bring back these heretical manuscripts.

Priscillian was finally condemned to death along with five of his disciples in AD 386 and tradition asserts that he was interred at Santiago de Compostela. Some scholars even argue that the cathedral shrine houses the remains not of St James, but those of the Gnostic teacher.

Whatever the source of Santiago de Compostela's ancient sanctity, the sheer fact that Priscillian de Avila's priceless library might prove to be the key to unlocking Christianity's final secrets would have appealed to the studious mind of the Black Alchemist. From Bernard's past mental link-ups with the man, it appeared he possessed a university background and had even worked as a researcher or librarian in an educational institute on the south coast of England. This would have given him the ideal academic approach to conducting archive research in some dusty records office in north-west Spain.

Clues offered by some obscure Gnostic treatise must have provided him with the inspiration to recover the seal and copper scroll at a location that, according to Bernard, had already yielded up Judaeo-Christian artefacts of great significance to our overall understanding of the Early Church.

So where had these artefacts been discovered?

Bernard shrugged his shoulders in resignation. 'All I know is that he was led to a rocky gorge where no one else would have looked.' But then he paused to think. 'No, more like where no one else would have bothered to look, because the thought of anything being found there would have seemed highly improbable.'

What about a country?

'Egypt or Israel.'

My bet was it had been found in Israel, on the West Bank of the Dead Sea to be more precise; and I suspected that the copper scroll was the clue.

Five years after the first Dead Sea Scrolls were unearthed by a Bedouin shepherd boy in 1947, archaeologists located a new, undisturbed cave at Qumran. Cave 3, as it became known, yielded up two oxidised cylindrical sections of a copper scroll about eight inches in depth and around a foot in length. When carefully separated into strips for reading purposes their inscribed text was found to be an itemised list of buried treasure. It included gold and silver bullion, ritual objects, temple vessels and even pots of money. Next to each entry were details of where exactly each item had been hidden. Unfortunately, the locations given could not be matched with any known topographical features in and around modern-day Jerusalem, squashing any ideas of archaeologists embarking upon what might have been one of the greatest treasure hunts of all time.

Debate over the origin of the copper scroll has raged in academic circles since the 1950s, the most plausible theory being that it represents a list of items removed from the Temple of Jerusalem just before the Romans captured the city and destroyed the Temple in AD 70.

All this seemed to suggest that the copper scroll seen to be unearthed by the Black Alchemist had been located somewhere in the Dead Sea region. Bernard's insinuation that BA had been aided by individuals who knew the area, and knew exactly where to begin the search, was a sure reference to the Bedouin tribesman who inhabited the West Bank. Since the first discoveries were made in 1947 they had scoured every conceivable cave searching for further scroll fragments, knowing that each one would fetch a high price either in Jordan or in their own country. Their clandestine activities in this respect were notorious, and it seemed beyond reasonable doubt that such people could be enticed to provide on-site guidance and expertise when it came to unofficial excavations.

'Well, I really don't know where the scroll was found or what's written on it,' Bernard admitted. 'I just feel that unearthing these items is very important to the Black Alchemist; particularly the seal, for some reason.'

Of more concern was exactly who would benefit from these discoveries. From what Bernard had suggested, BA had been funded to locate, retrieve and return these items on behalf of unscrupulous individuals belonging to a clandestine organisation with access to unlimited credit funds in a no-questions-asked Luxembourg bank. Any offers as to *their* identity?

'I thought you were going to ask that,' he said, a warm smile on his face. 'I don't know. But I would think that he made contact with them through his association with Rachel Goodison and her former associates in the Friends of Hekate. Now they have gone their separate ways he has seized the opportunity to establish a working relationship with this other mob.'

Were they in this country?

He shook his head. 'I don't think so. Continental.' He drew out the last word to emphasise its importance.

'D'you think they're connected with the Wheel in any way?' Debbie asked, playing with an empty glass.

'Almost certainly,' he responded assertively. 'Wheels within wheels.' He grinned at the thought. 'You'll never find the centre.'

Bent archaeologists, dodgy banks and international Wheel-linked organisations.

Very heavy stuff indeed, but was it over?

Another wry smile. 'Well, I hope so; don't you?'

25
The Black Cross of the Flame

Wednesday, 26 September 1990. Turning into the drive, Bernard depressed the brake pedal and brought the Montego to a halt. There was some paperwork he should complete after tea, but otherwise the evening was clear; it would give him a chance to catch a few programmes on television and read a little in the dining room.

Locking the vehicle, he approached the front door and let the key turn in the lock. It opened inwards and on the floor he found a single item of mail, a card sealed in a large white envelope. Funny, it was no one's birthday and it was certainly not an early Christmas card.

He reached down and picked it up, being careful not to stretch his tender back which had been playing up these past few weeks. The envelope flap said it was an Athena card made from recycled paper, giving him a good idea of its sender, and it was postmarked STRATFORD-ON-AVON 6.30pm 24 SEPTEMBER 1990.

Moving into the kitchen, he found a paper knife and slit open the lip. Peering inside, he saw only a slightly buckled card which he slowly removed. Its cover depicted the head and neck of a black leopard against a blurred background of greenery. The image seemed pleasant enough, but what about the message? He opened the gate-fold and found only a typed warning which read:

```
Beware of the Black Cross of the Flame.
European based Society of high funding.

Seeking ancient biblical scripts and relics
world wide.
```

```
Suspected of using an ancient ruin site as a
repository for the relics.
Attempt as been made to raise the Fallen Angel.

I am moving to different country.

R
```

The final 'R' confirmed its source of origin – Rachel Goodison, his old adversary.

He read the entire message a second and third time. 'Beware of the Black Cross of the Flame.' Who were they? He had never come across the name before. She appeared to believe they were a 'European-based Society of high funding'. Their apparent search to find 'ancient biblical scripts and relics worldwide' allowed him to link their existence with the baked clay seal and copper scroll the Black Alchemist had found and brought back to Europe sometime during the previous month. It also gave him some idea of where she had obtained this information.

Bernard pushed the switch on the kettle.

He knew the Black Alchemist was now being financed by a Wheel-linked organisation on the Continent who believed that by collecting power objects and manuscripts of ancient sanctity, they would greatly increase their wealth and influence. He knew little more, so had tried to mind-search just once to see if he could gain any further information. In response he had seen only a fleeting glimpse of Amsterdam. So was this where BA's wealthy supporters, the so-called 'Black Cross of the Flame' were to be found?

Black Cross ... Black Cross ... What did it mean? In response to his thoughts he saw the disturbing mental picture of a huge calvary cross charred black with fire. It was not a pleasing sight by any means, as it reminded him of the Ku-Klux-Klan.

Listening to the water in the kettle growing steadily more noisy, he decided that these people were not messing about. Whoever they were, they did not play by the Queensberry Rules. Yet through contacts in the United Kingdom they had been introduced to the Black Alchemist, who they believed would be

THE BLACK CROSS OF THE FLAME

of value to them, tracking down biblical relics and seeking out ancient manuscripts.

What of this 'ruin site' they were suspected by Rachel of using 'as a repository' for the relics? On this he picked up nothing at all, although it did appear to echo recent words from Debbie. Just hours after the card must have been dropped into a letter box in Stratford-upon-Avon, Andrew had rung him to relate some intriguing psychic imagery she had glimpsed at work that afternoon. She saw dark, musty catacombs with orangey-red pillars hewn out of solid rock. They formed interconnecting tunnels resonating an atmosphere of solemn morbidity. With these moving pictures had come the overwhelming impression that this manmade necropolis had been used both in the past and in more recent times for acts of necromancy – raising the dead through supernatural processes. She went further, however, believing it was here that the Black Alchemist had come to deposit the clay seal and copper scroll.

Debbie had been unable to give a location, but there had been mention of the Early Church catacombs in Rome, which made some sort of sense to him. The Athena card tended to confirm these impressions.

He made coffee before settling at the dining-room table with the card still clutched in his hand.

An 'Attempt has been made to raise the Fallen Angel.' By whom? The Black Cross of the Flame, perhaps? He supposed so, but which Fallen Angel did she mean? Lucifer? Satan? Belial? Some other devil? There were so many.

Rachel's final sentence said she was moving to another country. He understood why and possibly where she was going, even though he was under the impression that she had moved to France at the beginning of the year. Perhaps she had only been staying with her family and friends. Now it appeared the relocation was more permanent. It was possible she had met someone out there and had decided to settle down; get out of the occult completely.

He smiled to himself. Oh well, it was good to hear from her again. If she was going to continue sending him cryptic facts concerning the apparent activities of the Black Alchemist, then it was all right by him. It would certainly make life easier.

Lifting his mug of coffee, he realised he would have to give Andrew a ring and let him know about this enigmatic card. Maybe he could throw some light on the Black Cross of the Flame.

Friday, 28 September. 'The Black Cross of the Flame? No, I've certainly not come across that name before,' the book dealer responded.

I had expected this would be the case. Bob Gilbert is a well-known author and professional book dealer of international renown. His life is spent rooting out and purchasing rare and valuable books on all aspects of Freemasonry, mysticism and the occult. His work takes him to auction rooms and dusty bookshops across Europe and he, if anyone, would be aware of any organisation in Amsterdam which might specialise in buying Christian Gnostic documents.

'The main buyer of Gnostic and alchemical manuscripts in the Netherlands is J. R. Ritman, the owner of the *Bibliotheca Philosophica Hermetica* in Amsterdam,' he continued, wondering if this information would be of any use. 'Its library houses literally thousands of extremely rare books and manuscripts; in fact, it is the biggest collection of its kind in Europe.

'Ritman is a very reputable collector, but if you want to start looking for another collector of Gnostic material in Amsterdam, then I suggest you begin here.'

These were important words, for in the spring of 1988 Bernard felt sure the Black Alchemist had sloped off either to Belgium or the Netherlands to purchase a valuable alchemical work. Bob Gilbert had referred to the Ritman Gnostic library on this occasion as well, but the name had meant little at the time. Then a few months later David experienced a vivid dream in which he saw the Black Alchemist inside the Ritman Gnostic library in Amsterdam, without any knowledge of Bob Gilbert's words on the matter.

None of this implied any direct connection between the alleged Black Cross of the Flame and the library itself. It did, however, suggest that others with less honourable intentions might be taking an unhealthy interest in this priceless manuscript library, which contains items not just on Gnosticism, alchemy and Hermetica, but also mysticism and continental Rosicrucianism.

'"The Black Cross of the Flame" sounds like the sort of name some neo-Nazi occult group would use,' Bob mused, summing up his thoughts.

He was quite right, of course. In Trevor Ravenscroft's occult classic *The Spear of Destiny* there is mention of a 'Rosicrucian' meditation referred to as 'the Black Cross and the Seven Red Roses'. It was conducted in 1914 by Johannes Walter Stein – an early associate of Adolf Hitler's and one of the first Nazi precursors to realise the significance of the supposed 'Heilige Lance' housed in Vienna's Hofburg Museum. On this meditation Ravenscroft said:

> The separate symbols [the Black Cross and Seven Red Roses] never appearing together in the sense world, such a form of meditation was already a step towards sense-free experience. Besides this, the whole thought process of this particular meditation embraced the inner significance of the blood, the central theme of the search for the Grail.[1]

So much for the 'Black Cross' aspect of the name, but what about 'the Flame' – what did this mean? Almost certainly it was a reference to the perpetual flame once kindled in the Zoroastrian fire temples of ancient Persia, the modern-day Iran. Not only was the sacred flame seen as the sole representation of the monotheistic deity, Ormuzd or Ahura Mazda, it was also a symbol of absolute purity. When at St Catherine's Hill, Winchester, in March 1989 Helen had been 'given' the names 'Mazda', as in Ahura Mazda, and 'Ahriman', Ahura Mazda's dark counterpart, hinting at the role Zoroastrian fire worship may have played in the activities of the Friends of Hekate/Dark Council.

It is also known that during the Second World War Nazi occultists hijacked elements of the Zoroastrian, or Aryan, belief in racial purity and corrupted it for their own purposes.[2] A modern-day connection between Zoroastrianism and neo-Nazi occultism is unquestionable.

Yet aside from these perhaps obvious neo-Nazi associations,

any organisation known as 'the Black Cross of the Flame' was likely to mimic the aims, and therefore the style, of the Ku-Klux-Klan – who feature burning cross imagery heavily in their rites and symbolism. With strongholds still persisting in the southern States, among many other places, the Klansmen have fought against Black Americans since the Civil War period. They are still active today and have undoubtedly forged links with neo-Nazi bodies such as the Church of Jesus Christ Christian. These people blend together white Aryan propaganda and Norse mythology with Bible teachings to confirm their own racial superiority. A *Daily Mail* article dated 13 October 1986 claimed that this occult-linked American church already had thousands of supporters in Britain and would start establishing churches here 'in two years'.

The first country that comes to mind when talking about white superiority and racial purity is, of course, South Africa, whose white European roots and modern-day sympathies originated in the Netherlands. It was therefore not inconceivable that a Klan-like fraternity, with extremist right-wing and Christian tendencies, could establish itself in Amsterdam as Bernard had suggested.

Still, unless we established firm evidence of the Black Cross's existence and activities, there was little more we could do or say at this present time. There were, however, slight indications that the Black Alchemist had been flirting with the symbolism of the Spear of Destiny – the power object so important to Nazi Germany – during the lead-up to the Paradise Mound episode in August 1988. Where this had led him was only now becoming clear.

Bob and I turned to other more mundane matters before we said our goodbyes and I resumed making entries into the handwritten diary. As I took up the pen, one line in Rachel's card kept repeating itself inside my head: 'Attempt has been made to raise the Fallen Angel.' Something wanted to tell me that this was not a reference to the invocation of some Judaeo-Christian devil or demon; no, it was far more complex than that.

What the hell did it mean? I could not be sure, but I had the vague suspicion we were going to find out soon enough.

26
A Last Goodbye

Monday, 3 December 1990. She depressed the play button on the cassette player and the slow, melodic music of David Sylvian emerged from the mounted speakers on the wall of the upstairs function suite of a public house in Leigh-on-Sea. After adjusting the sound levels, Debbie joined the rest of the Earthquest group, who sat in a wide circle across the floor waiting to begin the meditation.

Most of those taking part were relatively new to the subject and part of their training involved an introduction to visualisation techniques. A meditational theme is chosen and afterwards those who wish can relay details of any imagery and impressions they may have experienced during the session. Most of what they have to say will be pure imagination, and this they know. However, out of imagination comes genuine psychic inspiration gained from levels beyond the conscious perception of the human mind.

Tonight there was no set theme; so, after taking the assembled group through the construction of a cone of mental power, I suggested they visualise the base of an idyllic green hill, capped with a circular copse of mature trees. This they were to climb, using their hands if necessary, experiencing the heat of the sun upon their exposed skin and a cool breeze rushing through their hair. They were to hear the leaves hissing gently as a mild wind blew through the swaying branches. Having arrived at the flat summit they were to look out over the plush, green landscape before rising into the air and beginning an imaginary journey of their own choice. That was the plan at least.

7.50pm. Debbie could hear Andrew babbling on about hills, the tree-tops and the wind rushing through your hair, but she was already deviating considerably from the prescribed course. In the darkness she pulled her way up a steeply wooded slope towards an altogether different destination. The setting was, however, vaguely familiar; she had been here before in dream.

Debbie had never visited this desolate place in a physical sense, but somehow she knew she was fast approaching the deep circular ditch and bank encircling the Iron Age hill-fort known as Chanctonbury Ring. Perched high up on the South Downs Way in West Sussex, it is approached through a miasma of dense woodland covering a treacherous 45° slope.

Unseen eyes followed her movements, gazing out from the shadows but not daring to move any closer. When she turned her head they would duck into the shadows, only to re-appear once she continued her arduous journey. She knew they were dusky elementals, familiar spirits of the woodland, the real hobgoblins of old; but they would not bother her tonight. They acted boldly sometimes, leaping around on their spindly legs and taunting her like playful monkeys, but sinking back into oblivion as she approached.

On reaching level ground, the dense woodland gave way to open scrubland and a fierce wind blustering maniacally across the exposed Downs. Its constant roar ebbed and flowed in time with the hissing of the black skeletal trees, which acted like dark sentries guarding over the ancient encampment.

She knew the fort had once been connected with the activities of the Friends of Hekate and wondered why she had been drawn here. Upturned tree trunks, their roots rudely exposed for all to see, lay scattered across its enormous circular plateau.

She became aware of more eyes watching her, this time from somewhere overhead. Glancing upwards, she perceived two charcoal-black forms perched upon a tendril-like branch jutting out of a weathered, though still upright tree trunk. Silhouetted in the greyish hue of the December night they appeared to be half-man, half-raven, as if they were the neglected souls of past great bird shamans who had once inhabited this place of vibrant power. They side-stepped over to a nearer branch and observed the movement below.

'Are you bird-men?' she called out, unafraid of these mutated site guardians.

One looked cautiously to the other. 'Maybe,' they responded in unison. Unexpectedly, their huge wings began to flap rhythmically until they lifted from the thin branch and took flight together.

Instantly Debbie felt them pulling her into the air, to join them on a journey. She sensed they had been expecting her and now wanted to show her something; wanted her to be with someone. With faith in their motives, she climbed steadily into the sky as the two bird-men led the way into a funnel of diffuse grey light, across the water to somewhere alien – a foreign place completely unknown to her.

In the darkness she could make out an unusual church – different from those she had visited before, French perhaps, and peculiar in style. She found herself entering this solemn place of worship, the two bird-men having disappeared from view. She passed down an aisle of loose wooden chairs and neared the high altar, its stark form made clearer by the flickering flames of candles burning in a side chapel.

Draped over this sanctified table of offering was a faded russet cloth with the words 'Noir, noir a lumière' embroidered across its well-worn frontal. Woven into the flat surface of its frail fabric was a perfect circle, one half the colour of fire and the other half sewn in threads of black. Set upon this aesthetic design was not the Cross of Christ, as might be expected, but a single twisted horn of carved ebony.

Suddenly there was a low, prolonged moan coming from female voices somewhere behind her, which increased steadily in level and potency as the atmosphere began to change. Fixing her eyes on the rectangular altar, she now saw a vaporous ball of lime-green light rise from the sewn circle and grow in size and brightness. Emerald-green tongues of fire then began lapping upwards as the amorphous mass slowly congealed into a hideous monstrosity, a vile beast of no godly origin. With the cold, verdant fire as a ring of protection, its claw-like feet came to rest and clenched the sacred cloth as its squat, bilious body crystallised before her eyes. She saw its reptilian scales in blue and white, its devilish forked tail and its claw-like hands ending in razor-sharp talons. Yet it was the crouching demoness's hideous, horned head that stole her attention. Its stark baldness, its yellow skin, its ruby-red lips and the sad, feminine face covered in browny-black stripes of dry blood made this the most disturbing beast she had ever encountered.

It was a picture of utter revulsion, but somewhere within its pathetic form was the distraught soul of its incarnate personification – the Black Sorceress of Arundel. This was a living thought form of the demonic mural found by Charles Walker painted on a barn wall next to Clapham Woods in 1979. It had been commissioned by members of the Friends of Hekate and it was an image that had haunted Rachel Goodison since those days, for it symbolised her allegiance to the Mistress of the Underworld.

The demoniac-like creation opened its mouth of razor-sharp teeth and emitted a burst of luminous green flame that cut through the air and formed a perfect ring of fire like a burning circus hoop just feet away from Debbie.

The ethereal side-show made no sense. Why had she been chosen to witness this stupefying spectacle?

Still the female voices continued their low chant.

Once more the repulsive entity opened its vampiric mouth and disgorged an arrow of fluorescent green fire that reached and passed through the flaming ring, missing Debbie's right shoulder by a matter of inches.

She flinched, suddenly breaking the unwanted vision. Once again she could hear the monotone voice of her partner slowly bringing the group back to the physical realm and closing down the circle of power.

It was over – both for her and for Rachel Goodison.

Tuesday, 4 December. Against the background hum of the early evening clientele passing their time in The Griffin, I waved to Bernard as he walked into the bar. He smiled in acknowledgement of our presence and after buying his token pint of Guinness, he moved across to the old wooden bench and took a seat next to Debbie.

The greetings over, he casually reached into his jacket pocket and pulled out a small piece of jewellery. 'What d'you make of this? It came last night.' He tossed the oval item on to the table. 'It's an apport. My first one.' He said it with a smile of satisfaction.

A LAST GOODBYE

It was a lady's cameo brooch mounted in a gold-plated clasp, showing the profile of a woman's head in white raised relief set against a background of black. Her hair was tied into a bun and although it was not old in a physical sense its design had almost certainly been copied from an early Victorian original.

I thought of Bernard's words for a moment. Yes, he was right, it would be the first ever apport, the first ever paranormally-produced object that had appeared at his home. So where did it come from?

'I found it on the table in the dining room. I heard this loud crack – I was in the front room at the time – and when I got there, this was on the side,' he explained casually. 'It wasn't there earlier or I'd have seen it, and the only thing I noticed when I picked it up was a distinct smell of burning – cordite, fireworks – something like that. This was just past eight o'clock.'

Bloody hell, that was at the exact time we were conducting the Earthquest meditation; something Bernard had no knowledge of at all.

'And this is connected with what's her name,' he revealed, fiddling with the cameo.

Rachel?

'Yes, and I shall keep it,' he added with a note of glee, not yet realising the extraordinary significance of the incident he had just described.

This was incredible. Debbie and I had concluded that her unexpected vision of the demonic mural in the French church symbolised the externalisation and passing on of Rachel Goodison's allegiance to Hekate, given to her as priestess of the Friends of Hekate during the 1970s. In this way she had finally rid herself of the sordid past she so wanted to leave behind.

Debbie agreed, sipping her glass of Malibu and orange. 'To achieve this I think she arranged a low-key ritual in a French church, possibly a private chapel. I feel it was conducted by a group of friends, all women, and may not have necessitated her presence at all.'

Bernard nodded; it felt right to him.

Debbie continued. 'They visualised Hekate manifesting as the demonic mural and then severed its connection with her forever.'

'Noir, noir a lumière', I found, translates from French into

English as *black, black into light*, in all probability a reference to her personal transformation at this time.

The strange thing was that at the same time Debbie had experienced this symbolic imagery, other Earthquest members were glimpsing similar themes. At least two others – one being new member Richard Ward – had been perplexed to find themselves at Chanctonbury Ring.

'I told you some while back that the demonic mural reflected a woman's extreme wish to break free from her involvement in ritual magic,' Bernard reminded me. 'D'you remember? I also said it was linked with someone in France.'

He did, back in February 1988, when psychometrising a colour print of the demonic mural.[1] Neither of us had realised then that the woman behind the troubled, yellow-skinned face was BSA, the woman we knew as Rachel Goodison.

Now Bernard had received a cameo brooch as a reality-defying apport at the same time Debbie had experienced a vision representing Rachel's ritualistic release from the clutches of Hekate. The cameo's existence could be seen as a final gesture to him, a final message conveying as pure emotional energy her magical transition from 'black, black into light'.

Noir, noir a lumière.

Apports occur when raw primal energy seen by psychics as coloured light or moving fire is transformed by paranormal processes into solid matter best befitting its original energetic state. It could therefore end up as anything; in this case a black and white lady's cameo brooch seemed perfectly adequate.

'It is her last goodbye,' Bernard announced, a glitter in his eyes. 'She's probably getting hitched to some Frenchman right now; I don't think we'll hear from her any more.'

A last goodbye, perhaps, but her legacy would live on and at the end of the day both she and the Black Alchemist were always just an air journey away.

Perhaps we should always remember that.

27
Trouble at Stonehenge

Sunday, 25 August 1991. Debbie lay on the floor of the Black Room, her head resting on a soft pillow, as she drifted into a semi-conscious trance state. The stereo system played slow, ambient music ideal for meditations and I had already directed her to our chosen target for the evening using creative visualisation. The blazing light of the full moon outside gave the darkened room an eerie quality and made the use of candles almost superfluous to our needs.

Something strange was happening in the barrow cemeteries surrounding Stonehenge and we needed to know what. Readying my pocket cassette, I waited patiently for her to establish contact.

Just two days ago Debbie had experienced a vivid dream concerning this most famous of prehistoric monuments. From Stonehenge itself her mind's eye had been drawn away to one of the neighbouring Bronze Age barrow cemeteries – one consisting of several low mounds and a few circular depressions somewhere in a flat, cultivated terrain. She found herself elevated on a slight rise and noticed snow lying round about. Close by, some youths leapt across a large circular depression on saddled ponies, a scene certainly not of this day and age as the kids today would probably use mountain bikes for the same purpose!

Later that same day she had experienced a further vision of the same location. Out of nowhere appeared an army helicopter and from its open door came a soldier on a winch, dressed in a 'drab grey boiler suit'. Another soldier, similarly attired, rose out of the circular depression to meet his colleague; all clear indications that the location in question was close to restricted military land on Salisbury Plain.

The circular depression was almost certainly a Bronze Age pond barrow, similar to the one found to contain the deep ritual shaft at Normanton Gorse during the 1960s. However, something told her she had not witnessed the Wilsford Pit on this occasion.

The previous day – Saturday, 24 August – Debbie had again dreamt about the snow-laden pond barrow. This time she saw a mature woman in grey named 'Anne' who asked Debbie if she had come to find the 'Amorea'. With these words the female spectre held out a polished, ruby-red garnet formerly set into the pommel of a Bronze Age dagger and placed in a barrow with other grave goods. Left in her mind was the strong impression that this woman in grey should *not* be trusted; all was not as it seemed.

The Stonehenge connection troubled Debbie for some reason, and in the hope that we could shed some light on this perplexing mystery we had decided to conduct a psychic session; nothing elaborate, just enough to give us a few simple answers.

After a few minutes of silence Debbie began mumbling in her sleep, a sure sign that the link had been made.

Switching on the cassette recorder, I moved in closer and asked her to tell me what she could see. I received no answer so put the question to her again, this time somewhat louder.

She mumbled below her breath before opening her eyes and looking towards me. 'What are you doing?'

Asking questions.

'You've wokèn me up, now,' she protested, more than a little indignant. 'Don't shout like that. All it does is jolt me out of the meditation.'

I told her I was sorry and tried to explain that I had not shouted.

'Well, it sounded like you did to me,' she insisted. 'You shouldn't do that. I've got a headache now.' Rising to a sitting position, she rubbed her forehead.

So it was my fault that the whole evening would now be aborted. Just because I had spoken too loudly when she was fast asleep; surely I could not take the full blame.

Heated words passed between us as I stood up, slammed the door and went to sit in the front room. In response, Debbie sauntered off to the bedroom and decided to get ready for bed.

Annoyed, I switched on the word processor, found an open file and attempted to do some work. I accepted that the meditation was over and now the two of us were not even speaking to each other.

Petty perhaps, but on the other hand it was strange fate as well. Sitting in the Black Room, with the soft lunar light glistening on the floor, had brought back cold memories of Helen attempting to draw down the full moon in her lounge almost exactly two years before. That night had also ended in tears and, more distressingly, it had acted as the final straw in our strained psychic relationship.

Frustrated, I closed the file and switched off the far too noisy machine. Unable to concentrate at this late hour, I retired to the bedroom and made my peace with Debbie; there was no point in disagreeing over such trivial matters.

Tired and with peace of mind, Debbie dozed off to sleep. Day-to-day memories flashed through her mind until they forged with night-time trivia and finally gave way to deep sleep.

Glimpses of Stonehenge continually plagued her dreamscape, ebbing and flowing until she could make out the ancient monument's ring of upright sarsens with their distinctive horizontal lintels and its inner horseshoe of five trilithons, slotted into place by the sweat and blood of ancient hands.

There was something markedly different about Stonehenge today. Its fallen lintel stones had been re-erected and there seemed to be no luridly dressed tourists filing past the great stones, cameras in hand. She saw no entrance tunnel, no car park packed to capacity and no English Heritage centre. She saw no traffic thundering past, in fact she could not see any roads at all, only exposed plains swept by freezing cold winds and covered with patches of snow and ice.

In the orange glow of the low winter sun Debbie approached the outer ditch beyond the sarsen ring and noticed a tall, fairly broad man standing on one of the horizontal lintels. He wore a multi-layered, cowled robe of orange, black and blue and supported himself with a long wooden pole. Drawing nearer, she saw he sported a wiry beard and his face had a rough, ruddy complexion caused through his constant exposure to the harsh weather.

Moving within shouting distance of this strange priestly figure she gazed upwards, wondering why she had been brought here to meet this man.

'I am Ptah,' he announced in an English voice her unconscious mind could understand. 'You wish to know of Amorea?'

To her it was a rhetorical question. 'And who is Ptah?' she responded, craning her neck to view him.

'You seek the place of the ancestors?' was his only response.

She did not answer.

Ptah used his long, slim staff to point towards the distant horizon. 'The place you seek is of the ring of five, west of the avenue of procession.'

She knew of no 'avenue of procession'.

Almost instantly her mind's eye was cast forth and soon she reached a new location beyond the sight of the Stonehenge monument.

She stood on the edge of a circular depression hidden in the grass, its shallow bowl filled with nettles and weeds.

But where was this place? Andrew said that without a name it could never be found as there were so many barrow cemeteries and so many pond barrows. She would have to know.

But Ptah was no longer there.

Monday, 26 August. Eating a bowl of muesli I listened to Debbie as she recounted her most recent dream regarding the unidentified pond barrow.

'Tar', the name of the priest, intrigued me. Debbie could only spell the name phonetically, so there had to be a possibility that this ancestral guardian of Stonehenge took his name in honour of Ptah, the Egyptian high god of Memphis, the ancient dynastic capital south-west of modern-day Cairo. In Egyptian cosmogony Ptah, pronounced 'tar', was closely associated with the primeval mound of creation.

Egypt might seem a long way from Stonehenge, but in fact many turquoise faience beads belonging to the Egyptian Amarna culture, *circa* 1370-50 BC, have been found in mounds belonging to the various barrow cemeteries in the vicinity of Stonehenge.

Archaeologists explain away this historical anomaly by either claiming they were traded to the Mycenaean culture of Crete before being re-routed to Bronze Age Britain by Phoenician mariners, or they were homemade reproductions of those exported from the Mediterranean. Both theories offer workable explanations, but I saw no reason why, if Egyptian beads reached these shores, then Egyptians themselves could not have hitched a lift on Phoenician trading vessels and dealt directly with Britain's Bronze Age culture. I therefore decided to accept the Egyptian name Ptah until a better derivation was given.

As to the priest's inference that the pond barrow singled out by Debbie represented one of 'a ring of five', located in a cemetery 'to the west of the avenue of procession', I could not rightly say. I presumed that 'the avenue of procession' was a reference to the Greater Stonehenge Cursus, situated approximately half a mile north of Stonehenge. Consisting of two parallel-running earthen banks and ditches between 196 to 420 feet apart[1], this earthen monument, although considerably defaced by modern agriculture, can still be traced for a distance of anything up to two miles.[2] Archaeologists believe it to be contemporary with the first phase of Stonehenge, dating it to around 2800 BC.

The first person to discuss Stonehenge's processional avenue seriously was the eighteenth-century antiquarian William Stukeley. He gave it the name *cursus*, the Latin for a race course, and since then the title has been applied to other earthen avenues of a similar description. It has also been noticed that the northern bank of the Greater Stonehenge Cursus is aligned upon other landscape features. Archaeologist J.F.S. Stone, who conducted excavations here in 1947, recorded that 'its axis, if projected 1,500 yards east, strikes Woodhenge and passes the Cuckoo or Cuckhold Stone by the way.'[3] Unfortunately, however, its westerly orientation is not aligned on any feature at all, no matter how much you twist a ruler. Furthermore, there were so many pond barrows scattered among the various different barrow cemeteries that any reference to 'a ring of five' was virtually useless.

Debbie listened as she made toast. 'Isn't there anything west of the processional avenue at all?'

No, not really; well, nothing that made obvious sense. There was a barrow cemetery at Winterbourne Stoke, some one and half miles west-south-west of Stonehenge, and it did contain a pond barrow. Perhaps this was the one.

Debbie did not answer, knowing she needed further words with Ptah. 'You know, I reckon this has got something to do with a power struggle between two opposing forces associated with Stonehenge's past,' she revealed for the first time.

Go on, I urged her.

'This is happening now, today, but it all stems back to a very real struggle between two Bronze Age characters – one a male warrior lord and the other a powerful queen. During their lifetime they were constantly warring and their differences were never resolved, even after their deaths; they took them to the grave and there they have lain dormant ever since. This tension has been carried into modern times on a subtle level and involves certain artefacts, including the Amorea stone, which I'm sure was once placed in the pommel of a Bronze Age dagger.' She slipped out the grill tray and turned over the slices. 'I also see a diamond-shaped breastplate in bronze.'

A gold, lozenge plate of this type was found by Sir Richard Colt Hoare, an antiquarian, and his colleague William Cunningham, when excavating the Bush Barrow in the Normanton cemetery group in 1808. It rested with the skeleton of a tall, warrior-like man, alongside three bronze daggers, a bronze axe and various other stone and metal implements. The barrow's grave goods have been dated to the Early Bronze Age, *circa* 2100 BC, and the lozenge breastplate is currently on display in the British Museum.

'D'you want toast?' she asked, withdrawing the tray and plonking it on the kitchen surface.

I shook my head.

'Unfortunately, I have a nasty suspicion that someone, I don't know who, knows of this eternal struggle and has been pumping up the female side. In doing so they are imbalancing the entire local energy matrix; I'm sure this is why I've been picking up on this theme so strongly.

'I also get the horrible feeling that whoever it is may have already found what they're looking for. Perhaps it's this breastplate, or the Amorea, I don't know; but whatever it is, it has become a crucial factor in turning the tides at Stonehenge.'

I broached the likelihood of whether we might be dealing with the People of Hexe.

'I don't even want to think about the possibility,' she responded, grabbing a plate. 'I don't know if I can handle it at the moment.'

For nearly two years we had known that Hexe were apparently utilising the Old Sarum ley that ran between Frankenbury Camp and Stonehenge, while down-loading their own resurrected psychic forces and entities into the British energy matrix at Normanton Gorse, a mile and a half south-south-west of Stonehenge. The Wilsford group of tumuli, in which the ritual pit can be found, is within spitting distance of the Bush Barrow in the Normanton group where the bronze breastplate was unearthed during the nineteenth century, so there had to be a connection somehow.

'Well, I'm pretty sure the pond barrow I saw was *not* at either Normanton or Wilsford. As I said, this priest says it's "west of the processional avenue".'

Now we were going round in circles. Until we obtained a better idea of where to look, we could take the matter no further. In the meantime I would borrow a few books on archaeology and attempt to conduct a brief study of the various barrow cemeteries in the Stonehenge area, maybe then any further cryptic clues from Ptah would make better sense.

Tuesday, 27 August. Debbie dreamt again. This time the entire Stonehenge landscape slowly evolved into a completely new picture as she found herself alone in a crude wooden boat rocking about in cold, icy waters.

Beyond the distant banks was a green rolling landscape flowing down to the shoreline of this temporary lake, created when a nearby river had swollen to flood these low-lying plains. The only things visible above the lapping waves were the rounded summits of various tumuli, dotted about over a wide area, showing that this vast inland sea was just a few feet deep in places.

Suddenly Ptah was with her, calmly gesturing with his wooden pole towards the gently rippling waters. 'This is a lake upon a down. Look down,' he proclaimed with a note of stern contentment on his weathered face.

Debbie did as he wished and found that the waters were so clear she could easily make out the flooded agricultural land beneath them. Glancing back to him, she was disappointed to find that Ptah had vanished.

As if by magic, the primitive boat neared and then beached on the crest of a round barrow. Without warning the lake unexpectedly drained to leave the boat on dry land. Now the grassy barrow slowly became crystal-clear until she could observe at its centre a hunched-up skeleton in a foetal position, flesh still clinging to its bones and a Bronze dagger held against its chest. Somehow she knew it was the mortal remains of the woman in grey she had encountered before. It was her final resting place, a timeless grave preserving her memory forever. Now she was restless; the warrior queen had been awoken from her eternal slumber to rekindle ancient feuds that had never been settled.

Darkness fell upon the barrow cemeteries of Stonehenge as Debbie rose to the point of consciousness and dimly registered the electronic *beep-beep-beep* of the Time Cube. She reached over and pressed its casing until she found the snooze button. It would give her five more minutes before it would force her to wake up again.

8.30am. Of course! Ptah had said: 'This is a lake upon a down. Look down.' It was a clue – a play on words, a mental pun, organised by her unconscious mind to help convey data being received from exterior sources associated with the local energy matrix in the Stonehenge area. The message was simple and quite brilliant and left me in no doubt as to the identity of the Bronze Age cemetery being referred to in the communications. It was *Lake Down*, a cluster of no less than sixteen barrows about half a mile south of the Wilsford group and only two miles due south of Stonehenge.

Leaving Debbie in the kitchen, I rushed to find the book that had recently become my 'bible' of archaeological information – *A Guide to Prehistoric England* by Nicholas Thomas. Flicking through its pages, I found the chapter on Wiltshire sites and read the entry for Lake Down (which, incidentally, is different to the quite separate Lake group of barrows, situated north-west of Lake Down).

Yes! Found them at last. I clenched my fists and punched the air in satisfaction. Although I had not noticed it before, Lake Down contains a cluster of *five* pond barrows, four together with one just a short distance away; this was Ptah's 'ring of five'. There were no other details on whether they had been excavated, just references to cremations found in some of the group's disc and saucer barrows.

Finding the OS map for the Amesbury/Stonehenge area, I moved into the kitchen and opened it out on the table. On locating Lake Down, I realised it did not lie due west of the Cursus; not by any stretch of the imagination. Yet if Ptah's message about the 'ring of five' was accurate, then surely the rest of his words should make sense as well.

So where did we go from here? Debbie had shown very little interest in actively pursuing this psychic quest. She knew full well it probably involved the People of Hexe, even though she did not want to admit it to herself.

This coming Sunday I had arranged a photo session with *You* magazine, who were putting together a piece on my psychic questing exploits for an up-coming feature on my book *The Seventh Sword*, due out in November.[4] They required location shots of myself and the group standing in a circle making contact with some spirit denizen or other to illustrate the piece and had finally agreed on a photo call at Waltham Abbey in north-east Essex. We had unfinished business here and in between the photo session we could at least try to conduct some real psychic work.

Now, however, there were alternative plans going around in my head. What if, instead of Waltham Abbey, we were to switch the photo call to Stonehenge, saying we had a few leads we wanted to check out there. If the group could handle the camera flashes and adverse attention from over-curious tourists, we could perhaps conduct a meditation inside the public walkway at Stonehenge. If this proved hopeful, then maybe we could go on to the Lake Down cemetery and see what was happening there.

Then another thought entered my mind. If we ended up unearthing an artefact at this pond barrow, while the photo session was in progress, then it might appear as if we had set up the whole thing; in many ways it might be best not to find anything at all.

No, this was a defeatist attitude. All we could do was play it by ear and see what happened. If a discovery was made, then we would worry about the consequences when it came to it.

28
The Bone Man

Sunday, 1 September 1991. Standing on the edge of the pond barrow, gazing down at the shallow depression alive with grass, scrub and spiders' webs, I felt jubilant. After nearly two weeks of constant psychic material we had finally reached our destination.

Debbie descended into the hollow while John Horrigan strolled around taking photographs. Professional photographer Richard Ansett and his female assistant set up their infinitely more expensive equipment as Tom Hibbert, the pale-looking ex-*New Musical Express* journalist assigned to compile the *You* magazine feature, looked on in mild amusement.

The day had started well. The weather was absolutely perfect, with clear skies and a pleasant early autumn sun, and I had managed to pull together seven members of the questing group for the occasion. Having arrived at the already overflowing Stonehenge car-park around lunchtime we had joined the constant procession of tourists making their way towards the 4,800-year-old prehistoric henge monument.

No real psychic information had resulted during an impromptu meditation at the Stones, just the feeling that we should continue on to the Lake Down pond barrow. This had appeared a simple task from the OS map, but after cruising the minor roads and farm tracks south of Amesbury for some while, we parked the cars and continued the arduous journey on foot.

After an hour of crossing ploughed fields – and a few tense moments when I led the party completely astray – we caught sight of the Lake Down group of Bronze Age barrows. The low tumuli looked wholly unimpressive and after a cursory surveillance of the shallow depressions marking the positions of the remaining pond barrows, Debbie found the one revealed in her dreams.

The example before us now was the deepest and best preserved of the three still discernible and, following a few last-minute pictures, the weary group descended into the earthen bowl and formed a circle on the ground. Aside from Debbie and myself, the group consisted of Kerry, John, Paul, Alex and Karl.

The warm, sunny weather aided our concentration as each person closed their eyes and used mental visualisation to link themselves with the ancient site's subtle energy matrix.

Click. Click. Click. From the outside edge of the pond barrow Richard Ansett completed the photo session. Tom Hibbert had already sauntered off for a quiet cigarette leaving his old cassette player to record the session.

Debbie focused her inner mind and watched for any gradually forming imagery. It was going to be slightly more difficult to concentrate than usual, but like everyone else, she had freed herself from embarrassment long ago.

Click. Click. Click.

She could hear the photographer and his assistant moving around, somewhere above them. In a strange sort of way their mundane presence was more a comfort than a hindrance, and they seemed nice enough people.

A sudden shift in perspective meant she could now see straight through the curved rim of the depression, into the constantly evolving world of the barrow's etheric counterpart. Its glass-like walls gave her a misty vision of strange sights. There were anguished faces peering out at her as if trapped in limbo. They were formless and unhelpful, yet appeared to be aware of her intrusion into their domain; each wanting her to free their soul from this eternal damnation.

Debbie shook her head slowly; she did not have the means with which to help them.

In front of her now was a woman in grey. She could make out her features more clearly this time; see her long grey frizzy hair and tattered cloth garments. It was the 'Anne' of her dreams, the ruthless queen awoken by the recent acts of others. Each side of her were human midgets dressed in plain leather leggings with a string of beads around their necks.

As with the formless souls, the dwarves were aware of her

presence in their midst and were gesturing with their fingers, pointing enthusiastically, saying one after the other: '*They've come to break the red ring of cursore. They've come to break it.*'

She had nothing to fear from them, but could the warrior queen be trusted and where was her rival, the noble lord with whom she had perpetually struggled during her lifetime?

Unexpectedly Debbie experienced movement, like an arrow in flight, shot from one site to the next, over cultivated fields of crop stubble and through a leafy clump of tall trees. She landed in another barrow cemetery, this one infinitely more menacing in atmosphere. In front of her was another deep depression – one she recognised as the ritual pit at Normanton Gorse. Entry to this hell-hole was prevented by something she had not seen before – a small padlocked door set into a tiny wooden shed which quickly melted away to reveal the dark, dank depths of the sanguine pit.

Debbie felt scared, but assistance was on the way, for into view came an ancient shaman, so thin he was virtually a skeleton. He wore only a loincloth and looked as if the sands of time had not succeeded in wasting away the shrunken remains of his frail body. Despite his gruesome appearance, his black eyes glistened with arcane wisdom and his golden aura assured her he meant no malice, for he was an ancestral guardian of the place.

'Are you bad?' she had to ask him as he lurched steadily forward.

'Do not worry about me,' he responded in a slow guttural voice as he came to a halt just feet away. 'Nobody knows I am here. I keep an eye on things.'

'What is your name?' she enquired, eager to learn the identity of this strange, boney man.

'I am Keez. Like Ptah, I am Lord of the Sun,' he proclaimed with some dignity.

Knowing that the original lozenge breastplate had been unearthed at Normanton during the last century, she asked him of the example she had seen in her dreams. Had it been found?

Skull-face gradually looked down into the sacrificial pit. 'It is down here. I breathe upon it and it will not be found, but its power is still in this place,' he replied, somewhat cryptically. 'You must go to the ringed cursore.'

'What do you mean?' She needed to know.

Keez's last words now permitted her a view of another grassy mound, this one larger than the rest and close to some woods. Seeing it made her realise it was an epicentre of chaotic activity, for encircling its base was a thin red ring of diffuse energy, choking its life blood and cutting it off from the surrounding sites and barrows.

Keez explained this mental image: 'Here you must amend the differences between the warrior and the queen. She must recognise him as her champion, only then will the power of the breastplate no longer be in their control.'

The image of Keez gradually dissolved, saddening Debbie slightly, for the unsightly bone man had exuded a warm, comforting presence. In his place came only the rhythmic sound of Andrew's voice closing down the circle of power.

Debbie opened her eyes and looked up at the gathered group seated among the undergrowth in the uninspiring depression. I had attempted to speak to her quietly on more than one occasion once Richard had completed the photo session, but she must have been completely out of it as she made no response at all.

Kerry, John and Karl lit up cigarettes as the rest of us fought off the irritating gnats, fruit flies and money spiders that seemed to infest this pond barrow.

Debbie kept her hay fever at bay as she began relating the sequence of images and impressions experienced during the tense meditation. She told of the grey woman, the midgets, the 'red ring of cursore' and her visit to see 'Keez', the guardian keeper of Normanton Gorse.

The 'cursore' had to be a reference to the Cursus or processional avenue half a mile north of Stonehenge. Since both *cursore* and *cursus* derive from a word root meaning 'to run' or simply 'running' they preserve the antiquarian view that the processional avenue was once a prehistoric race track! The description of the large mound situated close to woods was almost certainly the round barrow lying at the western end of the Cursus; I had noticed it earlier, marked on the OS map.

Suddenly, a realisation dawned upon me. Of course, this latest information made perfect sense of Ptah's message about a barrow of importance lying 'west of the processional avenue'.

THE BONE MAN

This ancient Priest of the Sun had not been referring to the location of the pond barrow, but to a separate round barrow at the very heart of the problem. Perhaps he should have made this clear!

Debbie wanted to interject. 'If I've got this right, I reckon someone has used ritual magic to set up a ring of dark red energy around the base of this mound. It is strangling the site's inherent power and the only way to restore some sort of balance there is to break the ring,' she concluded, before turning away to blow her nose.

It could be done.

'Only then can we even attempt to reconcile the warrior queen and her rival warlord, who I believe is connected with this mound.'

I threw up my hands in resignation. Whatever she wanted to do, we would do it. I have learned over the years simply to go along with what the psychic says as it usually produces the necessary results. Sometimes our understanding of such matters is less than adequate, yet utilising such energies, archetypes and symbols is like employing a form of mental logarithmic system to create the desired changes in a site's energy matrix through the process of non-locality. The actual mechanics behind such concepts are difficult to explain in a couple of sentences, but suffice it to say that shamans, mystics and magicians have successfully worked with these subtle forces since time immemorial, without them ever having understood the scientific nature of their actions.

So, with the *You* crew still in tow, it was time to leave the pond barrow and move on to the Cursus, where we would hopefully discover the real root of Keez's anguish.

Finding the A344 Devizes road, the four-car convoy filed past the Stonehenge monument with its busy car-park and headed out towards the extensive clump of evergreens in front of us now. Printed on the map as the Fargo plantation, it formed a visible point of commencement for the two-mile long Cursus.

All the vehicles gradually slowed down as their occupants scanned the approaching tree line for any sign of the huge mound of earth. One did then come into view, forcing the drivers to reduce speed and search for a parking space. It appeared to be located in its own sectioned off clearing at the very end of the impenetrable wall of coniferous trees.

Bringing his car to a halt on a dusty verge directly opposite the round barrow, Tom climbed out and spoke to Richard and his assistant. He still appeared quite bemused by our undaunted quest to solve the riddles of Stonehenge.

Other cars found spaces and disgorged their occupants, who quickly crossed the busy road. A wooden gate marked the entrance into the clearing containing the fifteen- to twenty-feet-high round barrow covered in bleached grass, which looked in desperate need of rain to revive its richness.

Standing at the base of the mound, Debbie blew her nose. 'This is it. I can't see it, but I know it's here all right – there's some kind of unbroken red ring encircling it. Unfortunately, there is nothing we can do until after dark. The red band grows with strength at night. Only then will I know what's really happening here. It's just too fuzzy in the daytime.' Looking around, she watched the *You* crew amble up behind us, not particularly worried by her assessment of the situation.

I listened carefully to her words. OK, we would return later, but until then there was little else to do but find a local hostelry and wait for darkness to fall.

29
The Walking Bone

'Better watch the time,' Paul suggested, finishing his glass of mineral water and looking anxious, 'it'll be dark soon.'

I acknowledged his concern and glanced out of the window. No, it was still only twilight; night would not descend for at least another thirty minutes.

Killing time, we stretched out our drinks in the Amesbury public house, having said our goodbyes to the *You* crew, who had decided to call it a day and make their way back to London.

I was on edge, I had to admit it. That familiar old churning sensation was there in my stomach as if I somehow knew that impending doom loomed ever nearer. Turning to look at the others, I saw they were still entertaining themselves, finding records on the jukebox, playing pool in the adjoining room or feeding money into the quiz machine.

It would soon be time, but not yet.

The air was changing as it does with the passing of daylight and the coming of darkness, and already Debbie had made a few strange comments. Coming away from the round barrow next to the Fargo plantation, she had experienced a sudden pain in the head and at the same moment she saw, in her mind's eye, an axe falling upon an old bone with such force that it sent splinters flying into the air. The only point she could add was that the bone appeared to be green with age.

I suggested it could signify the disturbance of the Bronze Age graves by modern-day archaeologists and treasure seekers of the past three centuries. She seemed unsure, and with the head pains still troubling her, I did not push the matter.

Sighing to myself, I decided to give it another twenty minutes, then we would go for it, darkness or not.

Night finally encroached around eight-thirty and within sight of the dark clearing, I slowed down the Orion and bumped it on to the dirt verge, John pulling in behind me in his company Peugeot 205.

One by one the remaining party crossed the A344 and made for the metal entrance gate. Once through, the seven silhouetted figures entered the sacred enclosure and moved stealthily into position, just in case anyone else happened to be lurking inside the dense tree line surrounding the black barrow.

Kerry and John advanced further with Debbie in close pursuit. Exchanging whispers they brought out and began concentrating on a carnelian stone in their possession. With their eyes firmly closed they visualised the mound illuminated by an ethereal light while Debbie attempted to focus upon its chaotic energies.

I looked on carefully, the pocket cassette already recording the proceedings. Anything could happen and I wanted to make sure I captured the lot on tape.

'Did you see that flash of light?' John said in a low voice. 'On top of the mound.'

I had not been looking in the right direction and it seemed of little consequence to the matter at hand.

'Right, I think you've got rid of the shadows here,' Debbie confirmed, watching Kerry, 'but the ring is still intact. I still can't see it; I can only *hear* it. It's like a thudding noise, like a chopper cutting through a cabbage. *Thud. Thud. Thud.*'

She looked around to make sure the others were all together before continuing her whispered assessment. 'There are several energy lines in the mound itself, but these have been deliberately blocked by the red ring. They will have to be set free. That's what we've got to do – *free them*. Yes, that's it.' She gestured with her hand. 'Come on, let's get to the top of the mound; I think we'll be safer up there.'

The questing posse advanced cautiously as Kerry made one final circuit of the small hill to ensure the coast was clear. She then joined the others in their ascent and once we had reassembled, I quickly raised the cone of power.

'I can see two people at the base of the mound,' John said, his head still bowed as if in prayer. 'One's a large bloke with long auburn hair. He appears to be naked and his hand is raised to his chest. He seems to be watching us. I'm not sure about the other one; I can't make out any detail yet.'

I recorded his words and looked around for Debbie.

She stood close by, unaffected by this new development.

'I can still see him,' John continued. 'He's holding something. In fact I can see more figures now, moving out of the shadows.'

Debbie began pacing around in a tight circle, her eyes closed, as though raising power. 'Don't worry, we're safe up here,' she muttered in a low voice to no one in particular. 'They can't penetrate the ring.'

I asked her if she was all right.

'Yes, I'm fine. Just wait.'

'How d'you feel, Deb?' Alex asked her.

After several moments she said, simply: 'Empty.'

'Death, from a blow to a head,' John announced. 'I don't know whether it's the warrior, or not.' He touched his forehead to concentrate further. 'I, I just keep feeling that I'm down there as him, and then I'm back here.'

'I reckon he's taking on the aspect of the Bronze Age warrior. Don't you?' Paul suggested, as we watched John struggle to determine what was imagination and what was reality.

I agreed with this assessment. John could see spectral figures of the past – Bronze Age spirits disturbed by our presence here on the mound.

All around us was total darkness. Only the muted whoosh of cars passing on the road beyond the enclosure, and the occasional sound of cows mooing in a distant field, broke the eerie stillness.

John continued unabated. 'This queen, she captured or took something from this warrior, a treasure,' he now explained. 'Something that was personal to him and she took it to the grave.'

Perhaps it was the Amorea, the bronze dagger or the lozenge-shaped breastplate; it was impossible to say.

Karl watched Debbie closely and listened as she told him cryptically: 'I don't want to feel for it, I just want to hear it.'

'Hear what?' he asked, placing a hand on her shoulder.

She did not answer, just continued to pace slowly around and around in a small circle. But then she stopped and glanced towards the north-eastern edge of the summit. 'Would you check to see if there's anything there,' she said to him.

Karl left her and moved across to the spot. 'There's like a shallow pit carved out of the earth, about a foot deep and five feet across,' he informed her, dropping to his knees and feeling the cool earth.

Her voice seemed strange as if she was beginning to fall into a light trance. The shallow ridge just below the summit we had noticed earlier; it was an obvious place to conceal an artefact.

Karl and Alex searched the pit while John continued his monologue. 'The shadows seem to be encroaching nearer,' he suddenly exclaimed in a low voice before opening his eyes, feeling he had seen enough. 'We haven't got much time. The warrior thinks *we've* got his treasure which the queen took, and now he wants it back. I don't think he's very happy.'

Everyone except Debbie, Paul and myself began frantically searching within the thick matted grass covering the floor of the shallow pit beyond the edge of the flat summit. Even with small pencil torches nothing seemed visible or hidden between the cracks and hollows of the baked earth.

'People,' Karl announced calmly. 'Over by the cars.'

The foraging stopped and the torches were extinguished as we all froze and looked across at this new source of concern. Yes, he was right – two vehicles, their engines and lights still on, had pulled up in front of our own cars. One, possibly two figures had emerged into the open air and were now approaching the cars. At a distance of some 150 yards I could not make out what was going on and only hoped they were just over-inquisitive kids out for the night. It could be police, however. But then car doors slammed shut and soon afterwards the vehicles slowly moved away, prompting a sigh of relief before the search resumed.

'Here, let me try,' Debbie at last agreed, moving across to join the others.

Knowing that despondency can often kill the day, and scrambling about in the dirt was not the best policy, I suggested she just attune for a moment or two. Maybe she could get a better fix on where and what lay concealed.

'I'm not even sure it's here,' Debbie admitted, a trifle concerned by her own vagueness. 'But I can still hear the thudding noise, though.'

'D'you know where it's coming from,' Kerry asked, still searching the grass with her fingers.

chest. He seems to be watching us. I'm not sure about the other one; I can't make out any detail yet.'

I recorded his words and looked around for Debbie.
She stood close by, unaffected by this new development.

'I can still see him,' John continued. 'He's holding something. In fact I can see more figures now, moving out of the shadows.'

Debbie began pacing around in a tight circle, her eyes closed, as though raising power. 'Don't worry, we're safe up here,' she muttered in a low voice to no one in particular. 'They can't penetrate the ring.'

I asked her if she was all right.

'Yes, I'm fine. Just wait.'

'How d'you feel, Deb?' Alex asked her.

After several moments she said, simply: 'Empty.'

'Death, from a blow to a head,' John announced. 'I don't know whether it's the warrior, or not.' He touched his forehead to concentrate further. 'I, I just keep feeling that I'm down there as him, and then I'm back here.'

'I reckon he's taking on the aspect of the Bronze Age warrior. Don't you?' Paul suggested, as we watched John struggle to determine what was imagination and what was reality.

I agreed with this assessment. John could see spectral figures of the past – Bronze Age spirits disturbed by our presence here on the mound.

All around us was total darkness. Only the muted whoosh of cars passing on the road beyond the enclosure, and the occasional sound of cows mooing in a distant field, broke the eerie stillness.

John continued unabated. 'This queen, she captured or took something from this warrior, a treasure,' he now explained. 'Something that was personal to him and she took it to the grave.'

Perhaps it was the Amorea, the bronze dagger or the lozenge-shaped breastplate; it was impossible to say.

Karl watched Debbie closely and listened as she told him cryptically: 'I don't want to feel for it, I just want to hear it.'

'Hear what?' he asked, placing a hand on her shoulder.

She did not answer, just continued to pace slowly around and around in a small circle. But then she stopped and glanced towards the north-eastern edge of the summit. 'Would you check to see if there's anything there,' she said to him.

'*Chipping – clicking – crawling.*' She paused for a moment. '*It's moving. It moved,*' she let out a sigh. '*It's moved. Where's it gone to?*' Another pause. '*Walking bone. Walking bone. Walking bone. Walking bone. The bone that walks.*' Then came physical agony: '*Pain in my leg,*' she cried out. '*Pain in my leg. Walking bone. Clicking bone. Bashing bone. Broken bone. Dots. Lots of dots. Dots. Dots. Lots of dots.*'

She began hyperventilating as her words increased in speed and frequency. It was if she was fighting off the incoming pain and fear by speaking them out loud.

'*Like on the face. Nasir. Robin Hood. Lots of dots. Walking bone. Walking bone. Thigh bone. Splinters. Lots of dots. Robin Hood.*' Another pause to catch her breath. '*Puppies. Feathers. Bumble bees. Horses. Ponies.*' She stopped again. '*Lots of dots. Pit. The lowest point in the tummy is the pit. It's in the pit.*'

She was still breathing erratically. I told the others to continue visualising an axe falling on to bone. *See it. See it in their mind's eye.*

'*Bunnies. Chocolate. Feather. Birds. Running deer. Bunny rabbits. Ptah. Ptah. Think about Ptah everybody, please.*'

What was she doing? She sounded like she was in deep trouble. I told everyone to see Ptah, the guardian of Stonehenge, the Priest of the Sun Debbie had encountered in dream. See him with us on the mound, giving her strength and protection.

'*Walking bone. One bone on its own, walking. Splinter's gone. Rabbit. Rabbit jumping on bone. Shotgun. Daggers. Skinning. Brown paint. Paint bowl. Stick in paint bowl. Dots. Dots. Lots of dots. Blood inside brown paint. Dot brown paint. Wooden bowl. Lots of dots. On stick. Must break the beam in a minute. Soon break the beam and just go. It cannot be amended. It can never be amended. Just break the beam and go. Her guardianship will be broken. Matrix may fight for itself. We cannot save it. Just break the beam and she will die again. Second death. Third death. Just break the beam. She will die. No hip. No walking bone. Walking bone. Lots of dots.*'

Then she cried out. '*Splinters everywhere. Crystal. Crystal. And a walking bone. Wet grass. Green bone. Green bone on wet grass,*' were her last words before she collapsed to the ground, her breathing even more erratic as if she had something lodged in her throat.

'Everywhere,' was her reply.

Still nothing could be found. No, this was no good, I pulled everyone back to the centre and attempted to restore some calm with a brief meditation.

The cone of power was strengthened and the energies visualised, and then came only silence. Suddenly, Karl looked disturbed. 'Oh, shit, I've just opened my eyes and seen two red eyes staring at me. They were right behind us, looking, as though watching and waiting . . . waiting for something.'

Nobody attempted to interpret the meaning of their presence.

The air was growing stranger and more oppressive by the minute, agitating the group still further.

Debbie broke the stillness. 'I feel we've got to draw out the power of the energy lines trapped inside the mound. See them breaking out of our own wall of protection.' She began counting, then added: 'There are six of them in all.'

I echoed her words as part of the visualisation, telling everyone to see six lines of light breaking free of the mound and pushing out into the surrounding landscape.

'They're attempting to stop us,' Debbie suddenly revealed, following a further period of silence. 'It's the warrior lord that John saw; he's the mound's guardian. He opposes the warrior queen, and yet he doesn't understand that we're trying to help him. Just ignore him and concentrate on the energy lines.'

All we could do was continue to visualise six bars of golden light bursting out of the mound and extending like spokes of a wheel into the surrounding landscape.

'I can see the ring,' Debbie said, excitedly. 'I can see the Red Ring of Cursore. It's just a single band, six inches in diameter, and I can see the six lines coming out. There are seven in fact, but one's blocked. Where is it blocked?' She was posing the question to her own mind; she needed to know. 'The only way to break the ring and free the final line is to remove the block. *Axe splits bone – chipping. Chipping bone splinter.*'

What was this? What was she talking about?

'*Splinter bone splinters. Sound. Kicking. Kicking. Clicking. Bone splitting – splitting bone.*'

It seemed she was building up power while homing in on the whereabouts of the alleged blockage. Were we to visualise this imagery as well? I assumed so.

This really was getting scary.

Kerry, Karl and I fell to our knees and tried to comfort her.

In severe distress, Debbie reached out, gesturing frantically towards the source of her anxiety. She attempted words, but in her struggle for breath managed only one: '*Pit.*'

Quickly, Kerry and John resumed the search, ripping and tearing at the grass roots, not caring where they looked any more.

Debbie still screamed out in anguish, as if pleading with unseen hands to stop choking her to death. '*Walking bone,*' she slowly cried one more time, her eyes still closed and her hand pointing towards the shallow pit. '*Walking bone. Oh, please. Take the walking bone away.*'

The scene was frightening, and other than comforting her I was no longer sure what to do. With my hands on her body I visualised light, *any light*, passing through me into her. Paul and Alex joined me as I tried to co-ordinate a visualisation using the chakra centres along her spine.

Still she reached out towards the source of her prolonged consternation. 'Right. Right,' she directed them, even though her head faced *away* from the pit. 'They're getting closer. *Please remove it.*'

Kerry, John and Karl followed her instructions.

'Please, please help me up,' she now pleaded, pushing herself off the ground.

Karl rushed across and threw an arm around her shoulders, allowing Debbie to stagger across to the pit. Falling down, she breathed erratically as her hand reached ground level and moved slowly over the surface. '*It must be here,*' she uttered in despair. 'Walking bone.'

I rejoined the search for the concealed artefact.

She stopped to pull up grass in the light of a pencil torch, a sign that others should tear at the same spot. Hands reached down and wrenched out roots a little more cautiously this time.

'Oh, it's got to be here,' she exclaimed. 'Let me stand up.' She regained a little more composure as more and more roots were torn away.

'God, *where is it?*' she asked desperately, her fears mounting by the moment.

More grass was ripped away by grasping hands.

'Oh my God,' Debbie yelled, withdrawing away. 'What's that?'

The torchlight had revealed an out of place object lying deep beneath clods of damp grass and white roots.

'Got it,' Kerry declared, taking it into her hand.

Debbie panicked as Karl ran to calm her.

'Oh God, yes, *look at the symbols on that*,' Alex declared, gazing into Kerry's illuminated hand.

Leaning across I saw the source of Debbie's suffering – a small animal bone around three inches in length absolutely covered in painted dots and markings.

We had found the Walking Bone.

I looked around for Debbie and saw she was already marching towards the edge of the mound.

Surely we could not just leave; what were we to do now?

'Come on, *just go*,' Debbie urged, in no mood to argue. '*Let's get out of here*.'

'Check the cars,' were her last words as the disconcerted and rather unnerved party gave up the mound and headed towards the entrance gate, beyond which was the open road back to reality.

Debbie Benstead, the psychic who began pin-pointing the apparent activities of the shadowy group known as the People of Hexe (author's pic).

Left: A graveyard cross in Romania bearing an inscription that translates as 'My God, save me from Dracula', clearly showing the modern-day reality in the power of 'dracul', the devil of Romanian folklore (pic: Douglas Hill).

Below: The head of the Norse demon–wolf Fenris emerging from the interior of the earth, having broken free of its bonds in the underworld. Did the Romanian people see its release in terms of the massive earthquake that shook the country on 30 May 1990? (pic: Richard Ward)

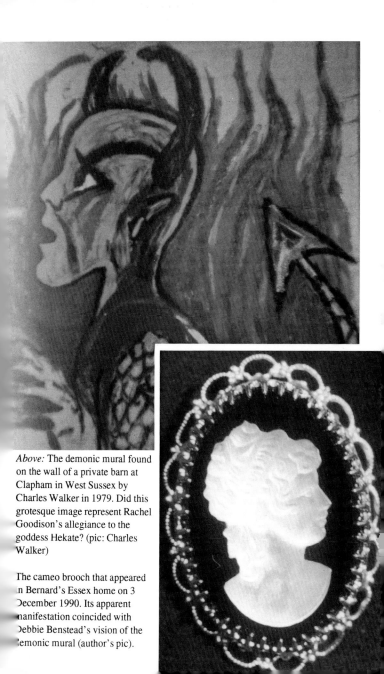

Above: The demonic mural found on the wall of a private barn at Clapham in West Sussex by Charles Walker in 1979. Did this grotesque image represent Rachel Goodison's allegiance to the goddess Hekate? (pic: Charles Walker)

The cameo brooch that appeared in Bernard's Essex home on 3 December 1990. Its apparent manifestation coincided with Debbie Benstead's vision of the demonic mural (author's pic).

Above: The Bronze Age round barrow by the Fargo plantation at the western end of Stonehenge's Great Cursus. It was here that the Walking Bone was discovered under dramatic circumstances on 1 September 1991 (author's pic).

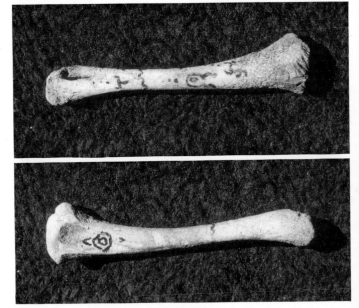

Above: Bram Stoker, the author of *Dracula* and many other Gothic horror stories of the late nineteenth, early twentieth centuries. Why have his spine-chilling novels repeatedly mimicked real-life events? (pic: The Dracula Society)

Left: The so-called Walking Bone found on the Fargo plantation round barrow by Debbie Benstead on 1 September 1991. Its distinctive symbols showed it had been placed in position by the People of Hexe (author's pics).

Below: The church of St Mary, sitting above the North Yorkshire town of Whitby, where Bram Stoker's Count Dracula took his first victim. Is Whitby's fictional past now taking on a life of its own? (author's pic)

Hier þiotra[?] **ASA R** Fenris
Ulfinn: Týr misser sijna adra
Hönd: en þr Aristera Ulfinn til Re-
gna Röckurs: so sem XXXX Eddu
Dæmisaga Utvijsar.

Above: The floodlit Whitby Abbey in North Yorkshire where the People of Hexe magically 'contained' the power of the Norse demon-wolf Fenris in November 1991 (author's pic).

Left: Illustration of Tyr who sacrifices his hand in order to ensnare the demon-wolf Fenris and prevent Ragnarok, the Doom of the Divine Powers. Taken from an *Edda* MS of medieval Icelandic tradition.

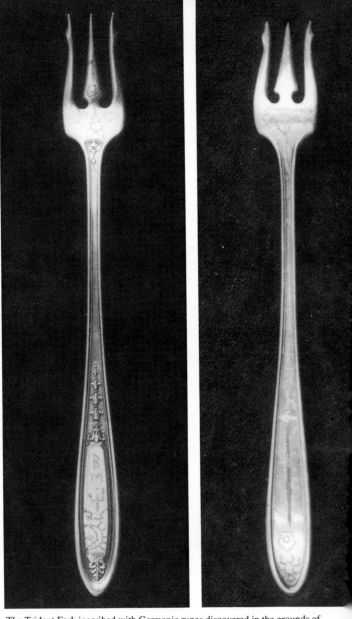

The Trident Fork inscribed with Germanic runes discovered in the grounds of Whitby Abbey on 2 November 1991. The magical signatures showed it to be the work of the People of Hexe (author's pics).

30
The Angry Moon

Monday, 2 September 1991. Leaving the car in the main road, Debbie and I made our way towards the front door of John and Kerry's Southend home. There were new developments to be discussed and I wanted to retrieve the Walking Bone, which they had taken home in their car.

John appeared behind the mottled stained glass window and let us in. He guided us through the hall and into the lounge.

'All right?' Kerry greeted us, tidying up the room.

'Not bad,' Debbie answered, descending into an armchair. 'I don't feel too brilliant, but that's only to be expected, really.'

John took his seat. 'OK, so what's been happening in your world since last night?'

I took a long breath and shook my head with a cautious grin. The disturbing events of the night before had not ceased upon our departure from the Fargo plantation. The car journey back to Essex had proved to be most peculiar. Alex was with us and for over an hour no one spoke a word. We finally stopped for a much needed cup of tea at the Fleet services on the M3, but even then the Walking Bone was still not really discussed. After resuming the long journey back to Essex the only strange comment Debbie had made was that the reddened, virtual full moon hanging low in the night sky was an 'angry moon', words she did not elaborate upon.

Then, just two miles from home, I saw blue flashing lights in my rear-view mirror, so came to a halt. A police motorcyclist pointed out that I had been speeding and booked me on the spot. It was my first driving conviction in fifteen years. Coincidental bad karma, I hoped, but my suspicions had been aroused on speaking to Bernard earlier that day. Without any knowledge of recent events he had spoken of an intense oppressive atmosphere hanging heavy in the air all weekend. It had affected him to such a degree that he had cancelled his plans for the previous day and stayed at home instead. With this heavy atmosphere had come a clear mental picture of a slowly revolving pyramid with red and blue bands of light around its vertical axis. It was only small, he said, and he had been unable to account for its presence in his mind's eye; it was also his first psychic image in several weeks.

The only logical solution I could offer was that it somehow represented the Fargo plantation round barrow we had visited the night before. There was, of course, no blue band of light involved in this story, although both Bernard and Debbie admitted this was the most likely explanation for his recurring vision.

He went on to relate three unfortunate incidents that had occurred earlier that day. He had crashed his Montego, putting it off the road and forcing him to cancel the meeting we had planned for the following evening. His wife had had her bag stolen and his cousin had written off his own car in a serious accident. This sudden cluster of unfortunate events Bernard had linked with the oppressive atmosphere which, he felt, was still around today. I told him I would reserve judgement for the moment, although I could vouch for the fact that he was not normally insistent about such matters.

'So what's the score then, Deb?' John asked, settling back in his chair. 'What did we achieve last night?'

She sighed, not really wanting to talk about the subject. 'Well, the removal of the Walking Bone has taken away the influence of the red ring. This will allow the site to restore its own energy balance.

'It's like setting free a wild animal caught in a trap. The animal must now be left to heal its own wounds. This was all we could do; I realised this when we finally broke through to the core of the problem. We were stupid even to think we could restore the balance in any other way.'

John nodded in acceptance. 'So what were all the funny words you were saying just before the bone came up?' he asked next. 'What was all that about?'

'At first I was merely describing what came into my head as

imagery, but then it became necessary to try and retain consciousness, like someone talking to stay awake.'

He smiled. 'Yeah, but at some points you were saying things like chocolate, horses and bunny rabbits!'

She tried to explain. 'The fear made me conjure images of things I found comforting; I wasn't aware I was saying them out aloud. Only in this way could I keep my focus on the root cause of the problem, which turned out to be this bone. I could see it walking, on its own, in between flashes of a wooden bowl containing a thick gouache-like paint and someone daubing it on to the bone.'

I felt it was time for John to go and fetch the offending item; we needed to study its markings, see what they meant.

'I'll get it.' Without further word, our host disappeared for a few moments before returning with the small bone in his hand. I reached out and took it from him as Debbie looked on rather apprehensively.

It was a fairly old animal bone, probably from a rabbit's leg, and covering its entire surface were strange symbols drawn in dark brown 'paint' with an ink-like texture. One resembled the astrological sign for the influence of Taurus; this I could recognise. There was also a stylised spider with six legs as well as a small pentagon inside a hexagon. Finishing the design were the lines of dots also described before its discovery.

Both the spider design and the pentagon inside a hexagon revealed its source of origin. One evening in March 1990 Debbie had doodled several signs and symbols in a notepad, adding that should we ever come across any of these, then we would know we were dealing with the People of Hexe. They were hex marks, she said, and although none of them matched the symbols inscribed on the bone, the similarity was beyond coincidence.

In Germanic tradition a hex mark was drawn with the appropriate incantations by an initiated *Hexenmeister* to evoke a specific supernatural entity or occult force. *Hex* is also a word prefix used to denote the number six, as in hexagon or hexahedron.

'It was left by Hexe alright,' Debbie butted in. 'It has their stamp all over it. The pentagon inside the hexagon symbolises their labyrinth, their own understanding of the energy matrix.

The six-legged spider is another of their signatures – it relates to the Web of Wyrd, the cause and effect resulting from their interaction with the energy matrix.'

'So why leave it at the mound?' Kerry queried from across the room.

Debbie frowned. 'The bone was specifically fashioned to create an energy blockage at the end of the Cursus. It stifled the guardianship of the warrior lord and allowed the spirit of the queen in the Lake Down cemetery to usurp his territorial power.

'This blockage took the form of a red ring encircling the mound and somehow just this one fixing marker – and possibly one other – caused a complete upset of the whole localised energy matrix,' she explained, trying to curtail the matter. 'There may be other stuff at the mound, but I'm certainly not going back there.'

'So what happened to the dagger, then?' John asked next.

'I feel it was confiscated from the warrior lord by the queen, who sought to dishonour him through jealousy. The influence of this dagger was used by Hexe to resurrect the grey queen and to rekindle the ancient feud between them in order to control and alter the local energy lines.' She looked down momentarily before adding: 'Unfortunately, I get the feeling Hexe actually have the dagger or perhaps just the stone, I'm not sure.'

I continued to study the Walking Bone. Some of its symbols were beginning to fade due to the length of time it had been out in the open, and adding this to its green staining on one side, I guessed it had lain in the grass for up to a month, so it had probably been placed in position on or around 1 August, the old Celtic feast of Lugnasadh. This was important, for I had discovered that ley-hunting pioneer Alfred Watkins found that the Old Sarum ley could be extended northwards from Stonehenge to St Anne's Hill 'the old name of which is Tan Hill (denoting a fire or beacon hill); on it is still held a fair on August 6th'.[1] This date was obviously unique to the area as St Anne's usual feast day in the Anglican calendar is 29 July. If the Old Sarum ley was being utilised by the Hexe group, then it looked as if they had taken advantage of this feast-day connection to link in with the local energy matrix.

Like St Catherine, St Anne – the legendary mother of the

Virgin Mary in Christian tradition – was seen as a dusky saint embodying aspects associated with fire and darkness. In Britain her cult enveloped the pre-Christian belief in Annis or Black Annis – a crone-like corn goddess associated with the red harvest moon and the burning and blackening of crop fields at harvest-time. Strange then that Debbie should gain the name 'Anne' in connection with the wiry-haired warrior queen apparently resurrected on or around a localised feast-day of St Anne. Could the spirit essence of the warrior queen have merged with the indigenous memory of Annis or St Anne in the ritual landscape around Stonehenge? If so, did Hexe use St Anne to resurrect the warrior queen?

The Walking Bone was our best evidence yet for the independent existence of the Hexe group and, if we were to accept this, then Debbie's understanding of their aims and intentions was not to be treated lightly.

There were other thoughts now going around in my head. OK, so we knew that Hexe saw a great importance in the Stonehenge complex of ancient sites and had been using both the Old Sarum ley and the Wilsford Pit to feed resurrected thought forms into the energy matrix, their labyrinth, for some years. Yet their sudden interest in the Cursus now made me recall Helen's psychic information about the Dark Council conducting suspect rites at nearby Woodhenge. This henge monument just happened to be aligned with the northerly ridge of the Cursus and so featured in the overall landscape geometry associated with the Stonehenge cycle of sites.

Was it possible that Helen had in fact been viewing the activities of the People of Hexe as far back as February 1989? If not, did it imply that the Friends of Hekate/Dark Council were intrinsically linked with Hexe's ritual activities or, worse still, that the two were working together? Whatever the answer, it did appear to suggest a cross-fertilisation of interests between the different groups. Were such bodies simply cousins in the same big happy family, collectively linked as one by the creeping tentacles of the Wheel?

One last thing before we could go home – what exactly were Hexe attempting to achieve at Stonehenge? Why the sudden upsurge of activity in that area?

Debbie huffed as though this was obvious. 'Hexe use the Old Sarum ley and Normanton Gorse as their place of entry into the energy matrix. Ever since last summer they seem to have stepped up their activities all over the country. In the Stonehenge area this finally became so critical that its surviving ancestral guardians – figures such as Ptah, Keez, even the warrior himself – began sending out psychic distress signals which we responded to.'

She sank back into an anxious state as though it had regurgitated bad memories. 'I just get this horrible feeling that although we may have turned the tides for the energies at Stonehenge, we are too late to stop the People of Hexe.

'Something big is brewing. I can't put my finger on it yet, but it's big, and I think Bernard can sense it as well. Hexe are up to something, and whatever they're doing, it's the culmination of years of work; some kind of unleashing of accumulated forces they have been gathering together for some time.'

'Any idea what?' John interjected, clearly intrigued by the thought.

She shook her head in resignation.

31
The Well of Revealing

Monday, 9 September 1991. Advancing on their heavy caterpillar tracks, the gigantic yellow bulldozers crushed a fresh path through the dense expanse of jungle. The roots and trunks of erect trees cracked and snapped as they admitted defeat and were wrenched out of their sockets by huge metal scoops and carried across to a waiting bonfire of enormous size.

The insipid air was hot and humid even though the day was still young. The first shift would not change for several hours and by then a further extensive area of Peruvian forest would have been cleared to make way for the new urban development meant to accommodate the sudden growth in population in central Lima.

The sound of moaning chainsaws reverberated across the extensive wasteland, which would soon support a modern housing estate, a new road system and vast commercial units for the anticipated business boom.

Dark-skinned workmen wearing hard hats and overalls, co-ordinated the mass clearance and surveyed ahead of the giant earth-movers as they sliced their way forward, consuming everything in their path.

Above the perpetual din, a check-shirted workman watched as the scoop bucket of a brand-new machine ripped out a mass of impenetrable scrub, partially shaded beneath a canopy of tall trees. Glancing down, he held up his arm as the driver of the fat metal monster reversed slightly and switched off its noisy engine.

Leaping to the ground, he joined his colleague, who pointed out the low masonry scattered around some sort of round hole or well about two metres in diameter. It had been exposed when the heavy, metal bucket had dislodged and then broken the worked stone slabs covering its sealed entrance; these now lay in fragments at the base of the four-metre-deep vertical shaft.

THE SECOND COMING

Other vehicles began grinding to a halt as they realised that signs of human habitation had been found. The owners in Lima had given strict instructions on what the workmen should do if they discovered archaeological remains as they cleared their way through this virgin territory, which had only ever been inhabited by superstitious Indians. All work would have to cease until a thorough inspection of the uncovered site had been made by outside experts.

Without further word the foreman left for the works office to contact the big bosses, leaving the driver and his mate to stare apprehensively into the circular pit.

Time passed and still the bulldozers did not move forward. They lay idle for the rest of the shift and for the one after that as well. The workforce were laid off until further notice with full pay, leaving only the security guards to watch over the now deserted wasteland.

As still another shift and then another were missed, rumours began to circulate. It was said the earth-movers had uncovered a very ancient site, one of special importance that the management had been told they would find. Another rumour spoke of buried treasure concealed in the strange shaft. No one dared go near it as the Indians believed the land was cursed by evil spirits and anyone removing holy relics would surely bring bad luck upon themselves and their families. Only foolhardy outsiders would dare to disobey the word of the ancient spirits by claiming the Indian gold for themselves.

Time passed and still the workforce enjoyed its unprecedented holiday. On the edge of the tree line the security guards occupied their time telling stories and smoking cigarettes until the outsiders finally arrived some days later. They came in a four-wheel-drive truck from Lima and were given instant clearance to enter the works site and approach the edge of the remaining forest.

The agile vehicle left behind the half-finished roadway and bumped across rugged ground until it reached the silent earth-movers. Coming to a halt, its driver stepped to the ground. Three other men emerged on to the dark brown carpet of bare earth, ironed flat by caterpillar tracks and tyre marks.

One was a slim male figure with slicked-back grey hair and wire-rimmed spectacles. He held a black Gladstone bag, attached to which was a small military-style shovel. He looked somewhat older in face, and the expensive casual clothes belied his university background, but there was no mistaking his identity – it was the man known in occult circles as the Black Alchemist.

The two other men, both South American in appearance and dress, removed a collapsible aluminium ladder from the truck and began the short walk through the huge grey beds of fire ash and the freshly sawn tree stumps scattered among the heaps of broken branches. A putrid smell of stale water permeated the air, adding to the growing tension among the three Peruvian members of the party.

The British man's pointing arm directed their gaze towards the newly-unearthed round pit. Quickly, the metal ladder was constructed and lowered downwards into the ancient well. The Black Alchemist descended, leaving instructions that no one should follow.

Under the shelter of the remaining tree cover, he spent the next hour clearing debris, the others having abandoned him to dig at his leisure. A couple of minor pre-Columbian artefacts told him the search would not be in vain, and then finally he struck a flat stone base. Wiping away the beads of sweat from his brow, he used the shovel as a lever to prise out the stones that had remained *in situ* for several hundred years, and then finally he saw it. It lay, like a coin in a slot, between two separate slabs.

Crouching down, he clutched the delicate piece; it looked insignificant, yet its purpose was truly awesome.

At that moment a flight of birds scattered from the surrounding tree-tops, their eerie cawing startling him momentarily. His heart beat wildly as he felt a rush of adrenalin shoot through his veins. He knew he would find it here at a concealed location in the path of the great earth-movers. His confidence had convinced his patrons in Europe to use their financial contacts in Lima to make the necessary plans with the site contractors and guarantee their complete discretion in this matter. All he could do then was sit back and wait for the expected telephone call.

Holding the small, round object, inscribed with geometric patterns and undecipherable characters in a forgotten script, he smiled gleefully.

The look of satisfaction on his reddened face burned like a firebrand into the astral domains as the disturbing implications of this single discovery sank into his cold, calculating mind.

Yawning in response to the sound of the alarm clock, Bernard knew it was time to rise. The clock said 6.30am and he would have to get ready for work. Left in his thoughts was the bizarre imagery revealed in the totally unexpected dream concerning the Black Alchemist's apparent trip to Peru.

Descending the stairs, he made coffee and prepared himself for the bathroom, his wife still dead to the world upstairs.

Should he dismiss the dream as pure fantasy? He shook his head. No, it had that same lucidity about it; that same realism that accompanies all psychically inspired imagery. Had he therefore witnessed real events taking place at that time in Lima, Peru?

Leaving his coffee, he moved into the bathroom. Squeezing the toothpaste, he caught the white gel on his brush and began cleaning his teeth.

The last time he had received unwanted glimpses of the Black Alchemist was in August the previous year, when the wretched man had discovered the clay seal and copper scroll on the Dead Sea somewhere.

So what was he up to this time?

He was now more sure than ever before that the Black Alchemist was being funded by a very shadowy, Wheel-linked organisation whose influence obviously stretched to building contractors in Peru. The discovery of the stone-lined well had been anticipated, predicted even. A few international telephone calls were all it had taken for him to be on the scene, ready to take away the prize.

Exactly what he had discovered was not made clear, but left in Bernard's mind was the firm belief that it was linked directly with the artefacts found by the Dead Sea; the next in a chain of power objects the Black Alchemist believed he would uncover before a predetermined date. Bernard hated to think what might happen when the last in the series was retrieved.

Now the Black Alchemist had found the Peruvian variation of his Dead Sea discoveries it would unlock further doors, giving him even more confidence. More disconcerting, however, was the gut feeling that this little episode would have serious repercussions at some point in the not too distant future.

32
Portents of Danger

Tuesday, 10 September 1991. 'I've written off the company's brand new Peugeot 205, the one I got the day after we came back from Stonehenge,' John declared on the other end of the telephone line. 'I crashed it this morning. No one was hurt but the car is an insurance write-off, I can tell you. Even stranger, its sister vehicle, purchased at the same time, was involved in a smack-up one hour later in Birmingham; and that one I was out in only yesterday!'

Car troubles again. First I get booked for speeding. Then Bernard and his cousin crash their respective cars, and now John writes off his new company car. The oppressive atmosphere around last week was obviously still about.

'It gets even more obscure,' he exclaimed, anxious to relay the final twist in the tale. 'The red Peugeot 205 I had when we went down to Stonehenge – the one I handed over the day after we got back – was written off in Liverpool *this afternoon*. How about that!'

For a brief moment my mind flashed back to the unnerving scene at the round barrow next to the Fargo plantation when those two cars had pulled in front of our own vehicles for a few brief minutes. At the time I had dismissed their presence, but now, well ... no, it was stupid even to think there was a connection.

'I'll ring you if anything else happens,' he sighed, ending the conversation. 'Oh, before I go, anything happening?'

Yes, there was just one potentially important development. Over the past few days Debbie had begun receiving the distinct impression that the People of Hexe would be conducting a major ritual in Yorkshire around Hallowe'en; something to do with the fulfilment of a prophecy, she believed.

I had tried to point out that Hallowe'en was not the usual time for occult adepts to conduct serious ritualistic events, but she had emphasised this date, saying it was important to them for some reason.

'But you've encountered Hexe before in Yorkshire, haven't you?' he reminded me.

In April 1990 we had visited a hill-top folly near Glusburn in West Yorkshire named Lund's Tower. Actor Mark Ryan – who played Nasir the Saracen in HTV's *Robin of Sherwood* series – had seen the place under hypnosis whilst in California and knew something untoward was occurring there. Debbie and I had accompanied Mark to the site, and without much effort we had unearthed a stone inscribed with a serpent spiral, left there, we concluded, by a suspect magical group indirectly linked with the People of Hexe. We knew then that this was just the tip of a much bigger iceberg.

Already Debbie was having doubts about going to Yorkshire. She had a sneaky feeling it would open a whole new can of worms and had seriously suggested it might be better to leave well alone.

'She's no fun, is she!' John jested, half-heartedly. 'Karl and I loved every minute of the Stonehenge sketch! If Debbie won't go, we'll go up there anyway and camp out overnight!'

I thought he might. Both he and Karl had only really become involved in our Earthquest team after reading *The Black Alchemist*. Now they were real characters in the gradually unfolding pages of its sequel, a position they relished. Debbie, quite naturally, viewed the whole black questing phenomenon as purely adding to her periodic migraines and bouts of illness; for her it was certainly no fun.

If we did decide to go to Yorkshire, then it would also be an unpopular decision in other quarters as well, for in the wake of our Stonehenge exploits there had been unease among our immediate group, with one or two challenging the necessity of involving ourselves in such detrimental pursuits. They argued that it brought only bad karma to those participating on the quest and was a hindrance to our spiritual development. What they did not seem to realise was that unless the energy matrix was cleared of such unwanted intrusions, then we could never hope to achieve success with our other, more beneficial activities associated with the Seven Swords quest. To advance our understanding of psychic questing we would have to take the rough with the smooth, otherwise we might as well give up.

Despite this internal anxiety, there were still nearly eight weeks before the end of October, and in that time anything could happen to change the setting and the circumstances of what was shaping up to be our next major encounter with the activities of the People of Hexe.

Wednesday, 11 September. I kept the car to 70mph along the quiet A127 London to Southend road, driving back from Debbie's parents' home on the edge of Greater London.

Debbie snoozed in the passenger seat and the time was well past midnight. I was beginning to yawn incessantly, and having just passed the Rayleigh Weir junction I estimated we would be home in some eight to ten minutes.

The headlights of distant cars could be made out in the rear-view mirror, while London-bound traffic passed by on the opposite carriageway. Other than this the road was unusually clear at this late hour.

There had been no more on Yorkshire as yet, but this was probably due to our time being taken up on other, more mundane matters (when your attention is directed elsewhere very little seems to happen on a psychic level).

I contemplated the day ahead, preparing for the publication of my book *The Seventh Sword* on Thursday, 7 November. There was still much to be completed concerning the publicity and promotion which I was co-ordinating in association with the publishers, Random House.

At that moment I thought I saw thick drops of liquid flicked on to the windscreen, forcing me to slow down and evaluate the situation. It had been like holy water thrown from a sprinkler, yet whatever it was gave me instant bad feelings and conjured a picture of the two cars pulling in front of our vehicles as we had stood upon the Fargo plantation mound, just ten days before.

Mentally I tried to dismiss this fleeting vision as a figment of my over-active imagination, but the churning left in my stomach made me doubt whether the car-related incidents of the past two weeks were all simply 'coincidence'.[1]

PART FOUR
Hellbound

33
The Coming Fear

The End of September 1991. Amid the ruddy-mauve clouds furiously bellowing across the darkening sky, John Horrigan watched as the lone schooner edged erratically towards the harbour below. It seemed controlled by unseen hands for no crew member could be observed aboard the foreign vessel, which oozed an air of death and ill omen.

With ease it cut through the angry waters as he watched it head into the pier directly below the great cliffs. Despite the distance and the fading light, a long dark box could be seen lying upon its wooden deck, its familiar proportions identifying it immediately. It was a single coffin being carried into the safety of calmer waters by the good fortune of the schooner's course.

Finally, after several long minutes of viewing, the strange, seagoing vessel was lost from sight beneath the rocky overhang, just before it docked in the quay, apparently without the aid of the harbour men.

Night fell and with it came a clearer sky sprinkled with bright stars and a virtual full moon, masked now and again by wispy clouds. Yet the peculiar change in weather had brought with it a ground mist that filled the midnight air and hung heavy in the lower areas of the town. Buildings looked silhouetted against the glare of this impenetrable grey fog, which remained firm even though a gentle breeze blew in from the sea.

Aside from the flickering yellow light emanating from the occasional window, the only sight that broke the dullness was a lone woman in a pale dress, standing in the elevated churchyard on top of the cliffs. She looked as though she was waiting for someone, a boyfriend perhaps or a guardian who would take her home at this late hour.

Closer and closer John moved towards the young lady, fearing she might be in difficulty or that she might need some assistance. Nearer and nearer he walked, as gradually her innocence and beauty began to take form. Her long hair flailed about in the light breeze and she appeared to be entranced.

Another fleeting figure in dark clothes now emerged from the shadows and made directly for the poor girl, reaching her shortly before his own arrival. John could plainly see a tall, slim gentleman about to embrace her. Perhaps he was the girl's father or her lover attempting to rouse her from her waking dream.

No more than a few yards separated him from the two figures as he realised the man was tilting his head towards the curve of her neck.

Oh my God . . .

Suddenly, the tall figure left the girl and darted across to John. He thrust his pallid face forward to reveal sharp canine teeth that left John in no doubt as to the nature of this supernatural denizen. His sanguine eyes of pure red fire burned holes into John's skull as he forced himself to regain consciousness and scream, instantly disturbing Kerry from her already restless slumber.

Fully awake at last, John realised his folly and tried to compose his thoughts.

Kerry was not happy. 'What is it, John?' she murmured, not really interested unless it was the house burning down. 'What's going on?'

He sighed under his breath. 'I hate vampires and I don't want dreams about them,' he admitted, twisting on to his back. 'If there's one thing I hate more than anything else it's bleeding vampires.'

'What are you talking about?' his wife still enquired, trying without success to make sense of his words. Giving up, she snuggled beneath the duvet, hoping he would do the same.

John was not amused. 'Bloody hell, Kerry, I've just had this dream about a coffin on a ship and a girl being attacked by a vampire.' He wanted her to respond sympathetically.

'Look, John, just go back to sleep,' she pleaded from below the covers.

John huffed and turned over. He would assume this was his inner mind's own warped idea of nocturnal amusement and forget about the whole thing.

No, he wouldn't; he would record it in his magical diary, just in case, and then he would forget about it.

34
Night Stalker

Sunday, 27 October 1991. Rolling over, Kerry returned to deep sleep, oblivious of the passage of time and unaware of her sister Lisa lying elsewhere in the same bed; the two having agreed to stay together as John was away on business.

With her astral body free to roam aimlessly in the space between space, the realms existing between the physical and spiritual, the sensation of flying was always welcome. She dreamt about it often and tonight was no different.

In the darkness below she could make out arched roofs of endless houses, neatly grouped between empty roads and acres of blackness that marked the positions of open fields and parks. Much larger factory buildings looked like enormous dominoes laid out for some unimaginable game of the gods.

Kerry then became aware that she was no longer alone in her ethereal night flight. She sensed she was being followed, and not wishing to break the dream and look behind, she decided to find cover, knowing that whatever had locked on to her astral form was gaining speed.

Like a jet fighter attempting to escape the nets of radar, she plunged lower and lower until she found herself zipping between the jutting rooftops of houses and shops. Her assailant still pursued her, unmoved by this deliberate act of evasion.

Skirting a tall, flat-roofed building, she slowed up and came to a temporary halt to assess the situation. She did not care to know who or what the night stalker might be, although grave fears accompanied even the barest thoughts of its identity. Her spectral body took flight once more, realising she would have to reach safety, for she would be in trouble if she fell victim to this predator.

Suddenly she felt relieved; she could see her destination. There was still danger, however. She would have to get even lower to avoid capture, so skimmed along the pavements, weaving a clear path through the deserted streets that were somehow familiar even though it was not her home town.

In front of her was a tall Georgian house, with a great stone portico and an inviting doorway. She would be safe here with her friends, here in this building she felt she knew so well.

Changing her ethereal aspect, she grounded herself and became a player in her self-induced dreamscape. Finding she could walk again, Kerry took no time in entering and searching each room for her friends. Opening a wooden-panelled door she found herself in a small hallway, and following her senses she came upon a further closed door, beyond which she could make out the faint glow of artificial light.

Beyond the door, she found stone stairs leading down to a room alive with muted conversation. She was relieved to find her husband John, her sister Lisa, and her close friends standing around a huge wooden table in the centre of a basement room. They had been awaiting her arrival and seemed aware of the mortifying evil advancing towards them from the dark domain outside.

Apprehensively Kerry looked around at the plaster walls of this underground basement, hoping and praying it was a sufficient barrier against the invisible malevolence. Fear welled up inside when she realised that she was still not safe.

She stared anxiously at the stone steps leading up to the closed door; could it still make an entry through here? Her only comfort was to see the door had been locked and bolted upon her entry.

Then she stopped her visual exploration of the basement and listened hard. There was a rising noise reaching her ears only, an unfathomable cacophony unlike anything she had encountered before. It could have been heavy breathing, or perhaps the exhalation of pressurised air, or maybe wind roaring through trees, or all of these and more besides.

It was getting nearer; very near indeed. The sheer intensity of these tortuous ululations was good evidence of the night stalker's hideous strength as it moved still closer.

Registering the disturbed expressions on the searching faces of her friends, she focused her eyes on the sealed wooden door at the top of the stairs; its only possible place of entry.

Suddenly, and without warning, the deafening crash of glass made her whirl around in absolute terror to witness a vampiric black beast – half wolf, half man – break through an unseen skylight window and plunge towards the assembled party.

She registered only its blazing red eyes as it lunged towards her defenceless body. All at once she screamed and screamed and screamed again, waking herself from the nightmare until her eyes recognised the uncertain shape of the bedroom.

She cried out, knowing that, although the horrifying experience was over, its loathsome memory would not leave her until the stillness of the night had given way to the first light of day – only then would she be allowed to question the purpose of this unprovoked confrontation with a werewolf.

It had been a long day. Late the previous night Debbie had received an unexpected visitation from the spirit of a Victorian gentleman wearing a russet suit, a frilly white shirt and a cream cape. He gave the name Edward Bingham and had spoken of a medieval castle perched high on a hill above the scenic village of Castle Hedingham in north Essex. Acting with our usual spontaneity, we had visited the area that afternoon and discovered that Bingham had been a potter who lived locally during the second half of the nineteenth century. His Hedingham ware had become quite popular and examples were still to be found in local museums. Unfortunately, however, other than to confirm his somewhat eccentric nature (he carried an umbrella in all weather), we could not establish why Edward Bingham should have wanted to pay us a visit.

Having arrived home during the mid-evening, we had abandoned the idea of a hot meal in favour of allowing the local off-licence to provide us with enough refreshments to satisfy our immediate gastronomic needs.

Debbie emerged with tumblers for Kerry, Lisa and herself. Between them they opened a bottle of peach-flavoured Concorde, their current tipple when it came to wine. On the settee John swigged from a can of Coke, in between devouring bags of crisps, as I sat on the floor, an open can of Guinness by my side.

'I had a really weird dream last night,' Kerry began, pouring wine. 'I dreamt I came face to face with a werewolf!'

For several minutes I listened with only a mild interest to her account of the semi-astral encounter with a night stalker.

'Funny thing was,' Lisa added quickly, 'I woke up during the night and I swear I saw figures surrounding the bed. They were talking to each other, but I couldn't make out what they were saying.'

Did they seem malevolent?

She shook her head apparently deep in thought. 'No, I don't think so. The whole thing just seemed weird, that's all.' She had not expected anyone to be particularly interested.

John leaned forward. 'You know, that's odd. Last week I had a dream about a vampire. I can't remember the details, and it wasn't the first time, either.'

I asked him to tell me more.

'The end of September I dreamt about this boat coming into a harbour below tall cliffs and a woman being attacked by a vampire. I didn't say anything as I thought it was only my imagination, but I put it in the diary. Anyway, I can't stand vampires.' His head shook at the mere thought of one. 'I hate them; it's the one thing that really gets me going.

'I once saw this vampire film at a cinema with this girl,' he continued with the hint of a smile. 'It scared me shitless. Anyway, I drove her back home and as a laugh she went for my throat. I just stopped the car and told her to get out! It freaked me out completely!'

Vampires and werewolves. What was all this about? Kerry's lucid dream the previous night could be put down to temporary insecurity with her husband away, but what about John? Could his genuine fear of vampires have triggered some kind of symbolic response to other more mundane problems in his life?

The thought of vampires brought to mind our intended trip to Yorkshire this coming weekend. If I was not mistaken Yorkshire had connections with vampires and werewolves through its links with Bram Stoker's Gothic classic *Dracula*, first published in 1897. In my childhood our family twice holidayed in Whitby on the North Yorkshire coast, owing to the acute abundance of fossils found on its local beaches. I could recall visiting the splendid abbey ruins and being told by my father that this was where Count Dracula first came ashore when he arrived in England. I thought he really meant it as I had no idea that Bram Stoker's work was fictional in those days. Something else told me that Stoker had featured Whitby as a setting in his book after learning it possessed genuine legends concerning vampires and werewolves; the exact details eluded me, but it could be checked.

For the moment I would say nothing, since it was probably irrelevant to our own as yet unconfirmed interests in Yorkshire, which suggested that we would be going to the town of Knaresborough in West Yorkshire, nowhere near North Yorkshire. Without making reference to Whitby, I light-heartedly floated the idea that John and Kerry's nocturnal encounters with vampires and werewolves *might*, and only might, relate to our intended visit to Yorkshire.

'That's it, I'm not going,' John jested in a loud voice. 'Any vampires and I'm off, crucifix, garlic or whatever; you won't get me near the place.'

Debbie did not quite know what to say, so simply shrugged her shoulders. 'I'm not sure whether there's a connection or not. We'll just have to wait and see. The one thing I do feel about this Yorkshire business is that we're not being given the full story, and this worries me slightly.'

'What do you mean, Deb?' Lisa said, having caught the possible significance of her words.

There was a sigh and a few moments of thought before she answered. 'I, I just get the impression that we're stepping headlong into a situation crucial to Hexe's plans, and if we bugger it up for them, I don't think they're going to be very happy.'

35
Nosferatu

Monday, 28 October 1991. 'Whereabouts is Whitby?' Debbie finally asked, settling down on the front-room settee after a long day at work with a local picture framer's – the position she had accepted after leaving the copying centre.

Abandoning the word processor, I turned around with what must have been an intrigued look on my face. 'Whitby?' I said, not believing my ears.

'Yes, Whitby,' she confirmed, surprised at my reaction. 'It's just that since last night I've had this feeling that Hexe will be there around Hallowe'en.'

I needed to know more; how did Whitby come into this story?

Debbie put aside her newspaper and thought carefully for a moment. 'Is Whitby connected with werewolves?'

I simply said it was.

'Well, I hate to seem clichéd, but I have the sneaky suspicion that John and Kerry's dreams actually mean something and relate to Whitby, somehow,' she revealed, unsure of how I would react. 'I think Hexe are pumping up some localised aspect of the town and using it for their own purposes. What exactly, I'm not sure, but it's definitely linked with werewolves.'

My mind was reeling – why Whitby? Were there *real* werewolf legends in Whitby? Why had Bram Stoker featured this North Yorkshire fishing town in his masterpiece? And, more importantly, why were Hexe so interested in the place?

I started by asking Debbie if she had ever read Bram Stoker's *Dracula* (I had never got round to reading it myself).

'I've seen the films,' she admitted eagerly. 'I really like the Hammer Horror movies with Christopher Lee and Peter Cushing; they're brilliant together, aren't they?'

They were, yes, but did she know that Dracula was linked with Whitby?

There was a stunned silence, before: 'With Whitby? Oh, you're kidding.'

I told her what I knew already and realised it was time to search out my original copy of Bram Stoker's *Dracula*; see if it could throw any light on this perplexing mystery. Afterwards, I would scan my books and files to establish whether there really were any local legends connecting vampires and werewolves with Whitby's misty past.

Tuesday, 29 October. Replacing *Dracula* in its vacant slot among the other books above the fireplace, I contemplated my findings so far.

Bram Stoker's Gothic classic focuses around the notorious Count Dracula, an East European aristocrat who has lived for hundreds of years in a secluded medieval castle, close to the border of three separate provinces – Transylvania, Moldavia and Bukovina – situated amid the snow-capped Carpathian mountains of what is today Romania.

Scholars generally accept that Count Dracula is based upon the infamous fifteenth-century Romanian prince named Vlad Dracula of Wallachia, better known as Vlad Tepes – the Impaler – who crucified hundreds of thousands of people in the most hideous ways possible. The name Dracula comes from the Romanian *dracul* meaning 'dragon', while in the native Wallachian language *dracul* means 'devil'. The dualistic association between dragon and devil is preserved in the Germanic-Romanian frontier regions where *nosferatu*, the vampire of European tradition, was seen as a serpentine creature of the night[1] – equated with both the devil in Christian folklore and the blood-sucking *lamaiai* of classical tradition. Fusing together these various different elements Stoker came up with the hybrid vampire – the immortal, blood-sucking, devil-like Count Dracula.

The story-line in *Dracula* has the hybrid, fictitious Count Dracula yearning for a new lease of life among the citizens of England. He secures, through the intercession of an Exeter solicitor, an estate named Carfax[2] at Purfleet, close to the River Thames in Essex. Finally, after imprisoning Jonathan Harker, the solicitor's young clerk, the Count departs for England in a tomb-like packing case lined with sanctified earth. Along with a number of curious 'boxes of earth' and a ballast of 'silver sand', he is shipped to the Black Sea port of Varna and loaded aboard a Russian schooner named the *Demeter*. Yet instead of the shipment being consigned to Tilbury, the London port closest to the Count's new home, it is despatched to Whitby in Yorkshire – one of only three locations found by Jonathan Harker to have been ringed on the Count's map of the British Isles (the others being Exeter and Purfleet).

Following an appalling sea journey, where the entire crew of the Russian schooner are either murdered or forced to throw themselves overboard completely insane, the sailing vessel is unexpectedly sighted off Kettleness, a headland north-west of Whitby, just as a fierce storm is about to break. The ship finally slides into harbour, its sails tattered and torn and the corpse of its last remaining crew member bound limply to the wheel – a rosary and crucifix clenched tightly in its hands! Below deck is the sleeping Count Dracula and after the mysterious Russian schooner docks, a large hound, also described as a 'wolf', is seen to leave the deck. That night the attacks begin. His first confirmed human victim is Lucy Westenra, a vivacious young girl who is assaulted whilst seated on a bench, situated over the grave of a suicide in a churchyard perched high above the town.

Dracula then travels to London before returning to Transylvania for the story's eventual climax. Whitby features no more in the book – other than the brief visit Jonathan Harker affords it to confirm the incidents reported earlier. Indeed, why Stoker should have wanted to include Whitby in the story-line is difficult to comprehend. The insinuation in the text is that the Count is attempting to confuse the issue, and thus evade discovery, by employing the services of a different solicitor in three separate English ports.

Biographers believe it was simply Stoker's summer holidays here that convinced him to include Whitby in his novel. Such an explanation seemed inadequate to me, raising the possibility that there may have been other, as yet undisclosed, reasons why he chose to have Count Dracula come ashore at Whitby as opposed to anywhere else in England.

Strangely enough it was whilst holidaying in Whitby during August 1890 that Bram Stoker first found reference to Vlad Tepes's grisly deeds in a library book entitled *An Account of the Principalities of Wallachia and Moldavia*, written by William Wilkinson and published in 1820.[3] This important discovery must have had at least some bearing on his decision to feature the town in his forthcoming novel.

Of more immediate interest, however, was the disconcerting fact that John's nightmare appeared to replicate the appearance of the Russian schooner in Whitby harbour as well as the Count's subsequent attack on Lucy Westenra – even though he had never read *Dracula*. There were differences, however, such as John's description of a black coffin seen lying on the upper deck of the vessel as it coasted into harbour. In *Dracula* the Count's body is safely inside its packing case below deck. John also saw the woman attacked whilst standing on her feet, whereas Lucy Westenra is assaulted when seated on a bench overlooking the town below.

More curious still were the less obvious similarities between Kerry's astral encounter with a werewolf and the plight of Lucy Westenra in *Dracula*. This includes the scene where Dracula transforms from a gigantic bat into a sinewy wolf and crashes through the bedroom window as she shares a bed with her poorly mother.

All this may seem quite absurd to the outsider, but over the years I had worked with many good psychics who have experienced waking visions or lucid dreams in which they inadvertently replay scenes from a work of fiction. This is despite them never having read the book in question.

So what is the solution? Either the information utilised by the book's author has been gleaned from factual material – which is sometimes the case – or the constant reading of the book by thousands, if not millions of readers gives life to its characters by making them into very real thought forms with their own separate existence.

Whitby's perpetual association with the *Dracula* story has almost certainly enabled the manifestation of such thought forms complete with their own Victorian mindscape. If so, then these will become accessible to any good psychic, either when attuning to the town or when present at any of the locations featured in the book. Was it therefore possible that John and Kerry had managed to attune to Whitby's Dracula current without actually making the more obvious connection with the town itself? In other words, if they had received the place-name 'Whitby' in connection with their vampire/werewolf encounters, then it would have put us on to the town's apparent relevance *before* Debbie had linked it with our quest the previous day.

And the intrigue does not end here, for myth can often reflect reality, and vice versa, especially in the case of Bram Stoker. In my book *The Seventh Sword* I outlined how the story-line of his 1903 classic *The Jewel of the Seven Stars* paralleled real-life events in more recent years. Its account of the discovery of a supposedly mythical Egyptian queen named Tera, and her subsequent raising at the hands of the book's main character, undeniably echoed the recorded life and modern-day summoning of an ancient Egyptian female king named Sobek-nofru-re in 1981.[4]

Writing to me on this subject, occult researcher Gareth Medway pointed out that *The Jewel of the Seven Stars* was not the only Stoker book to mimic known reality. Kettleness is the headland north-west of Whitby where the Russian schooner carrying Count Dracula is first sighted prior to the fierce storm. It was on this same beach at Kettleness during the 1950s that Dr Donald Omand – a priest and exorcist who has blessed Loch Ness and the Bermuda Triangle during his colourful career – encountered a phantom black dog, the same form Dracula took to come ashore at Whitby.[5]

Then during the 1970s Dr Omand was asked to exorcise a Swedish psychiatric patient who had developed a craving for human blood. Upon enquiry he established that the parents had visited England soon after their marriage and the father had mentioned how they had experienced 'an oppressive atmosphere' at a place named Kettleness, a point they saw as relevant to his son's condition. Omand had concluded that Bram Stoker must have been 'fey' or psychic.

More importantly, old Whitby residents once believed that a huge ogre of ill omen, a monstrous black hound known as the barguest, stalked the streets at night. It was said to possess 'huge eyes glowing like the fires of hell' and emitted a 'terrible shriek or roar, a sound which struck fear into the heart, for only those who were about to die could hear the howl of the barguest'.[6] Other names given to the Whitby hell-hound were padfoot, scriker or gytrash. Its greatest haunt was in the vicinity of Church Street, at the base of the stone steps leading up to East Cliff, where St Mary's church and the abbey ruins are prominently situated.[7] Further enquiries showed that the barguest was a familiar spectre of the Yorkshire moors where its appearance was often accompanied by the distinct sound of clanging chains.[8] So, had Bram Stoker been aware of the barguest legend when he wrote *Dracula*? I would have thought so.

Whether such supernatural denizens exist or not is irrelevant; it was archaic legends and beliefs such as these that the People of Hexe used for their own degenerate purposes. Combining this with the sheer power of any possible Dracula-based thought form currently residing in the etheric counterparts of Whitby, then their apparent interest in this quiet fishing town was beginning to make sense. But why? Why take an interest in Whitby when there were so many other more significant places of ancient power in Yorkshire, or anywhere else in the country for that matter?

Debbie believed we were not being told the full story, and I could only agree with her. All I knew for certain was that John was not going to like this sudden change in direction one little bit!

36
Something Silver

Wednesday, 30 October 1991. Lifting out a half-finished can of Coke from its plastic clasp on the edge of the car's window seal, John took a swig and steered with the other hand.

Long journeys for a sales representative get tedious and he was always looking for something to occupy his mind. Lighting a cigarette he skipped into the outside, overtaking lane of the quiet A34 trunk road between Stone and Stafford, having just completed his third business call since eleven o'clock. He sold scaffolding and other related building materials to contractors spanning the length and breadth of the country, meaning long hours on the road.

He slipped on a well-worn cassette, as the car approached and passed a slow-moving vehicle. Deciding to pull back into the nearside lane, he clicked up the indicator, glanced up at the rear-view mirror, and saw not the open road *but a gigantic wolf with long, sharp canine teeth, matted grey hair and fiery eyes full of hatred and venom*. It was just there, on the road behind, keeping pace with the vehicle.

The car swerved across the road as he pumped the footbrake and made the decision to complete the manoeuvre. Having pulled into the slow lane, John looked at the steering wheel and saw that his hands were trembling.

What the hell was going on? Dare he look up?

Glancing apprehensively at the mirror, he saw only the empty road. There was no sign of a huge wolf, anywhere.

John attempted to calm his nerves by suggesting to himself that the wolf had been either a stray dog, or the product of his over-active imagination; some kind of hallucination perhaps, resulting from too many hours of laborious driving recently. He then reasoned that he could not have witnessed a *real* wolf (or any dog for that matter) as he was doing in excess of 60mph.

All this talk of vampires and werewolves was obviously getting to him, but the lucidity of the wolf's presence, its eyes like burning coals and its thick, matted coat were all too real to simply ignore. After his next call, the last of the day, he would give Andrew a ring on the car-phone; see if anything further had transpired over the past few days.

Moving into the front room I answered the telephone. 'Yeah, Andrew? It's John. Look I'm on the car-phone, so I'll keep it brief,' he began, the clear sound of cars whizzing past in the background. 'Has anything happened your end since Sunday?' he asked, somewhat cryptically.

I mentioned Whitby by name and this prompted him to give me a vivid account of his extraordinary vision of the huge, running wolf seen in the rear-view mirror, earlier that afternoon.

It made no more sense of what we already knew. Perhaps this vampire mania really was getting to him!

'That's what I thought,' he openly admitted. 'But, ever since I saw the wolf, just one name keeps coming to mind in connection with this whole Hexe business in Yorkshire at Hallowe'en, and that's Fenris.'

The demon-wolf of Norse tradition.

'It's all that keeps coming to me. Fenris. Fenris. Fenris. So, what d'you reckon? Completely mad, or what?'

In medieval Norse and Icelandic sagas the myth cycle of the Fenris-wolf focuses around the age of Ragnarok, the Doom of the Divine Powers and the destruction of heaven and earth. The release of the Fenris-wolf is seen as one of the portents marking the commencement of the final days, equated in Anglo-Saxon times with the Christian concept of the Day of Judgement and the Second Coming.[1] Ragnarok is seen to have happened once before, and to ensure it never occurs again the demon-wolf is bound and shackled in the underworld by the magic threads of skilful dwarves. Here Fenris will remain until it finally breaks free of its imprisonment and the entire Ragnarok cycle begins once again.

SOMETHING SILVER

Practising occultists consider the power of Fenris to be an immensely potent force not to be awoken unless the implications are seriously understood beforehand, so if somebody *was* playing around with this supernatural entity at Whitby, then it could mean big problems indeed.

I thought about Whitby for a moment. Wait a minute; of course, a Fenris connection did make sense. The town's famous abbey, popularised in Bram Stoker's *Dracula*, was sacked by the Danes during the ninth century, giving the location an air of sanguinary domination and violence ideal for utilisation in Norse rituals associated with death and destruction. It was also close to this spot that the barguest supposedly stalked the streets at night, bringing death to those who could hear its howl. There was certainly food for thought here.

Saying goodbye to John, I returned to my publishing duties until Debbie arrived home a short while later. Passing through to the kitchen, she removed her overcoat and put on the kettle as I told her about Fenris.

'Wait a minute,' she demanded, falling silent and simply staring into thin air.

Working with psychics has taught me never to interrupt their train of thought during such moments of contemplation.

Looking up, she breathed a sigh. 'You mentioning Fenris triggered something off in my head, an image I glimpsed last night – an object made of silver leaving the raised hand of a tall man and tumbling over the shoulder of a dwarf or midget in a grey-cowled robe, who then runs away.'

She opened the fridge and pulled out a carton of fresh milk. 'I get the feeling it's connected with Whitby and what's more, I think you'll find that Hexe were conducting some sort of ritual there last night; I could sense their presence.'

Pouring hot water into the teapot, I asked her if she could recall the background setting to this ritualistic event she had witnessed, bearing in mind she knew nothing about Whitby.

'It was dark but I could see lots of long grass and a ruiny sort of place made of brown stone,' she replied, bowing her head.

She was probably describing the abbey. So what was going on there?

'I'm not sure,' she said thoughtfully, still waiting to change out of her work clothes. 'I tried to concentrate on the hand to see what the silver object might be, but I didn't get any more.'

In Norse tradition warriors inscribed their spears with runic symbols to empower them with the force of Odin. These were thrown over the heads of their opponents to bring them under the control of the god who would then ensure they were defeated in battle.[2]

I assessed the situation once more. Debbie now believed that the People of Hexe were currently active in Whitby, having visited what appeared to be the abbey ruins the previous night. Here they had conducted a ritual or some sort, possibly one involving Norse pagan magic and the Fenris-wolf. The implications were that they would stay in the area and conclude their activities on Hallowe'en; although why this date should be important to them had still not been made clear.

Was it possible that John and Kerry's interaction with this fantasy-realm-made-real was triggered because of Hexe's new-found interest in Bram Stoker's legacy? Perhaps they were harnessing and utilising Whitby's indigenous vampiric, wolfish energy in association with the Fenris-wolf. Using the abbey ruins made complete sense as it was at Tate Hill Pier, beneath East Cliff, that Bram Stoker had Count Dracula bounding ashore as a wolf-hound. What's more, Lucy Westenra, the Count's first confirmed victim in England, is attacked while sitting on a stone bench in St Mary's churchyard, opposite the entrance to the abbey grounds. It is underneath this same bench, inside the grave of a suicide, that Dracula sleeps during his short stay in Whitby.

None of this information was openly known to Debbie, Kerry or John, making their psychic experiences of the past couple of days even more extraordinary, although where all this would lead was totally beyond me.

37
Harbinger of Destruction

Saturday, 2 November 1991. Bumper to bumper the Ford Orion edged its way through the several miles' long tail-back on the M1 motorway, somewhere north of Northampton. With John, Kerry, Karl and Lisa in the vehicle behind, Andrew drove in silence while Debbie, crouched up in the passenger seat, slipped drearily into sleep.

Vague flashes of insignificant imagery finally gave way to a clear mental picture of massive walls of tawny-brown stone, supporting soaring Gothic archways and huge, open windows devoid of their original decorative tracery. Somehow the setting seemed vaguely familiar, even though she had never visited this ancient place before.

Debbie found herself passing the murky depths of a shallow pond and was soon walking on a carpet of grass between an avenue of column stumps towards the high altar at the eastern end of the crumbling chancel ruins.

A crisp, winter breeze blew in from the sea, giving the impression of airiness and elevation. Was Whitby Abbey situated on high ground? Andrew had not said. Yet then came another, more disturbing realisation. She could sense something out of character in this place of Christian sanctity – an overbearing canine odour growing stronger by the moment. Glancing around, she saw the source of her concern.

Walking into view through the impressive entrance arch was a tall, imposing man aged around thirty-five, with broad shoulders; a square, clean-shaven face, strong jaws and thick bushy eyebrows. He wore a long, grey-green, double-breasted frock-coat, and his head of thick, dark hair was topped by a distinctive Russian winter hat. And yet it was his pale skin and small, deep-set grey eyes – of the lightest shade she had ever seen – that struck her the most and, when combined with his other prominent features, left her in no doubt as to his East European origin.

It was from him that the strong canine smell appeared to emanate; yet not from his clothes, like someone who might work around dogs all day, but from his overall persona, as though it was permanently within his psychic aura.

He looked powerful and strangely familiar.

At that moment their eyes met, in response to which a slight smile touched his lips. She did not understand this sign of recognition until they linked as one in mind.

His name was 'Hagal', she realised before suddenly finding she was no longer in the abbey ruins.[1]

They were now on the bleak and windy Yorkshire moors, standing on a rug of thick moss that kept at bay the encroaching heather and scrub surrounding them on all sides. Here and there exposed bed-rock jutted out of the harsh, rugged landscape constantly pounded by the cold, icy gales blustering in from the North Sea.

Completely encircling them were small wooden stakes, carefully inscribed with runic symbols of arcane power.

With an amused grin on his face, Hagal outstretched a hand and gestured towards the perimeter of this ring of runic stakes. He wanted her to choose one, and somehow she realised that by removing the correct rune she could gain her escape from this desolate place.

The raging blizzard increased in ferocity, making her shiver uncontrollably. She had to get out of here and make her way back to the abbey.

Hagal began to laugh.

She began checking each rune stick knowing that extracting the wrong one would bring poison to her soul.

Which one? Which one?

Still he laughed.

No, she could not choose, Debbie decided, as she gazed up at the Romanian runemaster, who was still revelling in her unfortunate plight.

And then she knew. The joining of minds told her where she had seen him before and why he had travelled from afar to be here on the deserted Yorkshire moorland.

Ravastack. Ravastack.

Yes, that was it. Of course . . .

Opening her eyes, Debbie glanced nervously out of the side window and saw that the car was no longer in a traffic jam. It cruised along at 80mph in the outside lane of the M1 on its journey ever northwards.

'Oh God, I've just had this really weird dream,' she revealed, still rubbing her eyes and looking around for the carrier bag full of drinks and snacks. 'I think I was at Whitby Abbey and I saw this man there named Hagal.'

Hagal? That was a strange name.

'I think he's Romanian, as he was wearing a thick trench-coat and one of those Russian hats,' she explained, yawning openly and finding a packet of crisps. She revealed the contents of the dream as the vehicle passed through Leicestershire and into Derbyshire.

I shook my head. Her description of masonry trailing into a shallow pool or pond inside the abbey grounds had to be wrong as the ruins were, as she suggested, situated on top of a steep cliff, overlooking the town. Still water would obviously filter into the top soil and drain away through the porous, sub-surface rock.

'I'm only telling you what I saw,' she emphasised, a little indignantly. 'I tell you, I saw water there.'

Anyway, what was this Romanian or Russian gentleman doing in Yorkshire? I picked up a small carton of service-station pineapple juice and pushed the flexi-straw through the foil-covered hole.

'I have this horrible feeling that he was there when they raised Fenris during the Romanian earthquake,' she revealed, a note of concern in her green eyes.

Almost choking on the juice, I turned around and asked her to repeat those words slowly; I wanted to make sure I'd heard this right.

She leaned against the vibrating window and tried to clarify her thoughts. 'I now realise that what happened in Romania was just part of a series of events coming to fruition at this time; possibly even this weekend.

'This Hagal bloke has transported the power of Fenris to Britain on instructions from the People of Hexe,' she said next. 'I hope I'm wrong, but the way I feel at the moment is that the force of Fenris was deliberately raised by indigenous Romanian shamans to fulfil a prophecy spoken of from generation to generation among their own kind.

'They actually believe they are descended from the wolf. It's a kind of tribal shamanism connected with the sons of Odin, or something. The blood of the wolf runs through their veins and with it comes the power to release Fenris at the appointed time.

'Hagal's family knew that one day someone would come knocking at their door saying: "It is time". If not the current generation, then knowledge of this prophecy would be handed down to the next generation and the next until they finally came.'

And I assumed it *had* finally come.

She nodded slowly as the Orion sped into the fast lane with John's car in close pursuit. 'Yes, somehow Hexe got on to these people and managed to convince them they were working for the greater scheme of things.

'They told them they were important and that by raising Fenris they were not just fulfilling the prophecy, they would become prime movers in the coming world changes.

'What the Romanians don't realise is that for Hexe they are not the only fish in the sea.'

Did these people believe they could initiate the age of Ragnarok simply by releasing Fenris?

'I believe so, yes. However, for them it will signify the commencement of great change, seen symbolically as the re-awakening of their own Germanic race. The Romanian earthquake was confirmation that the prophecy was being fulfilled.'

Her words made sense. At the time of the Romanian earthquake I had established that the Germanic races of northern Europe – who probably carried with them the core of the original Ragnarok story – had reached Romania sometime after AD 350. Many of today's Hungarian and Romanian races still have Saxon blood running through their veins.

As I already knew, one version of the Ragnarok story spoke of 'a distant forest in the East [of the Germanic territories]' where 'an aged giantess brought into the world a whole brood of young wolves whose father was Fenrir'.[2] Perhaps Hagal and his family believed they were lineal descendants of this 'brood of wolves' and decided that at the right time they would fulfil the prophecy by releasing a form of Fenris, which would climb into the sky and swallow the sun – imagery blatantly echoed in Debbie's vision of the ritual event thought to have taken place during the Romanian earthquake of 30 May 1990.

Just five months beforehand, Romania's Ceauşescu regime had collapsed, and with the dismantling of the Berlin Wall and the demise of other Communist Block governments in the wake of President Gorbachev's *Glasnost* and *Perestroika* policies, the winds of change had certainly swept across Eastern Europe in 1989 and 1990. Could this have been instrumental in convincing Hagal and his family that a new age of Ragnarok was upon them? But why should this man believe he was descended from the wolf? Was he some kind of wolf shaman?

'Don't you realise, *lycanthropy is in their blood*,' she declared. 'They will probably possess ancestral wolfish tendencies and actually believe they have control over wolves themselves. Yes, they are wolf shamans.'

So, was Hagal the man she had seen throwing the silver object over the shoulder of the midget?

'No, I don't think so,' she decided, picking up an apple. 'I don't feel he's been in the country for very long. I'm not even sure if he's down-loaded the Fenris energy yet. If he has, then it can only have occurred in the last twenty-four hours and may not be over yet, which means that we could have company when we finally reach Whitby.'

Oh great, she was now telling me there was a good possibility of us encountering a fully fledged Romanian wolf shaman in Yorkshire! I shook my head in dismay. This story-line really was becoming like the script for a bizarre B-movie, and yet it was throwing light on a number of quite separate issues. For instance, we knew for a fact that the Romanian earthquake of 1990 rocked the border area between the Romanian/Soviet provinces of Transylvania and Moldavia – the region where real-life vampire and werewolf legends were still rife, and where Bram Stoker set his fictional Castle Dracula.

Count Dracula transfers his seat of power from Transylvania to Whitby in search of new life. With the aid of this Hagal figure, Hexe appeared to be mimicking his sea voyage by transferring the Fenris-wolf from its place of resurrection in Romania to the same port of destination in Britain.

Slipping back into the centre lane, I reduced my speed. This was mind-boggling material, and I just hoped we achieved some hardcore evidence of its reality.

Debbie continued the dialogue. 'Fenris is, I believe, the most potent energy form so far harnessed by Hexe. It's to be used in some kind of binding ritual and if we don't prevent or stall this action in some way, then there are going to be unfathomable repercussions, I'm sure of it. This is why John, Kerry and myself have been picking up on this material about vampires and werewolves – the real Count Dracula is the Fenris-wolf.'

I had already worked this out. The age of Ragnarok of the later Norse and Icelandic sagas was equated with the Day of Judgement by the Anglo-Saxon Church. The two were merged into one as can be seen from the tall, decorative 'Viking' cross standing in the churchyard at Gosforth in Cumbria (close to the Sellafield nuclear power station). Here Loki, Fenris and the monsters and demons of Ragnarok struggle with the gods of Asgard. To the pre-Conquest Christians Ragnarok was synonymous with apocalypse, and there is no doubt that the Norse god Loki, who gave birth to Fenris and the other monsters of Hel, can be equated with both Satan and the devil.[3] So if Satan's son is Antichrist, might the spawn of Loki be seen as a Norse interpretation of the Great Beast, one of the forms of Antichrist?

Count Dracula can easily be compared with Fenris through his connection with the wolf, the animal most associated with his transformations. He is Bram Stoker's living embodiment of both the werewolf and the vampire, who, as I had already established, is seen as a devil, the 'dracul' of the Wallachian language.[4] There is no doubt from the reversals of Christian belief and ritual in Stoker's *Dracula* that the Count himself is being portrayed as a form of Antichrist.[5]

Accepting that Dracula was now a powerful thought form in his own right, then it seemed possible that Hexe were seeing the energy of Antichrist, Fenris and Dracula (devil) as merely externalisations of the same supernatural force; in their minds there were no differences. Christ, this was beginning to sound serious! What the hell laid ahead of us in Whitby? And how did all this begin?

'It started years ago.' She took in a deep breath before continuing. 'I feel our visit to Stonehenge in September followed an intensive series of rituals Hexe had been conducting in the area for some years. These climaxed in August and all we did was clean up the mess; it was too late to reverse their long-term activities.

'This will not be the case at Whitby. I'm still unsure exactly what's going on at the abbey, whether we'll find Fenris tethered in chains there or not. What I do know is that this is a crucial nexus point for Hexe. We can never stop their activities, but if we can achieve our objectives this weekend, then it will delay plans which they and others such as the Black Alchemist and the Friends of Hekate have been working towards for some time now.'

Of course, it was all becoming crystal clear. Ever since the Great Storm of 1987 we had known these dark groups and individuals were attempting to create an apocalyptic entity associated directly with the influence of Hekate in her guise as Lykaina, the she-wolf. The very night that the hurricane devastated the south of England psychics across the country experienced horrific visions of either demonic wolves or Lykaina herself. 'The wolves are running' were the words used the following morning by psychic Marion Sunderland, after hearing about the trail of devastation left by the hurricane.

Shortly afterwards Bernard and I had discovered the ape dagger speared into the blood-soaked heart left beneath a hurricane-struck tree in Danbury churchyard. An assessment of its magical inscription had strongly indicated that whoever had placed it in position was proclaiming the conception of some form of questionable entity that would henceforth 'gestate' inside the conceptual womb of a barren crone, the she-wolf herself.

Nine months later, in the scenario surrounding the Paradise

Mound outside Eastbourne on 8 August 1988, there were further clues that a diabolic entity had been 'born' upon the astral planes, and that its existence symbolised the resurrection of the Fallen Angel. Once again there had been clear indications that it was of wolfish origin.

Rachel Goodison's Athena card received by Bernard the previous September had also spoken of the resurrection of the Fallen Angel in association with a sinister, Wheel-linked group known as the Black Cross of the Flame. At first I had assumed this to be a reference to either Satan, Lucifer or Belial, but now I was beginning to realise that it was none of these . . .

'No, Andrew,' Debbie interjected, shaking her head. 'It is all of them combined, just as the Fenris energy form is an amalgamation of these immensely powerful forces in Britain today. As the barren she-wolf gestating the Fallen Angel in her womb against the laws of nature, Hekate has provided the lifeblood that will sustain and nurture the power of the Fenris-wolf – the harbinger of destruction in Norse mythology.

'If released in the way Hexe and others intend, then it will symbolise the commencement of their own variation of Ragnarok, during which time the world will undergo immense ecological and economic changes, or so they believe.

'In doing this they hope to subtly shift the centre of gravity in favour of the Wheel worldwide. It is this they have been preparing for – their own warped vision of Ragnarok, Judgement Day, the Second Coming, call it what you want.

'Whether or not these people can really achieve their ultimate goals is irrelevant, the sheer fact that they actually *believe* this power can give them control is sufficient to cause ripples upon the Web of Wyrd that will ultimately affect each and every one of us. That is why we must succeed this weekend.'

38
Omens of Despair

Somewhere on the outskirts of Whitby, in the darkness of the early evening, I propped the OS map against the steering wheel and attempted to find the abbey ruins. The urban developments, factory units, roundabouts, one-way system and heavy traffic seemed a far cry from Bram Stoker's Victorian vision of a slumbering seaside town. For some stupid reason I had imagined that time would have stood still and nothing would have changed since the publication of *Dracula* almost a hundred years ago.

The continuing journey took us through housing estates and an assortment of T-junctions before we rose to the level of East Cliff and followed the last few hundred yards of the coastal road towards the abbey car-park.

A tall stone wall lined the left-hand side of the road and somehow I knew we had reached our final destination. Soon afterwards I saw the vast ecclesiastical ruins jutting skywards beyond the secure enclosure, and suddenly I developed the same sinking feeling that had accompanied us on our departure from Knaresborough earlier that afternoon. We had found nothing to further our quest here, so had unanimously decided to move on to Whitby as quickly as possible, realising it would be dark by the time we arrived.

Now there were new worries I should have contemplated an awful lot earlier. High stone walls were generally meant to keep people out as well as to ensure that a token payment is made before such majestic ruins can be appreciated by visitors. Since it was just after six o'clock on a dark November evening, I realised the abbey was going to be closed.

The quiet road opened out into a small car-park separated from the edge of the cliffs by a further stone wall. To its left, in full view of the town below, was the squat, somewhat ugly church of St Mary, immortalised in the pages of *Dracula*. On the opposite side of the road was the huge, arched wooden gate leading into the abbey ruins, next to which was a house belonging to the monument's live-in custodian and his or her family. Blazing lights coming from more than one window made it clear they were at home tonight. Worse still, more than one of those windows faced out towards the ruins.

I also realised that every part of the jagged masonry exposed above the eight-foot high wall – topped with broken glass, I might add – was illuminated by powerful floodlights strategically placed at ground level.

How could I have been so stupid? Fancy thinking we could just waltz into the grounds of an English Heritage monument in the pitch dark and conduct the odd meditation here and there.

John's new Peugeot 205 pulled in next to the Orion and slid to a halt. Car doors opened and out poured the remainder of the questing posse, pulling on warm coats and readying themselves for a long night ahead.

'It's not open, is it?' John observed, staring up at the gatehouse.

Gradually the whole group moved towards the huge locked entrance, with Karl trying to tell people to keep their voices down. Within earshot of the custodian's home, I distinctly saw a figure appear briefly at a window before disappearing from view; it was obvious that someone had looked out to see what was going on.

I had seen enough. The party was over; there was no way we could enter the abbey that night. We would have to make a return visit at some later date.

'Don't be daft. It's no problem,' John concluded with a broad grin. 'You can get over those walls, what's the matter with you?'

'Come on,' Karl said calmly. 'Let's take a walk.'

We traced the extent of the boundary wall back along the coastal road and after a distance of some 200 yards it had lowered sufficiently to be scaled without too much problem. Illegally entering property was not something I did commonly, but under such circumstances there seemed to be no other alternative. I did not think that knocking on the custodian's front door and asking for permission to enter officially would go down well at all.

'Well, it's here all right,' Debbie announced, concentrating more on what was beyond the wall.

'What is?' Lisa asked.

'Fenris,' she replied. 'I can't see anything, but I can hear it. It's like a rhythmic breathing, rising and falling.'

I assessed the situation. We now had a means of entering the abbey grounds and provided we could move swiftly and silently across to the ruins themselves, avoiding the floodlights, then we stood a good chance of succeeding in our mission. According to Debbie the Fenris-wolf was already in position (I imagined it as a huge floating wolf tied to its moorings).

What we needed now was time to talk this through, gain some 'Dutch' courage and then return a little later. I suggested a quick drink and a bite to eat in one of the pubs in the harbour.

'There are some steps by the side of the church,' Kerry confirmed, zipping up her decorated leather jacket. 'I think they lead down to the pier or something.'

I knew them from *Dracula*. They were featured within its pages and descended to Church Street – the traditional haunt of the monstrous barguest.

With her hands lost in the pockets of her overcoat, Debbie seemed pensive. I asked her to share her thoughts.

'It's Hagal. He's here somewhere,' she announced, as we moved back to the car. 'I also have the feeling that he has not yet completed the down-loading of Fenris, and that both he and members of Hexe are still in the area.' Debbie opened the passenger door and picked up her shoulder bag. 'I also feel they were here yesterday.' She looked at the cloudy sky as though Hagal's presence could be sensed in the air.

Unlocking the Peugeot, John fiddled around with walking boots and rucksacks as the rest of the party sauntered across to the edge of the churchyard. Slamming the car boot, a moment of silence followed before John swore. 'Shit. I've just locked me keys in the boot,' he exclaimed loudly. 'And I've got to get into the car to get mine and Lisa's coat, and you're gonna want torches later.'

'Oh, John, you are a prat, sometimes,' Kerry told him in all seriousness. 'Now what are you going to do?'

'No problem, is it?' he replied with a smile. 'I just need a piece of plastic cord and I'll slip it between the door frame and pull up the latch.'

Karl shook his head. 'Should be easy to find on a Saturday night. Plenty of places open.'

Someone was trying to tell us something, I was sure of it. When we returned from the harbour we were going to have to wait for John to break silently into his own car before we could even attempt to enter the abbey. And if we were not careful, any adverse noise would arouse the suspicion of those inside the custodian's home just 150 yards from the cars. I could see the chances of a result this evening fading away fast.

Bar meals in the Duke of York public house on Church Street were wholesome and the beer wet and welcome. The atmosphere was light-hearted though tense.

Debbie was going over some of the material we had covered on the journey into Yorkshire that morning. Our raised voices wafted through the bar, arousing the interest of some of the locals, who were casting disparaging looks in our direction.

Having sorted out our plan of action, I wondered whether Debbie had any last-minute thoughts about the situation inside the abbey grounds.

She shook her head. 'I just sense that Fenris is being kept in position by a fixing marker, possibly more than one,' she explained, glass in hand. 'All we can really do is place a spanner in the works, so to speak.'

Kerry and Lisa stretched across the table, listening to the conversation. Karl, sitting the other side of Debbie, nodded in agreement, while John was away trying to find something with which to open his car door.

In the Ragnarok story Fenris is bound in the underworld by six fine cords that grow tighter the more it struggles to break loose. They were fashioned and set in position by a group of dwarves, so maybe this explained her vision of the silver object she saw being thrown over the shoulder of a dwarf or midget.

'I don't know; possibly,' she acknowledged. 'I think the midgets I saw are real people associated with Hagal; they're important to him in some way.'

'What about protection?' Karl asked.

'I don't think we're going to have time,' she replied. 'It really *is* going to be like some sort of commando raid, because if Hagal and members of Hexe *are* still around, and they sense something is going on down at the abbey, they are sure to respond. We are just going to have to get the whole thing done before the warning bells start sounding.'

Lisa looked confused. 'How did Hexe get into the abbey, then?'

'I think they were there during the early hours of yesterday morning,' Debbie said, finishing her drink.

Those beating butterflies were in my stomach once more and sooner or later we were going to have to climb the seemingly never-ending steps, open John's car and then enter the abbey grounds. It looked like being a fun night ahead, I could just feel it.

John returned clutching a piece of plastic binding cord and seemed eager to leave right away.

'Right, let's kick it,' Karl urged, standing up. 'I suppose it's now or never.'

The rest of the group rose lethargically and looked towards the bar staff to say goodnight. As we did so more than one person ceased their conversation and for the last time tried to guess what the shifty-looking Londoners were really doing in Whitby that night.

39
The Form of the Wolf

The seemingly never-ending Church Steps, dating from the time of the medieval monastery, petered out at the foot of the dreary churchyard. Here the souls of old mariners bide their time, awaiting the Day of Judgement, whenever that may come.

Approaching the final stone steps, Kerry caught sight of something human-like and nimble, crossing between the shadows. 'Oh my God, what was that? I saw something among the graves,' she suddenly exclaimed.

'So did I,' Lisa confirmed. 'Like a moving shadow.'

'Yeah, that's it.' Kerry pointed. 'Over there.'

'Isn't this where Dracula claimed his first victim?' Lisa queried, recalling some mention of the fact.

A flash of silver in the churchyard interrupted Debbie's train of thought, and with this came the fleeting glimpse of something else, something out of place. 'I've just seen a trident,' was all she could say as the two sisters attempted to analyse their own brief moment of mystery. Debbie gazed towards the graveyard in the hope that it would yield up some sort of explanation. But none came. 'You saying that about Dracula's first victim seemed to trigger something in my head.'

Not only was this the fictional setting for Count Dracula's first attack on Lucy Westenra, it was by association the location of John's nocturnal encounter with a vampire back in late September.

No one understood what had actually taken place, or whether Kerry and Lisa had really witnessed a dark figure flitting among the graves, and it did not seem to matter; the three girls simply dropped the subject and headed back to the cars.

In a virtual silence unusual for our group, John and Karl

padded over to the Peugeot and played around with the door frame using the newly acquired length of plastic cord. As they did so, I took in details of the other cars parked in the muted darkness. Around one was a sensible family, fresh from their brisk walk along the cliff-top. They gave us a suspicious look before opening the car doors and climbing inside.

In another vehicle a courting couple sat motionless, unnerving me slightly, especially as John and Karl actually looked like car thieves. I then saw they had opened the driver's door as Karl punched his clenched fist in the air. 'Yes! Thirty seconds is all it took me!' he jubilantly proclaimed.

Glancing around, I noticed a smooth white car coming into view. As it slowly made its way towards our vehicles, my heart was in my mouth. *No, please, not tonight.*

The police car came to a halt and for too long its patrolmen simply sat there, following our every movement. I could not bear the suspense, and nearly hid my eyes when I saw John and Karl walking over to them. There was no way in the world that we did *not* look like we were loitering with intent.

'Calm down and just be patient,' Debbie told me. 'They'll go in a minute.'

Sighing loudly, I unlocked my own vehicle and pulled on an old coat. I realised it was getting cold up here.

The police car began to roll away as John and Karl waved it goodbye. Soon it had made a U-turn and was racing out of sight.

My hands were trembling slightly, I admitted to Kerry and Lisa who stood close by.

'No worries,' John said, ambling across. 'I told them that if they get any calls about someone breaking into a vehicle in this car-park, it was only us.'

This was like a living nightmare. Not only had we aroused the whole neighbourhood, we had now alerted the local constabulary to our suspicious actions!

'Oh, they were OK,' Karl tried to convince me. 'Look, they've gone, haven't they?'

Let's just do it now, whilst I was still in shock.

Locking the cars, the six of us walked casually down the road and followed the stone wall as it decreased in height from around eight feet to first seven, then six and then finally five feet.

Jumping up we could see into the grounds. Those churning butterflies were now conducting some kind of synchronised manoeuvre inside my stomach, so I breathed in slowly and continued the pace.

Further along the road our problems rapidly diminished when we spotted a five-bar gate set into the wall. It marked the entrance to a farm track that joined the eastern boundary of the abbey grounds. John and Karl made the climb without another word. 'Come on,' Karl urged those lagging behind, 'there's only a barbed-wire fence to get across and we're in the grounds.'

Without further delay we followed their tracks and readied ourselves for the final assault on the floodlit abbey which stood some 300 yards away. A gap between the fence and the wall was quickly located and one by one we each squeezed through. There was no turning back now.

'Keep your cover and move forward only when you've checked to see if the coast is clear,' John emphasised, his former army service coming out as it often does under such circumstances.

He and Karl led the way, advancing swiftly from shadow to shadow until they reached a low earthen mound hiding a solid brick building. Suddenly there was a frantic commotion as a large group of geese took flight, disturbed by our close proximity. Everyone hit the deck and stayed there for a tense minute before finally getting up and advancing to the edge of the abbey's soaring walls, silhouetted clearly by the bright floodlights.

A low dry-stone wall now formed our cover as we scurried through well-lit open land and came within spitting distance of the spectacular Gothic ruins.

Finally it was a dash across to the base of the abbey's enormous east wall. Gradually the group reassembled, puffing and panting but still thankfully keeping their silence.

The harsh wind had begun to bluster across the open cliff-top, breaking the earlier stillness. I then noticed a feature of the abbey grounds that greatly excited me. To our right beyond the low wall was a long pool of glistening water, a medieval fish pond perhaps. The foundations of the fair-sized wall appeared to sink below the water line, just as Debbie had described during the car journey that morning; and I had doubted her word!

'I can hear it breathing,' Debbie exclaimed in a loud whisper

'I'm not sure where it's coming from.' She listened again. 'Seems to be all around us.'

I assumed she meant the Fenris-wolf.

'Although I can't see it, I know it's sleeping.' There was another pause. 'Yes, it's asleep and will only be awoken on command. Three chains. Three markers. I get the feeling it's bound with three chains. I see a pentagram with three lines, like individual chains trailing away. One of them is over there.' She motioned beyond the huge wall. 'One over there.' She swung around and pointed to the darkened pond. 'And there's one on the far side,' she concluded, directing our eyes towards the furthest corner of the empty stone shell. 'The one by the water is the closest. Whether it's a bone, a crystal, or what, I don't know.'

So what were we to do? I looked at the pocket cassette already recording her comments.

'If we remove one it will make the whole thing unstable,' she whispered. 'If we remove any more of the markers it could mean releasing Fenris. In fact, I feel that if we visualise anything at all, it could wake up.'

The rest of the group nodded in acknowledgement of her words before waiting for the command to go for it.

'OK, come on,' I said, as we crouched down and made for the narrow, black pool. The final dash involved a scramble over the loose rocks making up the dry-stone wall before ducking down on the other side.

Still the biting wind increased its potency, having reached speeds in excess of 30-40mph (I had made a point of guessing wind speeds since the 1987 hurricane).

'I need time to listen,' Debbie said quietly, Lisa by her side. 'If it's here I'll have to hear its trace, and in water this is more difficult.'

Kerry crouched by the water's edge, while John and Karl opted to keep watch on the other side of the wall.

'I need to perambulate,' Debbie was saying, holding back her long blonde hair as she looked down into the murky waters. 'It's here somewhere. But where?'

Hearing nothing, she moved on a few feet and listened again before continuing the process and eventually moving back to a position some five to six feet from the base of the stone wall. 'Lisa, look down there in the mud. Feel around with your hands.'

She did so without further question.

'Look down there, Andrew. See if it's there.' I crouched low and plunged my hand into the cold water. Carefully, I sifted through the silty mud and decaying matter resting on the bottom. A few stones were pulled up and looked at before being cast to one side.

Lisa continued her search with Kerry by her side.

'There are three markers – one silver, one copper and one of another substance which I'm not sure about,' Debbie informed us, reaching down with her fingers. 'I don't know which is which yet.'

All four of us continued the search.

Suddenly the wind took a new turn, roaring violently across the water surface towards our position. The gusts were definitely increasing in strength and duration.

'I hear it. Somebody's touched it – Lisa, I think. Shhh, listen.' Debbie whispered, placing her hand to her ear and remaining still. 'It's like a whistling sound; like a tuning fork.' She listened again. 'A very high-pitched tonal sound.' She immersed her hand in the soft mud, close to where Lisa was still probing below the shallow waterline. 'We've definitely touched it, we're close,' she exclaimed in a low, excited voice. 'It's getting louder. Dig deeper.'

'Get down,' John and Karl whispered loudly. 'There's a car over by the gate; the one we came through.'

All movement and noise ceased for a few tense moments. Near gale-force gusts bellowed incessantly, sending an unnerving chill down my spine. Something was happening here; the atmosphere was changing rapidly.

Debbie frantically resumed the search, sinking her hand downwards as the wolfish winds climbed to an ululating crescendo. Her fingers sought and explored, finding the touch of cold metal at last. 'I think I've got something,' she revealed clutching the object fully before withdrawing it. All at once her hand rose out of the gloomy water holding something long and slim, from which dripped mud and slime. Instantly she began to hyperventilate. 'My God, it's like ice. I can't move.'

Still in a kneeling position, Debbie held out the offending item as though gripping an electric fence coated with liquid nitrogen

She seemed unable to move a limb, as if whatever it was she held was freezing her arm solid.

As the hyperventilating grew more erratic she could no longer hear our words. Kerry and Lisa reached out and cupped Debbie's extended hand, one each side of her, not quite knowing what to do next.

'*Illiath. Disbat. Brecon. Argot. Colway. Leth. Hel. Ardwillian col* . . .' were strange, unknown words Debbie began reciting almost somnambulistically as she gradually lost consciousness.

Debbie no longer cared what was happening; there was no sense of direction any more, just the excruciating pain of the fierce frostbite now searing through her whole arm.

In its place came only icy-cold wastes of unabating hailstorms cast in a perpetual darkness. No people, no abbey and no civilisation, just the growing realisation of a gargantuan presence of seething malevolence towering above her, a huge bestial shadow of no recognisable form. Slow, rhythmic exhalations of its red-hot breath, like the blistering rays of a thousand swallowed suns, caused acute burning sensations on her head and shoulders, raising the physical torment to an overwhelming level.

And this was all she experienced in this protoplasmic domain – two contrasting realms vying for superiority inside her senses, both in a state of constant flux and mutability; intense heat and freezing cold, fire and ice together as one chaotic force coexisting beyond the furthest reaches of time and space.

This was the form of the wolf.

'Debbie. Debbie, are you OK?' Kerry and Lisa were asking her, their voices rising in pitch.

Still the psychic clutched the unidentified artefact, which appeared to be around seven inches in length and made of silver.

'I'll never get it out of my hands. I'll never get it out,' Debbie uttered at long last, although still seemingly oblivious to the alarmed words of her friends. 'It's stuck to my hand. Three lines – *Brecon, Illiath, Hagal*. Oh my God. Don't remove it from me. It'll tear my hand off.' She looked up now.

'The car's gone,' Karl responded, hearing her words. 'Some

people got out, but I don't know what they were doing. It headed off towards the car-park.'

'We can go,' Debbie said next. 'But don't remove it from my hand.'

So we departed, climbing back over the wall, with Kerry and Lisa still cupping Debbie's hand, as though it was completely frozen in ice. Together they walked through the grounds until the strange party finally reached and tackled the barbed-wire fence, John and Karl having gone on ahead. I crawled through with the pocket cassette still recording, the fierce winds having noticeably subsided. Out on the road, I felt elated, though concerned for Debbie's safety. She seemed to be completely out of it.

It looked very strange – Kerry and Lisa aiding Debbie along the road with the silver object still wedged in her closed hand. Silly perhaps, but the close contact restored her physical strength and helped sustain the sudden energy loss that always accompanies the paranormal discovery of a concealed artefact.

Eventually the cars were reached and, with only Lisa still holding Debbie, the two entered the Orion.

Doors slammed shut and moments later the two vehicles left the car-park and found the coastal road that would take us away from this place of hidden hell.

Reaching Whitby harbour, alive with crowds of youths sounding off on their way to and from local pubs, we followed the road looking for parking spaces. Two came into view outside a funeral director's and rolling the vehicles to a halt, the anxious party reconvened on the pavement just as a crowd of skinheads marched past, jeering at a rival gang on the opposite side of the road.

The whole setting was surreal, but there was no time to absorb local customs. Quickly, I dug into my portable questing kit and pulled out a bottle of spring water, gained from an ancient well at Knaresborough earlier that day.

Lisa held Debbie's wrist as I poured the vibrant water over her clenched fist, while the group visualised thick ice gradually melting into water.

Very steadily she began to loosen her grip on the silver object before letting it go completely. It tumbled out of her hand and into Lisa's waiting palm, thereby allowing its identification at last. It was a finely worked, antique pickle fork, its three prongs fashioned to resemble a devil's trident and its surface literally covered in occult symbols, painstakingly pecked into the silver plate on both sides.

Clearly visible in the torchlight provided by John was a pentagram from which emanated three lines, the symbol of the three chains mentioned earlier by Debbie. I could see the two Hexe signatures found on the Walking Bone – a hexagon inside a pentagon and the sinister spider design. There was also a crescent moon with five bars radiating out of its convex edge and the rest of the symbols were clearly Germanic or Norse runes.

Debbie rubbed her hand. 'Bliss. It's like I've had no feeling at all in one hand; like I grabbed hold of a live wire. It felt as if I was freezing cold and burning hot, both at the same time.'

We took it in turns to examine the water-soaked Trident Fork as customised cars and wild youths paraded past, oblivious to our own absurd predicament, here tonight in Whitby harbour.

'It's covered in runes,' John confirmed, studying the fork closely. 'Someone's had a good ol' go at this, haven't they? It must have taken them hours to do all this lot.' He turned it over again.

Debbie looked on cautiously. 'That's one of them,' she nodded. 'There are two more like it at the abbey – one made of copper. They were put in position yesterday. Fenris is still there, chained by three, sorry, two markers, now.'

Lisa looked thoughtful. 'So if we removed all three, we'd be . . .'

' . . . in serious trouble,' Debbie cut in. 'And I'm not going back there. Not tonight; no way. We've done enough. By removing just one of the three we will have destabilised the whole Fenris thought form, and provided that Hexe can't replace it immediately, then this'll be a serious set-back to their overall plans.'

'So have we got to go back, or is that it?' Karl asked, still reeling from the events of the evening.

Debbie looked up. 'It's like removing a cork from a bottle of champagne, it will now go flat. It's all we could do. Anyway, I just think we should go home, there's nothing more we can do here tonight.'

'Yeah, let's move it,' John agreed, realising there was an outside chance of getting back to Essex at a sensible hour.

Returning to the cars, we promptly rejoined the one-way system and left behind the hustle and bustle of modern-day Whitby, with its noisy pubs and boisterous youth culture. I was glad to get away, for the lucid image I had gradually formed of this Victorian seaside town from its graphic portrayal in Bram Stoker's novel, no longer existed. Like an illusion, it had been shattered and replaced by the vivid memory of our own nocturnal assault on Whitby Abbey.

40
The Lantern's Force

Tuesday, 19 November 1991. There was a noticeable rise in clientele in The Griffin tonight, due in part to the threatened pop quiz, which was scheduled to kick off around nine o'clock. Hopefully, much of what I had to tell Bernard would be over by that time, although there was a lot to get through in just one and a half hours.

'Where's Debs tonight?' he asked, strolling across to the window table and taking a seat.

She could not join us as she had been unwell of late, so she sent her regards instead.

'I'm sorry to hear that,' he responded. 'Effects of recent events?'

I nodded, quickly turning the subject of discussion to the discovery of the Trident Fork in Whitby just over two weeks before. Bernard listened carefully and waited until I pulled out and placed the Trident Fork on the table.

I pointed out that the maker's name – R. A. Jones & Sons, a fashionable London manufacturer of silverware during the first half of the century – had been purposely erased from the rear surface of the handle to ensure its presence would not interfere with its runic influences. Inscribed from edge to edge across this maker's mark was a zigzag pattern similar to that noted on the Stonehenge Walking Bone. This, Debbie believed, represented a sharp, constant snapping of the artefact to allow a controlled release of its accumulated magical energies.

I drew his attention to more of the symbols, such as the lunar crescent, with five strokes radiating out of its convex edge. This appeared to signify a date five days *after* a new moon. Since the nearest new moon had not been until Wednesday, 6 November, this gave us a date of Monday, 11 November, which made no obvious sense at all.[1] Only by suggesting that the five strokes symbolised five days *before* the new moon could we reach Friday, 1 November – the day Debbie believed the markers had been placed in position.

As to the series of runes pecked into its surface, there were twelve, possibly thirteen, in all. Neither Debbie nor I had studied runic magic and no books on runes were to be found in my extensive library. I had therefore asked three people who did have an in-depth knowledge of runic magic to study sketches of the Trident Fork and let me know the results. Each one had concluded that whoever had inscribed these sigils of power possessed an accomplished understanding of Germanic runelore.[2]

I also learnt that one of the runes inscribed on the fork is known as *hagalaz*, meaning 'hail' or 'hailstone'. Sometimes this is shortened to *hagall*, the magical name of the Romanian runemaster who had apparently transferred the Fenris-wolf to Britain. Edred Thorsson, in his excellent book *Runelore*, says that *hagalaz*, the H-rune, 'contains the complete model of absolute potential energy, as it holds the full dynamism of fire and ice in its form'.[3] Reading these words made me recall Debbie's intense sensations of fire and ice upon first touching the Trident Fork.

In the days that followed our return from Whitby, Debbie had complained of severe pains in the hand and wrist she had used to clench the Trident Fork. Since then she had deteriorated in health and was still unwell, hence her non-appearance that evening, and there had been further disconcerting dreams as well.

Without another word, Bernard picked up the Trident Fork and held it tightly for a few brief seconds before rolling it on to the table and touching it briefly, like a cat might play with a dead mouse. He then withdrew his hand and shook it lightly. 'Do you want to know what I get from this?'

Naturally I did, so readied the pocket cassette in anticipation of his words. Would they confirm Debbie's evaluation of what we knew so far? On psychometrising the quartz crystal found at Bygone church in March 1990, he had placed it down after just

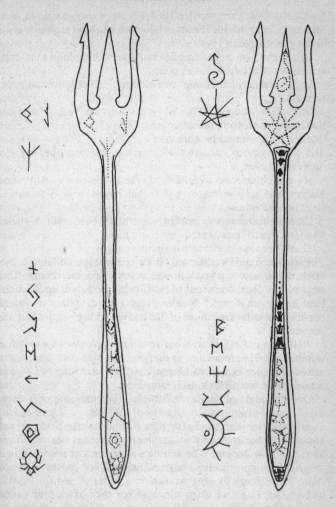

Author's sketch of the Trident Fork inscribed with Germanic runes discovered in the grounds of Whitby Abbey on 2 November 1991. The magical signatures showed it to be the work of the People of Hexe.

few seconds with the words: 'Well, I'll leave that to spin its own little web,' and this had been without him knowing anything at all about the People of Hexe.

'A red eye,' he began cryptically. 'Twelve people in long dark trench-coats, all dressed the same.'

Long coats probably implied coldness – a cold environment, perhaps.

'Right,' he nodded. 'They're on a trackway, with a bracken-like moorland setting on either side.'

Such as that found in Yorkshire?

'I think so, yes, and this dirt track leads to a building – a dilapidated barn.'

My mouth opened wide. Oh my God, this was exactly what Debbie had been seeing ever since our return from Whitby. Go on, I urged him.

Leaning towards the pocket cassette he said with a smile: 'Andrew's getting excited!'

That's because Bernard was right!

'Part of the roof's collapsed. It's a beamy-type building in old brick. I can now see you running in front of some others. You stop, turn around and shout to those behind: "Hurry up, because I've got to get it out." You're in an excited state and you're heading towards this building.' He paused. 'That's it, I don't see any more.'

Well, I could relate to what he'd just said almost exactly. I watched the DJ enter the bar carrying the twin-deck and heavy boxes of golden oldies, so I knew I did not have long before our conversation would be killed stone dead.

Over the night of Sunday to Monday, 3/4 November – twenty-four hours after our return from Whitby – Debbie had experienced an extraordinary dream. She unexpectedly found herself in a harsh, windy environment with sleet beating down hard upon the ground. The setting was an ancient trackway in a rough, desolate moorland region. Beyond her on the unmade road was a gaunt-looking woman in a tattered and torn dirty-white robe. Her feet were bare and her long, dark hair flailed about in the gusting winds. Her hands were clutching her body as if she was desperately trying to keep warm amid the terrible blizzard raging around her.

In spite of never having seen her in this form before, Debbie recognised this woman as Elen, an Iron Age goddess of Europe. In Welsh bardic tradition she was Elen of the Hosts, who presided over the prehistoric trackways spanning the entire length and breadth of Britain, and whose name is preserved today in the Sarn Elen roads of Wales.

Debbie approached Elen, who appeared sad for some reason. In response the goddess simply turned around and pointed up the track, saying: 'Along the Pennine Way'. Her mind's eye was then thrust forward to view a ruined stone building without a roof. It looked like a farm building, a barn, but Debbie gained the distinct impression that it was a sanctified site connected with St Helen, Elen's Christian counterpart.

This was all she could recall, although the same dream occurred twice more that same night, emphasising its apparent importance.

Upon waking, she was left with the overriding impression that it was here that the People of Hexe were incubating the force of Hel, the Norse goddess of the underworld, in connection with certain concealed fixing markers. For the moment, however, the influence of Hel lay dormant.

The Pennine Way is Britain's longest ancient trackway and runs roughly north-south through Derbyshire, Lancashire, and Cumbria before entering the Scottish border region. It is a remote and often bleak terrain that frequently cuts across open moorland and steep hills, much of which is known to be associated with folklore, legends and strange phenomena.

'Did anyone say anything about a lantern or a light?' Bernard asked, completely out of the blue. 'Or do you envisage seeing a light or lantern? A ball that could be construed as a lantern; a will-o'-the-wispy thing?'

I realised immediately what he was talking about. The Pennines were renowned for their strange light phenomena as can be seen from Jenny Randles's book *The Pennines UFO Mystery*. Often these small, ground-level lights were seen in terms of lanterns in the hands of supernatural denizens.

Paul Devereux's excellent book *Earth Lights Revelation* speaks of a moving light seen in the vicinity of Glossop, a village in the south Pennines. It is known locally as Peggy o' th' Lantern – an appellation remembered in the place-name Lantern's Pike, a nearby beacon hill. At its base is a pub called The Lantern which bears a signboard depicting an elemental holding up a bright lantern. Whether this figure of folklore is associated with the Yorkshire end of the Pennines, I could not say. In spite of this, a lantern connection with the earth lights peculiar to the Pennines was undeniable.

'What d'you make of this, then?' he said next, removing a small slip of paper from his jacket pocket. Passing it across the table, I read, then re-read, its message as my heart began thumping:

Message 6.40. Male/No name.
'Tell Deborah to beware of the Lantern's force at The Griffin tonight.'
Reply: 'I'm not sure what you mean.'
Answer: 'Just tell her.'
Phone put down.

Someone had made this telephone call *to him* earlier that evening?

'Yes. I just picked up the phone and the voice said, "Is that Bernard?" I thought it was someone I knew, so I said "yes". The rest of what they said you've got there.'

The immediate point of interest was the caller's use of the name Deborah. No one knew her by her full Christian name, only those who had read my book *The Seventh Sword*. Furthermore, the caller knew that Bernard and I, and in their mind Debbie as well, would be at The Griffin *tonight*.

'So who was it, then?' he asked again, the matter having concerned him slightly.

The easiest answer was to suggest it was someone who had followed our plight through the last two books and knew from the final chapter of *The Seventh Sword* that the three of us met in The Griffin on an irregular basis. Yet how did they obtain Bernard's ex-directory telephone number? No one knew this number, not even my closest friends. Furthermore, how did they know that Debbie was working on fresh psychic material that would make sense of their warning concerning 'the Lantern's force'? We had told no one about the Pennines connection as yet, so how had they known?

Perhaps the caller was a psychic who had picked up on Hexe material in some symbolic capacity and saw the corrupted influence of Elen in terms of 'the Lantern's force'. Feeling this could be of some relevance to Debbie, he rang the message through to Bernard. Any other explanations were just too bizarre to even think about, so we would not even try.

What sort of voice did this man have?

'Gruffish,' he replied, sitting back. 'Not smooth, but sort of abrupt, and quite deep; a bit broken, really.'

This made no sense. We had no hope at all of identifying this anonymous caller, so it was best to heed his warning, then quietly forget the matter.

I recognised the DJ as the bloke who beat me into second place during the finals of a pop quiz in Wickford some years before. Perhaps I could get my own back tonight. He was now limbering up for his own quiz by spinning a few less-than-memorable pop tunes of the past three decades.

Leaving the twin-deck, he moved around the room scattering typed questionnaires on each table. I picked one up and saw that each entrant had to use a 'team name'. So what was our team name going to be?

'The Knights of Danbury?' Bernard suggested.

No, I had an idea . . .

Looking up, I noticed that the small bar had swelled to capacity in readiness for this hour or so of light entertainment.

Allowing the conversation to drop, Bernard bought a round of drinks and cautiously eyed the twin-deck as he sat back down.

'*Right, here is your first question*,' the scraggly-haired DJ began as the sound of Status Quo's all-too-familiar guitar riff begun chugging out the fifties' classic 'The Wanderer'. '*OK, I want to know who had the original hit with this record?*'

'Dion, wasn't it?' Bernard responded, twisting his head round to see the source of this mild amusement. 'It's easy, isn't it?'

I asked him what he thought about the discovery of the Trident Fork and our assessment of the Whitby situation.

'I think you've got to be careful,' he suggested, lighting a cigarette. 'You're not just dealing with lone figures here, are you? These people, rightly or wrongly, have been planning all this for years and they're not going to simply sit back and allow you to mess it all up, are they?'

Probably not.

'I mean, it's all right you crashing about the countryside pulling up objects, but sooner or later these people are going to feel you've become more than just a minor irritation. Aren't they?'

Yes, but were the People of Hexe already aware of our activities?

He simply grinned. 'Well of course they are, you published details of their activities in *The Seventh Sword*. Groups such as the People of Hexe are certainly going to know of your interest in their activities.'

'*And now for a little change in mood,*' the voice exclaimed over the PA. '*Which beat group put this record into the charts during 1967? When you think you know the answer, write it down.*'

I recognised the tune. It was a record by The Herd entitled 'From the Underworld'.

Bernard sipped spring water. 'I think what you've done at Whitby is to cause a delay in someone else's plans, and in doing so you've gained a little extra time.'

So how was the Black Alchemist linked in with this story? I gulped down beer and watched as the groups of youths on other tables scratched their heads and contemplated the last pop question.

'It's all connected, isn't it? It's like a fast-moving river current. Once you jump in, you're swept along with the tide like everyone else. It's inevitable that there's always going to be a crossover of people, places and ultimate goals. It's like what happened up here a few years ago.' He nodded in the direction of the church beyond the green. 'You know, after the 1987 hurricane; it's all part and parcel of the same thing. I told you at the time there were a lot of wolves about. Then again when you went down to that mound in Eastbourne. When was it?'

August 1988. Yes, but how did this relate to the release of Fenris in Hexe's own variation of the Ragnarok saga?

'Only indirectly, really, through the intentions of this Wheel-based organisation on the Continent; the one with the big bank account in Luxembourg,' he answered humorously. 'They will all have directives and when these are added together it will begin to form an overall picture. It's got to be that way, hasn't it? Otherwise it would be too easy.'

What about the Black Alchemist's apparent discovery of artefacts in the Dead Sea region and in Lima, Peru? What was all that about?

'Don't know,' he admitted. 'Didn't get any more on that, did we?' He thought about the question before going further. 'More artefacts will be found.'

How many? And why?

He shrugged his shoulders. 'I don't know. Anyway, changing the subject for a moment, have you heard from Helen?'

Not at all. All I knew was that she had completely turned her back on the psychic scene in favour of reviving her ladies' afternoon group – fortune telling being considered a slightly less harrowing alternative to investigating the Dark Council.

More pop questions came and went as the slow, disjointed conversation stopped and started in between chit-chat on originals, cover versions, years of release and lead singers. The completed form looked good. With our combined efforts we stood a good chance of winning, provided everyone else had experienced temporary brain seizures.

OK, so one last question before I closed the book. Where did he feel it would go from here?

'Home, I should think. It's past ten o'clock.'

He could not leave before they had announced the winner!

Bernard shifted in his seat and tried to avert his eyes from the barmaid clearing away the used glasses from the busy table. He turned back to me and looked serious for a moment. 'I feel it will not be until the Seven Swords are finally brought together next August that you'll really start to understand how to combat those who intend to control the British energy matrix,' he cryptically revealed. 'Then the fun will really begin. Anyway, I'm going, now.'

I made him wait until the DJ had marked the papers and added up the final scores. After announcing the runners up, he looked at the winning sheet. '*And in first place, with nineteen out of twenty, give a big hand for . . .*' he looked down and absorbed the team name. '*A big hand, please, for THE BLACK ALCHEMIST.*'

A loud cheer went up as I left the chair and headed towards the twin-deck. Having taken possession of the cheap bottle of white wine, I settled back down for a brief minute before we gathered together our belongings and headed towards the exit. With no more than a cursory wave to the landlord and his wife we stepped out into the cold night air.

Epilogue

Saturday, 17 April 1993. The very first thing people will ask after reading *The Second Coming* is whether or not the story is true. Well, the plain and simple answer is yes, the book is an accurate portrayal of the events it describes. Everything has been written as it occurred from my own perspective as Andrew Collins, author and psychical researcher.

Whether the contents of the many dream sequences presented in this book are accurate reflections of the real world is a lot more difficult to determine. Bernard's dream of the Black Alchemist in Peru is truly amazing, and if I did not have faith in his ability as a psychic then I would not have included it in this work. At the end of the day only the Black Alchemist himself will be able to tell us whether this dream was accurate or not. So all I can do is reproduce it in good faith and leave any interpretation until such times as further information becomes available.

One comment frequently made to me by readers of my previous work *The Black Alchemist* is something along the lines of: 'Loved the book. Shame about the ending.' This is usually in reference to the fact that by the end of the book the Black Alchemist has not been caught, unmasked and led away by the police following an awesome supernatural battle worthy of a good Dennis Wheatley novel. I could write such an ending if you like, but then the book would become a work of fiction and not fact. Unfortunately truth does not always grant us convenient endings ideal for use by non fiction authors such as myself.

The final chapters of this present work were decided because they climaxed suitably as a sequence of events involving the People of Hexe. The Whitby episode acted as a cut-off point in the narrative and allowed me to sum up the proceedings during the get-together with Bernard at The Griffin on Tuesday, 19 November 1991 (by the way, the unexpected pop quiz did seriously curtail our conversation that night!)

I could have gone on to detail many more visions, dreams and episodes featuring the People of Hexe. However, space does not permit this, especially as I had to drop at least ten additional chapters from the book for this very reason. What follows is just a sample of the obscure events that have taken place since November 1991. During the summer of 1992 John Horrigan traced and spoke to an Irish tramp in Kent who had been clairvoyantly seen by Debbie and is believed to have become involved with a Hexe ritual in the churchyard where he sleeps. On Dartmoor in Devon at Hallowe'en 1992 our group were led to recover two inscribed artefacts from a remote double circle of stones where, later that same night, John Horrigan and Karl Dawkins watched just yards away as three members of the Hexe group turned up in the darkness. There have also been further problems at Yorkshire abbeys, and Hagal, the Romanian wolf shaman, turned up again at Whitby to complete his work. In addition to these episodes, there has been Hexe activity at ritual sites in Sweden, on the Isle of Anglesey, in west Wales and in the Scottish northern isles.

In contrast, Bernard has received no further inspiration at all about either the Black Alchemist or Rachel Goodison since their final appearances in this book. Of course, I get literally dozens of letters from people who believe they know something about the Black Alchemist or the Friends of Hekate, and they might be right, I don't know. However, the only real interest I have in any of these groups or individuals is through the words of psychics such as Bernard and Debbie, who have consistently produced accurate and verifiable information on this subject for some years now. Bernard will not attune to the activities of the Black Alchemist, as he hopes that for him the show is over. Yet somewhere at the back of his mind he knows it will never be over.

So the story goes on. I write books such as this not because of the supernatural drama, but because I genuinely believe that others should have an understanding of these psychics; the way they work, the type of material they produce and where it all leads. At the end of the day, when you stand there with a newly retrieved artefact in your hand, it tells you good and proper that something has happened; it is not simply the delusions of a few gullible people with over-active imaginations. Something is really happening out there and I felt you should know about it – this is why I wrote *The Second Coming*.

Those wishing to be kept up to date on new publications, forthcoming events and future projects concerning the subject of psychic questing can write to me, Andrew Collins, at SKS, St Aldhelm, 20 Paul Street, Frome, Somerset BA11 1DX.

Appendix I – The Cult of St Catherine

Following her first visit to St Catherine's Hill, Winchester, on Sunday, 12 March 1989, Helen made contact with the spirit of a monk named 'Markus de Capelin'. During this psychic communication he said he 'walks the paths every day, but not those used by the Dark Council'. When asked who he meant by 'the Dark Council', Helen referred to the sixteen figures thought to have conducted the ritual libation at St Catherine's Hill several weeks beforehand. Based on this assumption I have used this title when referring to the activities of this particular collective – who almost certainly include former members of the Friends of Hekate. However, during the writing of this book Debbie Benstead and I re-examined Markus de Capelin's words and now feel we can shed new light on this curious title.

I was never able to confirm the existence of a medieval chaplain named Markus de Capelin officiating at St Catherine's Chapel, Winchester. In spite of this I see no reason to doubt his existence as a composite site guardian, created through Christian reverence when the chapel was still attached to the see of Winchester and the cathedral monastery of St Swithun.

Markus himself claimed he was connected with a religious house in Winchester. If this can be accepted then, as a primary intelligence of essentially medieval composition, Markus would only be able to store and communicate information using terms familiar to the time of his creation. So if people were interfering with St Catherine's Hill in 1989, he would only be able to explain what was going on in terms already programmed into his vocabulary by past human interaction. Was it possible therefore that when Markus referred to the modern-day intruders as the 'Dark Council', he was in fact using a term previously applied to a group of this name who existed during medieval times?

APPENDIX I – THE CULT OF ST CATHERINE

The chapel on St Catherine's Hill, Winchester, was constructed during the mid-twelfth century under the patronage of Henry de Blois, the bishop of Winchester, when, according to one historical source, the 'cult of St Catherine' was at its height.

In Chapter 16 of this book artist Chesca Potter produces some remarkable psychic material linking the cult of St Catherine with the mystical power of the full moon eclipse, the so-called 'Midnight Sun' or 'Sun of St Catherine'. This information proved to be important to our understanding of the ill-fated events surrounding St Catherine's Hill, Winchester, in August 1989. Was it possible, therefore, that we inadvertently chanced upon information concerning the pursuits of an influential body of medieval high churchmen known as the 'Dark Council' who practised a form of heretical Gnosticism in Winchester during medieval times? If so, did their devotions include the mysteries of St Catherine?

As a saint, Catherine of Alexandria was adopted by medieval Crusaders following the success of the First Crusade in AD 1099. There had been, however, in existence since *c.* 1063, a military order named the Knights of St Catherine at Mount Sinai. According to my colleague Bernard, they were said to have lived under the rule of St Basil and used a badge of office consisting of a wheel of six spokes, over which was a sword, positioned upright.

St Catherine's first recorded reference in England is in connection with a miracle play celebrating her life, performed during the year 1100 at Dunstable in Bedfordshire.[1] She subsequently became a patron saint of the Knights Templar as suggested by the prominent bas-relief depicting St Catherine with her spiked wheel cut into the wall of the Royston beehive cave in Hertfordshire, *c.* 1150-1308.

Ean Begg in his book *The Cult of the Black Virgin* links St Catherine of Alexandria with Gnostic beliefs in a female 'wisdom' or *sophia*, an outlawed Christian devotion forced underground during the fourth century AD, only to re-emerge at the time of the Crusades. The name Catherine he said, derives from the Greek root *cathar-*, meaning 'pure', suggesting that her Gnostic devotion may well have re-surfaced in the twelfth-century Albigensian or Cathar worship of southern

France. He also associates St Catherine with the cult of the Black Virgin, with whom she was often linked, as well as with other dusky Christian divinities such as the 'Queen of the South', a form of the Queen of Sheba.[2]

The popularity of St Catherine grew extensively after Queen Matilda, the wife of King Stephen, founded the first chapel dedicated to her memory on the banks of the River Thames, close to the Tower of London, in 1148. Chapels and churches dedicated to St Catherine began appearing all over England, and it was for this reason, along with the archaeological evidence unearthed between 1925 and 1928, that the chapel on St Catherine's Hill, Winchester, was given a foundation date of *c.* 1140-50. These dates make perfect sense as its founder, the former Cluniac monk Henry de Blois, was the brother of and advisor to Stephen of Blois, who had seized the throne and proclaimed himself king in 1135.

Furthermore, from 1126 till his death in 1171, Henry de Blois was abbot of Glastonbury in Somerset, a monastic settlement which has been frequently linked with unorthodox religious practices of a Christian Gnostic nature. A fourteenth-century seal from Glastonbury Abbey shows the Virgin Mary – the abbey's principal dedication – flanked by St Catherine of Alexandria and St Margaret of Antioch (the reverse shows three male saints connected with Glastonbury tradition). There is no mention of St Catherine's association with the abbey anywhere else. So why was she given such a prominence on an official seal? Could Henry de Blois have introduced St Catherine to Glastonbury Abbey during his incumbency? If so, then did he also inspire his sister-in-law, Queen Matilda, to found the first chapel dedicated to St Catherine in 1148? More intriguing still, did he found the chapel on St Catherine's Hill, Winchester, *before* or *after* the foundation of the London chapel? And does any of this have any connection with Markus de Capelin's 'Dark Council'?

Henry de Blois was an influential churchman, highly regarded for the many religious buildings and monastic houses commissioned at his expense, but there are clear indications that he over-stepped the limits of his monastic vows when it came to personal indulgences. In his 1988 book *Glastonbury Abbey*,

APPENDIX I – THE CULT OF ST CATHERINE

James P. Carley referred to the reactions of leading contemporaries to Henry's notorious antics by admitting that: 'His love of fine things . . . extended well beyond any limit tolerable in a man vowed to monastic poverty and the ascetic St Bernard of Clairvaux contemptuously labelled him variously a rival pope, the old wizard of Winchester, and the whore of Winchester . . . Indeed, the contemporary chronicler, Henry of Huntingdon, referred to him with contempt as "a new kind of monster, a monk-soldier"'.[3]

I have no idea whether Henry de Blois possessed any obvious Gnostic leanings, although he was certainly familiar with the written works of Early Church Gnostics such as Origen – which he is recorded as denoting to the library at Glastonbury Abbey during his incumbency. It is also interesting to note that when the coffin of Henry's predecessor at Glastonbury Abbey, Abbot Seffrid Pelochin, was opened in Chichester many centuries after his death, his skeletal hand still bore an episcopal ring made of jasper bearing an image of the Gnostic serpent god Abraxas. This discovery led James P. Carley to hint at Gnostic tendencies among the abbots at Glastonbury,[4] but whether this religious undercurrent stretched to Henry de Blois we shall never know.

I do feel that Henry de Blois would have played some role in our hypothetical Dark Council, whatever its nature. I am also quite sure that he was responsible for the spread of interest in the mysteries of St Catherine during the second half of the twelfth century. What's more, I believe there is a good chance that, in addition to the chapel upon St Catherine's Hill, Winchester, Henry de Blois could well have been responsible for the construction of the original turf-cut Miz-maze.[5] Further research into these matters would, I'm sure, throw much light on the medieval development of the cult of St Catherine.

Notes and References

The full bibliographical details, when not cited here, are to be found in the Bibliography.

The Proclamation
1   Horapollinis, *Hieroglyphica*, B.i.15: 'For at the exact instant of the conjunction of the moon with the sun, when the moon becomes unillumined, then the male Cynocephalus neither sees, nor eats, but is bowed down to the ground with grief, as if lamenting the ravishment of the moon. The female [baboon] also, in addition to its being unable to see, and being afflicted in the same manner as the male, emits blood from the genitals; hence, even to this day Cynocephali are brought up in the temples, in order that from them may be ascertained the exact instant of the conjunction of the sun and the moon.'

Chapter 2 – The Foul Pit
1   Ronan, S., ed., *The Goddess Hekate*, 'Chaldean Hekate', p. 102, fr. xlix. I had no real knowledge of the *Chaldean Oracles* until reading Stephen Ronan's excellent book on Hekate in early 1993. It was felt, however, that this material was so pertinent to the story-line that it should be included in the main body of the text. A full study of the *Chaldean Oracles* may provide important clues as to the Greco-Roman magic employed by the Black Alchemist.
2   Ibid., p. 102, fr. l.
3   Ibid., p. 98, fr. xxxv.
4   Toyne Newton informs me that the plague pit in Clapham Woods was filled in and levelled in the wake of the extensive damage caused during the 1987 hurricane. Exactly when this

incident took place is not recorded, although it is thought to have occurred sometime around 1989.
5   Newton, T., *The Demonic Connection*, p. 39.

Chapter 5 – Forbidden Fruit
1   Garinet, J., *Histoire de la Magie en France*, Foulon & Cie, Paris, 1818. See also Davidson, G., *A Dictionary of Angels Including the Fallen Angels*, p. 82.
2   Woods, W., *A History of the Devil*, pp. 206-7.
3   The complete sequence of events revolving around this period, including the apparent significance of Hurricane Gilbert to the native Mexicans of the Yucatan peninsula, was told on *The Black Alchemist Tape* released in 1988.

Chapter 6 – The Hosts of Hekate
1   Ronan, S., ed., *The Goddess Hekate*, p. 106.
2   Lowe, J.E., 'Magical Hekate', in *The Goddess Hekate*, ed., S. Ronan, p. 15.
3   Luck, G., *Arcana Mundi*, pp. 169-70.
4   Rohde, E., 'Hekate's Horde', Section I, in *The Goddess Hekate*, ed., S. Ronan, pp. 65-8.
5   The Greco-Roman invocation to Hekate was taken from Francis King's *Sexuality, Magic and Perversion* and reads:

> Come Infernal ... Bombo, Goddess of the broad roadways, of the cross road, thou who goest to and fro at night, torch in hand, enemy of the day, friend and lover of darkness, thou who dost rejoice when the bitches are howling and warm blood is spilled, thou who art walking amid the phantom and in the place of tombs, thou whose thirst is blood, thou who dost strike chill fear into mortal heart, Gorgo, Mormo, Moon, [other names for Hecate] of a thousand forms, cast a propitious eye upon our sacrifice.

Compare the two incantations to observe the subtle differences. Francis King saw Gorgo and Mormo as simply names of Hekate, although this is not supported by the words of Professor Luck or by Fiona's psychic information.

Chapter 9 – The Wheel of Destruction

1 The psychic session with Helen on Sunday, 26 February 1989 included material on such matters as Robert Devereux, the sixteenth-century Earl of Essex, as well as references to unfinished business for me in Derbyshire. Space does not permit its inclusion in this book.

Furthermore, I would like to make it clear that Helen came out with a considerable amount of material on various different topics during 1989 and subsequently upon her return to the fold in 1990. However, as none of it is directly relevant to this book, it cannot be included, giving a slightly one-sided perspective of her psychic abilities.

2 The name 'Kathlin St' and 'St Cathirin' was first mentioned by Helen in a letter to me dated Sunday, 5 March 1989. In it she describes clairvoyantly glimpsing the hill at Winchester and obtaining the aforementioned names. She also describes seeing a turf-cut maze below her and approaching from the north, i.e. from the direction of the city. Due to space it has been necessary to include these details at an earlier point in the text. During the psychic session on Sunday, 26 February 1989 she did, however, say that the name of the hill in Winchester began with the letter 'C'.

3 Brian Vesey-Fitzgerald in his 1953 book *Winchester* suggested that the two hills in Hampshire bearing St Catherine place-names – i.e. St Catherine's Hill, Winchester, and St Catherine's Hill, Christchurch – as well as St Catherine's Down, near Chale in the Isle of Wight, gained their appellations not from a Christian saint, but from their former Celtic name of 'Kader Ryn', the fort of the river. Although he accepted that each possessed its own chapel, he said there was evidence for only one of these – St Catherine's Down, Isle of Wight – actually being dedicated to St Catherine. In Winchester's case, he argued that the chapel was already present on the hill in Saxon times, so could not have been dedicated to a saint who only gained popularity during the mid-twelfth century.

In answer to these claims, I have this to say. First, there is no written evidence for any of these hills ever being named Kader Ryn. So his argument bears no consequence at all for the Christian dedications borne by these three chapels.

Second, there is no convincing evidence of a Saxon chapel on St Catherine's Hill, Winchester. Excavations between 1925 and 1928 could not confirm a Saxon foundation to 'the early chapel at the east end of the main building' and there is certainly no mention of any pre-Conquest chapel in the Doomsday Book.

Third, there is ample written evidence for the dedication of the chapel on St Catherine's Hill, Winchester. From its first surviving mention in the Calendar of Charter Rolls, 1257-1300, vol. II, p. 273, till the end of the thirteenth century, St Catherine's Chapel gets three, possibly four, separate references in extant records (See C.F.C. Hawkes, etc., *St Catherine's Hill, Winchester*, Warren & Son, Winchester, 1930, pp. 193-4). Furthermore, St Catherine's Hill, Winchester, is recorded as 'Monte Sancte Katerine' as early as 1208. I fail to see how the hill's name could have been changed from Kader Ryn to St Catherine's Hill just sixty years after Queen Matilda first popularised the saint in 1148 with the foundation of a St Catherine's Chapel in East London (where St Catherine's Dock is situated today).

Chapter 10 – Markus of the Miz-maze

1   See Appendix I – The Cult of St Catherine.
2   Saward, J., *The Book of British Troy Towns*, pp. 9-10.
3   Ibid., p. 22.
4   From the words 'stay with the hills . . .' to the end of the psychic session has been taken from a letter written by Helen to me dated Tuesday, 14 March 1989 – two days after our return from St Catherine's Hill, Winchester. I quote: 'I asked Markus for help again, now this might be important. He said stay with the hills below and above the eight . . . [she had drawn a map of England with a figure eight vertically imposed and the word 'Kent' arrowed towards its south-eastern base] . . . follow the path, draw a map (Azimuth, do it) . . . Peg out the line, the path, it can be done. Follow the path and you will find. I then asked for a starting point and what I saw was Ide Hill. I have never been there but I know this info. is correct. So they double back on themselves.'

This was her first ever mention of Ide Hill.

I have included this information at this earlier point in the text as it relates directly to the psychic session of Sunday, 12 March 1989.

Chapter 11 – The Energy Matrix

1   Brian Vesey-Fitzgerald in his 1953 book *Winchester* referred on p. 37 to a long-distance ancient pathway of 'Neolithic' origin, linking Winchester and its surrounds with a string of Iron Age hill-forts across Hampshire and beyond. According to the author it 'enters the county [of Hampshire] at Quarley Hill and runs, by way of Danebury and Woolbury, to St Catherine's [Hill] and thence on over Old Winchester Hill and Butser Hill to the South Downs of Sussex and Beachy Head'.

No such track exists on modern-day Ordnance Survey maps and, as Vesey-Fitzgerald readily admitted, it is by no means straight. If the line is extended back into Wiltshire it passes some miles to the north of Woodhenge. Despite this, knowledge of such ancient trackways could, I'm sure, be utilised for magical purposes by groups such as the Friends of Hekate/Dark Council.
2   Kimmis, J., 'The Hermetic Labyrinth', *Caerdroia*, No. 15, The Caerdroia Project, Thundersley, Essex, 1984, pp. 25-7.
3   Easton, M.G., *The Illustrated Bible Dictionary*, Bracken Books, London, 1989, p. 205.
4   Michell, J., *The View Over Atlantis*, pp. 119-22.

Chapter 14 – Octavia's Hill

1   The 'Hecate's Wheel' illustration is taken from Elizabeth Pepper and John Wilcox's *Magical and Mystical Sites in Europe and the British Isles* (Weidenfield & Nicolson, London, 1977). I wish to thank Charles Walker and Toyne Newton for allowing me to use this material in advance of the publication of their forthcoming book *Ring of Darkness*.
2   For a full explanation of the Dark Council see Appendix I – The Cult of St Catherine.

Chapter 15 – Cracking the Crucible

1   Another coincidence I noted only on a return trip to Ide Hill during the evening of Saturday, 1 May 1993 was that Jane Boaks's memorial cross also bears an inscription to her husband, John, who died on 16 August 1932 at the age of ninety-five; 16 August

being the date we accompanied Helen to St Catherine's Hill, Winchester, in 1989.

Chapter 16 – Midnight Sun
1   See Appendix I – The Cult of St Catherine.

Chapter 18 – Rachel's Anguish
1   Bernard said the car was a powerful Ford Capri, with fast acceleration. Acting on the knowledge that it was silver in colour and C registration (i.e. 1985-6), I consulted my brother Michael – who is a car mechanic – and after due discussion we decided that the model in question was likely to have been a Capri 2.8 injection. Its engine size would have given the vehicle the sort of acceleration spoken of by Bernard. What's more, in 1985/6 – the last years the 2.8i was made – the principal colour scheme was Caspian blue metallic and silver.

Chapter 22 – The People of Hexe
1   Although Debbie first crystallised the Hexe material following her vision of the Wilsford Pit in November, she had alluded to this organisation in psychic material as early as Sunday, 17 September 1989. Inside St Paul's Cathedral on an Earthquest field trip she encountered the spirit of an ecclesiastical figure who gave his name as Erconwald, the first bishop of the East Saxons for London, *c.* AD 675 – whose shrine inside the cathedral was venerated as a place of pilgrimage during medieval times. He spoke anxiously of people conducting chthonic rites beneath the city of London. With this communication had come visions that same night of the Iceni Queen Boudicca decapitating Romano-British prisoners on the River Walbrook after razing London in AD 60. Debbie felt this modern-day group were attempting to resurrect not just Boudicca, but also a dark, corrupt form of the goddess Epona which they intended to embody in a bronze statue of a serpentine *lamia*. She spoke of seeing a locked steel door within an underground river tunnel sealed with 'hexing rituals'.

Bishop Erconwald told Debbie this 'hexing' group of six would induce the *lamia* to possess a woman. Through her they could attain great power as well as conversation with the 'foul spirit'.

He went on to say: 'They wish to resurrect a magic of total magic and demons, as well as the secret knowledge of all the different cultures. Their purpose is an awakening . . . to control the world mind.'

2 Pennick, N., and Devereux, P., *Lines on the Landscape*, pp. 25-6.

3 Ashbee, P., Bell., M., and Proudfoot, E., *The Wilsford Shaft*, English Heritage, London, 1989.

4 Burl, A., *Rites of the Gods*, pp. 205-6. A ritual spike in a Late Bronze Age shaft at Swanwick in Hampshire was found to contain traces of dried flesh and blood. Another example is the Iron Age spike pit at Holzhausen in Germany, where traces of blood, flesh and fat were detected on its upright timber.

5 Ibid., p. 96.

6 Crittall, E., ed., *Victoria History of Wiltshire*, vol. 1, part II, Oxford University Press, 1966, p. 383. Despite repeated attempts – the latest in May 1993 – I have been unable to locate the exact whereabouts of the Wilsford Pit, and can only assume it was filled in once the excavations were completed in 1962. If anyone can confirm its precise location, perhaps they can let me know.

7 Both in this book and in my previous work *The Seventh Sword* I use the spelling *hexe*, as opposed to *hex*, to denote the activities of the aforementioned magical group. This has been more by accident than design, as I recently discovered that Debbie's first-ever written reference to the group in March 1990 uses the spelling 'Hex'. I now recall obtaining this alternative spelling from Kenneth Grant's book *Cults of the Shadow*, where on p. 55 he refers to a Germanic form of Hekate named 'Hexe' – a claim I have been unable to substantiate.

8 Ravenscroft, T., *The Spear of Destiny*, p. 327.

9 See Appendix I – The Cult of St Catherine.

Chapter 23 – The Doom of the Gods

1 All information on the Romanian earthquake of 30 May 1990 was confirmed with David Redmayne of the British Geological Survey in Edinburgh and supplemented with news stories from the following sources dated Friday, 31 May 1990: *The Independent*, *Daily Mail* and *Evening Standard*.

2 *New Larousse Encyclopedia of Mythology*, p. 275.

NOTES AND REFERENCES

3 Thorsson, E., *Runelore*, 1987, p. 12.
4 Jackson, N. A., 'The Shamanic Vampire', *The Cauldron*, no. 66, 1992, p. 7.
5 Hill, D., 'Vampire', *Man, Myth and Magic*, Orbis, Purnell, 1971, p. 2924.

Chapter 25 – The Black Cross of the Flame
1 Ravenscroft, T., *The Spear of Destiny*, p. 192.
2 The Aryan teachings of Zoroaster were introduced into Nazi Germany between the two World Wars by figures such as Alfred Rosenberg and through the teachings of Rudolf Steiner and Helena Blavatsky (See Howard, M., *The Occult Conspiracy*, pp. 130-1).

Chapter 26 – A Last Goodbye
1 Collins, A., ed., *The Black Alchemist Supplement*, ABC Books, Leigh-on-Sea, 1988, p. 54.

Chapter 27 – Trouble at Stonehenge
1 Pennick, N., and Devereux, P., *Lines on the Landscape*, p. 50.
2 Clayton, P., *Archaeological Sites of Britain*, p. 90.
3 Pennick, N., and Devereux, P., *Lines on the Landscape*, p. 53.
4 The *You* magazine feature finally appeared under the rather dubious title of 'Go Quest, Young Man' in its issue of 1 December 1991.

Chapter 30 – The Angry Moon
1 Pennick, N., and Devereux, P., *Lines on the Landscape*, p. 26.

Chapter 32 – Portents of Danger
1 The next time I visited these same locations was on Saturday, 8 May 1993 when taking photographs for inclusion in this book. After giving up trying to find the ritual pit in the Wilsford barrow group, we departed for the round barrow at the Fargo plantation, north of Stonehenge. As we drove away my Ford Sierra hit an unseen bump, ripping a two-inch hole in the £160 radiator – a

problem necessitating the Automobile Association 'relaying' Debbie, myself and the car back to Leigh-on-Sea. It was the first problem I had experienced in one and a half years of driving the vehicle.

The previous weekend I had fallen over and broken a rib attempting to take night-time photographs of Ide Hill church in Kent! Furthermore, on the morning of Tuesday, 11 May Debbie said to me 'You want to be careful, these things usually come in threes!' Five minutes later she slipped on the kitchen floor and broke a toe! So, is there such a thing as bad karma?

Chapter 35 – Nosferatu
1   Leatherdale, C., *Dracula the Novel and the Legend*, p. 95
2   *Carfax* is a corruption of the Latin *quatre face*, four ways, as in the four cardinal points or a crossroads. Could Bram Stoker's use of this name be a cryptic allusion to Hekate as goddess of the crossroads? According to Kenneth Grant in his book *Cults of the Shadow*, Carfax is 'A synonym of Carrefour or Kalfu, God of the Crossroads', as well as 'a form of Baron Samedhi, Lord of the Underworld and of the Dead' in Haitian Voodoo tradition (see pp. 42, 212).
3   Leatherdale, C., *Dracula the Novel and the Legend*, p. 88.
4   Collins, A., *The Seventh Sword*, 1991, pp. 227-8.
5   Medway, G., private communication, late 1991. Taken from *The Devil Hunter* (originally titled *To Anger the Devil*) by Marc Alexander.
6   McDermott, P., *The Whitby Ghost Book*, p. 15.
7   Ibid., pp. 16-17.
8   Bord, J. and C., *Alien Animals*, p. 80.

Chapter 36 – Something Silver
1   Ellis Davidson, H.R., *Gods and Myths of Northern Europe*, pp. 178-9.
2   Thorsson, E., *Runelore*, pp. 14-15.

Chapter 37 – Harbinger of Destruction
1   At this point in the proceedings Debbie actually woke up and described what had transpired in her dreamstate. She then returned to sleep and the rest of the dream sequence took place.

Due to space it has been necessary to join these two dreams together.
2 *New Larousse Encyclopedia of Mythology*, p. 275.
3 Ellis Davidson, H.R., *Gods and Myths of Northern Europe*, p. 179.
4 Leatherdale, C., *Dracula the Novel and the Legend*, p. 95.
5 Ibid., pp. 192-3.

Chapter 40 – The Lantern's Force

1 According to Bram Stoker's *Dracula* the Count is destroyed on 6 November, something I only realised when researching this book. This was the date of the new moon connected with the crescent symbol inscribed upon the Trident Fork found at Whitby Abbey. Clive Leatherdale links Stoker's choice of this date with the Irish custom concerning the feast of St Martin, held each year on 11 November – the forward date suggested by counting the five strokes accompanying the crescent symbol. Apparently, to fulfil their annual obligation to the saint, blood had to be shed in the nine-day period between All Saints' Day and St Martin's Eve, otherwise the unlucky family could expect only ill-fortune during the coming year (see Leatherdale, C., *Dracula the Novel and the Legend*, p. 79).

This information makes sense of the utilisation of the Dracula theme at Whitby around Hallowe'en by the People of Hexe, also of the time frame suggested by our interpretation of the crescent symbol on the Trident Fork.

2 Thanks to Angela Reeve, Tim Dedopulos and Ian Read, editor of the journal *Chaos International*, for their respective analyses of the runes pecked into the surface of the Trident Fork. All three are in agreement that the runes were Germanic, not Norse, in origin. Ian Read – who has made an extensive study of Norse magic – also wanted to point out that Whitby Abbey has been used before by exponents of runic magic.
3 Thorsson, E., *Runelore*, p. 121.

Appendix I – The Cult of St Catherine

1 Vesey-Fitzgerald, B., *Winchester*, p. 33.
2 Begg, E., *The Cult of the Black Virgin*, pp. 122-3
3 Carley, J.P., *Glastonbury Abbey*, p. 20.

4 Ibid., p. 17.

5 The Winchester Miz-maze is a square, debased version of the so-called 'Chartres' design, which first made its appearance in the tiled floors of French Gothic cathedrals during the first half of the thirteenth century. It is essentially a christianized version of the much earlier 'Cretan' style maze, common throughout the Mediterranean in classical times.

The Chartres maze takes its name from Chartres Cathedral, where the earliest known example was laid out in tiles during the building's construction between 1194 and 1220. If this assessment is correct then it means that Henry de Blois could not have constructed the Winchester Miz-maze before his death in 1171. However, there is a good chance that the Chartres design existed before this date and was exported to Britain by church-building ecclesiastics such as Henry de Blois. There is also a likelihood that earlier mazes existed both at Chartres and on St Catherine's Hill before the thirteenth century.

Bibliography

All titles are either the current or last known editions of the book used by the author. The date of any relevant first editions is given in brackets.

Archaeology and General History

Burl, Aubrey, *Rites of the Gods*, J. M. Dent & Sons, London, 1981

Carley, James P., *Glastonbury Abbey*, The Boydell Press, London, 1988

Clayton, Peter, *Archaeological Sites of Britain*, Weidenfeld & Nicolson, London, 1976

Saward, Jeff, *The Book of British Troy Towns*, The Caerdroia Project, 53 Thundersley Grove, Thundersley, Benfleet, Essex SS7 3EB, 1982

Thomas, Nicholas, *A Guide to Prehistoric England*, B. T. Batsford, London, 1960

Vesey-Fitzgerald, Brian, *Winchester*, Phoenix House, London, 1953

Chaldean and Greco-Roman Magic and Mythology

Begg, Ean, *The Cult of the Black Virgin*, Arkana, London, 1985

Luck, Georg, *Arcana Mundi: Magic and the Occult in the Greek and Roman Worlds*, Crucible, Wellingborough, Northants, 1987

Ronan, Stephen, ed., *The Goddess Hekate*, Chthonios Books, Hastings, East Sussex, 1992

Demonology and the Occult

Cavendish, Richard, *The Black Arts*, Routledge & Kegan Paul, London, 1974

Davidson, Gustav, *A Dictionary of Angels Including the Fallen Angels*, The Free Press, New York, 1971

Gettings, Fred, *Dictionary of Demons: A Guide to Demons and Demonologists in Occult Law*, Rider, London, 1988

Grant, Kenneth, *Cults of the Shadow*, Frederick Muller, London, 1975

Howard, Michael, *The Occult Conspiracy*, Rider, London, 1989

Newton, Toyne, *The Demonic Connection*, Blandford Press, Poole, Dorset, 1987

Ravenscroft, Trevor, *The Spear of Destiny*, Corgi Books, London, 1974

Woods, William, *A History of the Devil*, Panther Books, Frogmore, Herts, 1975

Earth Mysteries

Bord, Janet and Colin, *The Secret Country*, Paladin Books, London, 1978

Devereux, Paul, *et al*, *Earth Lights Revelation*, Blandford Press, London, 1989

Michell, John, *City of Revelation*, Garnstone Press, London, 1972

Michell, John, *The New View Over Atlantis*, Thames & Hudson, London, 1983 (1st edn., 1969)

Michell, John, and Rhone, Christine, *Twelve Tribe Nations*, Thames & Hudson, London, 1991

Pennick, Nigel, and Devereux, Paul, *Lines on the Landscape, Leys and Other Linear Enigmas*, Robert Hale, London, 1989

Folklore and Legends

Bord, Janet and Colin, *Alien Animals*, Granada Publishing, Frogmore, Herts, 1980

Folklore, Myths and Legends of Britain, Reader's Digest Association, London, 1973

McDermott, Paul, *The Whitby Ghost Book*, Anderson Publications, Blaby, Leics, 1987

Germanic and Norse Magic and Mythology

Branston, Brian, *The Lost Gods of England*, Thames & Hudson, London, 1957

Ellis Davidson, H.R., *Gods and Myths of Northern Europe*, Penguin Books, Harmondsworth, 1964

New Larousse Encyclopedia of Mythology, intro. by Robert Graves, Hamlyn, London, 1974

Thorsson, Edred, *Runelore*, Samuel Weiser, York Beach, Maine, USA, 1987

Psychic Questing

Bates, Brian, *The Way of Wyrd, Tales of an Anglo-Saxon Sorcerer*, Century, London, 1983

The Black Alchemist Tape, ABC Books, Leigh-on-Sea, Essex, 1989

Collins, Andrew, *The Black Alchemist*, Arrow Books, London, 1992

Collins, Andrew, *The Circlemakers*, ABC Books, Leigh-on-Sea, Essex, 1992

Collins, Andrew, *The Seventh Sword*, Arrow Books, London, 1992

Phillips, Graham, and Keatman, Martin, *The Green Stone*, Granada Publishing, London, 1984

Phillips, Graham, and Keatman, Martin, *The Eye of Fire*, Grafton Books, London, 1988

Vampirism and the Dracula Legend

Alexander, Marc, *The Devil Hunter*, Sphere Books, London, 1981

Farson, Daniel, *The Man Who Wrote Dracula – A Biography of Bram Stoker*, Michael Joseph, London, 1975

Leatherdale, Clive, *Dracula the Novel and the Legend*, Desert Island Books, Brighton, East Sussex, 1993

Stoker, Bram, *Dracula*, Pan Books, London, 1992 (1st edn., 1897)

Index

Abraxas, Gnostic god, 313
Aeson, 35
Ahriman, 89, 209
Ahura Mazda, Ormuzd, 89, 209
Akboud, seal name, 199, 201
Albigensians, Cathars, 311
Alchemy, 23-4, 97-8
Amarna period of Egyptian history, 220
Amorea, garnet stone, 218, 220, 222, 235
Amsterdam, the Netherlands, Wheel links, 206, 208, 210
Andrew, Prince, 53
Anglesey, Isle of, 308
Angra Mainyu, 89
Annis, Black Annis, 245
Ansett, Richard, 227-8, 230, 232
Antichrist, 36, 280-1
Apollonius Rhodius, 35
Armenian earthquake of 1988, 193
Arundel, W Sussex, castle, 34, 154-5; church of St Nicholas, 149-50, 154-5
Asgard, gods of, 195, 280
Athos, Mount, Greece, 76
Avebury, Wilts, 33, 85, 97

Balder, Norse god, 196
Baron Samedhi, 322
Barguest, 269-70
Baruch, demon, 55

Beachy Head, E Sussex, 318
Beatrice, Princess, 53
Bedouin tribesmen, 203
Benstead, Debbie, 168-9, 198, 297, 308, 310, 322; intro, 166-7; and Bygone church, 173-9; and demonic mural vision, 211-6; Edward Bingham visits, 262; dreams of Elen on Pennine Way, 301-2; encounters 'Hagal', 275-80, 322; on Lake Down pond barrow, 227-31; on the People of Hexe, 178, 180-184, 252-3, 319; 'sees' Roman catacombs, 207; 'sees' Romanian earthquake of 30.5.90, 187-92, 195-7; and Stonehenge barrow groups, 217-26, 246; search and discovery of Trident Fork, 285-95; search and discovery of Walking Bone, 233-45; on Hexe in Whitby, 265-6, 269, 273-4
Begg, Ean, 311
Berlin Wall, 194, 279
Bernard, 57-8, 63, 86; and Arundel astral visitation, 149-51; and BA story, 23-4; dreams of BA in Peru, 247-51, 305, 307; 'sees' BSA in small hall, 48; and broken sword-stick, 68-76; and cameo brooch apport, 214-6; and Carreau affair, 55-6; crashes car,

INDEX

241-2; 'sees' discovery of clay seal and copper scroll on Dead Sea, 198-200, 202-4, 305; on dagger found in heart, 281; receives Dark Pool calls, 160-2; encounters Rachel Goodison/BSA in derelict house, 52-3; receives Rachel Goodison's card of 2.1.90, 164-6; receives second card of 24.9.90, 205-8; and Gozo head, 17-18, 71; and Lantern's force telephone call, 302-3; on Mercurial influence at Ide Hill, 99; and Paradise Mound, 20-6, 37-41, 43-44, 47; 'sees' ritual pit libation, 27-30; on St Catherine's Hill, 97; finds serpent bangle in casket, 166; encounters silver Capri, 151-58, 160-1, 319; summoned by BA to derelict house, 65-8; psychometry of Trident Fork, 298, 300

Bibliotheca Philosophica Hermetica, Amsterdam, 208

Bingham, Edward, 262

Black Alchemist, 20-4, 29, 31, 34, 37-41, 43, 46, 49, 53-4, 57, 67-8, 73-6, 90, 96-7, 115, 161, 165, 281, 308, 314; and Black Cross of the Flame, 206-8; finds clay seal and copper scroll by Dead Sea, 200-1, 305; in Lima, Peru, 247-51, 305; in Spain, 75, 165, 201-3; and the Wheel, 186

Black Cross of the Flame, 205-10, 282

Black Sorceress of Arundel, BSA – see Goodison, Rachel

Black Virgin, cult of, 312

Blavatsky, Helena, 321

Boaks, Joan, 126, 318

Boaks, John, 318

Bombo, 315

Boudicca, Iceni queen, 178, 319
Braila, Romania, 193
Brasov, Romania, 193
Brighton, E Sussex, 129, 144
Bucharest, Romania, 191, 193
Bukovina, 266
Bure, River, Norfolk, 174, 177
Burges, William, 144
Burland, C.A., 157
Bush, President George, 193
Butser Hill, Hants, 318
Bygone, Norfolk, ruined church at, 174-7, 182, 298

Caduceus, 98
Canute, Cnut, Danish king, 23
Cardiff Castle, Glamorgan, 144
Carfax, name derivation, 322
Carley, James P., 312-3
Carpathian mountains, 193, 266
Carreau, 55-6
Carrefour, Kalfu, 322
Carter, Lin, 56
Castle Dracula, fictional setting of, 266, 280
Castle Hedingham, Essex, 262
Cathars – see Albigensians
Ceauşescu, Nicolae, 194, 279
Ceauşescu, Nicu, 194
Cefalu, Sicily, 82
Cerberus, 46
Chaldean Oracles, 32, 60, 314
Chanctonbury Ring, W Sussex, 212, 216
Chartres Cathedral, France, 324
Christian Gnosticism, 75, 201-2, 208, 311-3
Church of Jesus Christ Christian, 210
Clapham, W Sussex, church, 53; demonic mural, 33, 213-6; plague pit, 34-6, 314; village, 34; woods, 33-7, 40, 54, 85

Clearbury Ring, Wilts, 181
Communism in Romania, 194
Constantine the Great, 122
Copper Scroll, found in 1953, 203
Crete, 221
Crowley, Aleister, 81-2
Croydon, Surrey, 82
Cuckoo Stone, Cuckhold Stone, Wilts, 221
Cunningham, William, 222
Cynocephalus, 14, 314

Danbury, Essex:
– church of St John the Baptist, 19, 35, 127, 151, 154
– Country Park, 69-71, 155, 161, 166-8
– Cricketers Inn, The, 69
– Griffin p.h., The, 17-18, 25, 51, 56, 94, 153, 201, 297, 302
– Iron Age hill-fort, 19
Danebury, Hants, 318
Dark Council, as medieval church body, 185, 310-3; as revised Friends of Hekate, 91-7, 100, 114-5, 118-20, 129-32, 135, 143-7, 209, 245, 305, 310, 318
Davey, Richard, 30-1, 34, 36, 44-6, 85
David, Essex psychic, 125, 131, 144, 147, 208
Dawkins, Karl, 175-7, 228, 230, 235-7, 239-40, 253, 284, 286-91, 293-95, 308
Dawkins (né Mundy), Lisa, 175, 260, 262-4, 286-9, 291-5
Dead Sea, Israel, 203
Dead Sea Scrolls, 203, 250
Dedopulos, Tim, 323
Dee, Dr John, 106
Delphic Oracle, Greece, 95
Devereux, Paul, 181, 301

Devereux, Robert, earl of Essex, 316
Dionysus-Bacchus, 117
Dracula, Victorian novel – see Bram Stoker
Dracula, name derivation, 266, 280
Dracula, Count, fictional character, 264-70; equated with Antichrist and Fenris, 280-1
Dracula, Vlad – see Vlad Tepes
Druids, 180
Dulcimer, 84, 98-9
Dunstable, Beds, 311

888, root of, 36; influence of, 53
Eastbourne, E Sussex, 24-5, 53, 90, 304; Paradise Mound, 20-2, 23-5, 27-8, 31-2, 37, 40-9, 54, 91, 127, 210, 282
Easter, 112
Earthquest, 40, 106, 112, 211, 319
Eclipse, full moon, 134-5, 139-41, 144
Edgar, king of England, 23, 127
Elen of the Hosts, 129-30, 301, 303
Elle folk, 129
Energy matrix, 96-7, 100, 129, 183, 253
Epona, 319
Erconwald, Saxon bishop of London, 319
Eshton, W Yorks, St Helen's Well, 135
Essenes, 75
Exeter, Devon, 266-7

Fargo plantation round barrow, Wilts, 231-42, 252, 254, 321
Fenris, Fenrir, and the Romanian earthquake of 30.5.90, 195-7, 272-4, 277-82, 304; at Whitby Abbey, 286, 291, 295, 298

INDEX

Fields of the Nephilim, rock band, 57

Fiona, girl downstairs, 31-2, 59-63, 87, 118, 315

Fomorians, 173

Fortuna, 118

Frankenbury Camp, Wilts, 181, 223

Friends of Hekate, 29, 33-4, 76, 85, 87, 90-1, 95-7, 119, 155, 185-6, 204, 209, 212, 215, 281, 308, 310, 318

Gardner, Gerald, 41

Garinet, Jules, 55

Gematria, 36

Germanic races, 196, 278-9

Germany, re-unification, 194

Ggantija, Gozo, 17-8, 71, 74

Gilbert, Bob, 208

Glastonbury, Somerset, the Tor, 95; abbey, 312-3

Glossop, Derbs, 301

Glusburn, W Yorks, Lund's Tower, 253

Goat of Mendes, 116-18

Goat's head dagger, 109, 115, 117

Goodison, Rachel, 28-32, 34-6, 40, 48, 50-7, 63, 68-9, 74-6, 87, 90, 149-51, 154-5, 158, 160-2, 204, 214-6, 308; card of 2.1.90, 164-6; card of 24.9.90, 205-8, 282

Gorbachev, Mikhail, 193-4, 279

Gorgo, 60-61, 197, 315

Gorgons, 61

Gosforth, Cumbria, 'Viking' cross, 280

Gozo, Maltese island, 17-18

Grandier, Urban, 55

Grant, Kenneth, 320, 322

Great Beast, 36

Great Leighs, Essex, St Anne's Castle, 73

Great Storm of 1987, 13-14, 29, 34-5, 41, 281, 304, 314

Greco-Roman alchemy, 23, 90, 201

Greenwich, SE London, 147

Guerrero, Mexico, 194

Hades, 46

Hadleigh Castle, Essex, 146

Hagal, Romanian wolf shaman, 275-80, 286-7, 298, 308

Hagalaz rune, 298

Harker, Jonathan, 267

Heilige Lance – see Spear of Destiny

Hekate, 29, 32-5, 40, 44, 46, 56-61, 63, 85, 117, 215, 281-2, 314-5, 322; and 'Hecate's Wheel', 118, 318; hosts of, 61-2, 197; and wolves, 46

Hel, Norse goddess, 129, 301

Helen, London psychic, 81-4, 305; and Dark Council, 91, 97, 103-4, 305; and goat's head vision, 111; and Ide Hill, 93-4, 99, 101-3, 105-15, 117-23, 125-7, 317; Larkhill/Woodhenge, 93, 96; and 'Mr Goat', 122-3; and Seven Swords, 128-9, 144; split in August 1989, 145-8, 219; and Winchester, 85-94, 97, 125, 129-41, 143-8, 310, 319

Henry de Blois, bishop of Winchester, 85, 134, 311-13, 324

Henry of Huntingdon, 313

Hermes, 76, 98, 117-8

Hermetics, 76, 98

Hex marks, 182, 243

Hibbert, Tom, 227-8, 232

Hill, Lady Octavia, 113, 126

Hitler, Adolf, 184, 209

Hoare, Sir R. Colt, 222

Hofburg Museum, Vienna, Austria, 184, 209

Holzhausen, Germany, ritual pit, 320
Horning, Norfolk, The Ferry Inn, 174-5
Horrigan, John, 125, 133, 135, 137-9, 141-3, 145, 147, 173, 175, 227-8, 230, 239, 241-4, 253, 274, 280, 308; car troubles, 252; Dracula dream, 257-9, 263-5, 268-9, 288; visions on Fargo plantation mound, 234-6; and wolf vision, 271-2; in Whitby, 284-92
Horrigan, Kerry, 125, 133, 135-6, 141, 143, 145, 147, 175, 228, 230, 234, 239-41, 244, 258-9, 274, 280; night stalker/werewolf dream, 260-65, 268-9; in Whitby, 285, 288-9
Howard, Robert E., 56
Hurricane Gilbert of September 1988, 315

Iceni tribe, 178
Ide Hill, Kent, 93-4, 96-7, 99, 101-3, 105-15, 125-6, 147, 317; church of St Mary, 94, 115, 127-8, 322
Ionia, Asia Minor, 118
Iron Age, 19
Istanbul, Turkey, 193
Itchen, River, Hants, 136, 138-9

Jason, 35
Jerusalem, Temple of, 203
Judgement Day, Anglo-Saxon concept of, 272; and Ragnarok, 280, 282

Keez, Stonehenge spirit guardian, 229-31, 246
Kemsing, Kent, 126

Kettleness, N Yorks, 267, 269
King, Francis, 61, 315
Kishinev, Moldavia, 193
Knaresborough, W Yorks, 283, 294
Knights of St Catherine at Mount Sinai, 311
Knights Templar, 185
Ku-Klux-Klan, 206, 210

Labyrinth, Cretan, 183
Lake Down barrow cemetery, Wilts, 224-8, 244
Lake barrow group, Wilts, 224
Lamaiai, 61, 197, 266, 319
Langstone, Alex, 112-3, 119-20, 125, 128, 133, 135, 137-9, 141, 143, 145-7, 174-7, 179, 228, 235-6, 241
Lantern's Pike, Derbs, 302
Larkhill, Wilts, 93, 97
Leatherdale, Clive, 323
Leigh-on-Sea, Essex, 30, 40, 146, 187, 211
Levi, Eliphas, 116-8
Little People, elementals in Arundel churchyard, 149; fire elementals in The Ferry Inn, Horning, 174-5; at Chanctonbury Ring, 212
Lima, Peru, 247-51
Lockyer, Sir Norman, 181
Loire Valley, France, 56, 165
Loki, Norse trickster god, and Ragnarok 195; equated with Satan, 280
London
– St Paul's Cathedral, 95, 319
– St Catherine's chapel, Tower Hill, 312, 317
– St Catherine's Dock, 317
– River Walbrook, 319
Loudon, Devils of, 55
Lovecraft, H.P., 107

INDEX

Luck, Georg, 315
Ludham, Norfolk, dragon legend of, 174
Lugnasadh, 18, 244
Lullington, E Sussex, 23, 90
Luxembourg, 200
Lycanthropy, 279
Lykaina, 13-14, 29, 281

Markus de Capelin, Winchester spirit guardian, 91-3, 95, 119, 130, 185, 310, 312, 317
Mary, Sussex psychic, 87, 131
Mary, Virgin mother, 115, 312
Matilda, queen of England, 312
Mazes, 'Chartres' design, 323-4; 'Cretan' design 323-4; turf-cut, 91-2
Medea, 35
Medusa, 60
Memphis, Egypt, 220
Mercury, 98-100, 114, 117-8
Mereworth Woods, Kent, 54
Merron, Johnny, 40, 42, 44-5
Michell, John, 95, 99-100, 114, 181
Minotaur, 178
Moldavia, Russian republic, 191, 193, 266, 279
Monas Hieroglyphica, 106, 110, 118-9
Mormo, 60-1, 197, 315
Moscow, Russia, 193
Moyo Bamba-Rioja, Peru, 194

Nazism, and the occult, 184, 209-10
Netherlands, the, 206, 208, 210
Newton, Toyne, 31, 33-6, 40, 61, 85-6, 96-7, 131, 314, 318; *The Demonic Connection*, 31, 33, 35, 61, 85
Newton, Joan, 86
North Downs, Kent, 94

Normanton barrow cemetery, Wilts, 181, 229; Bush Barrow in, 222
Normanton Gorse – see Wilsford Pit
Nosferatu, 266
Nuremberg, Germany, church of St Katherine, 184

Odin, and ritual spears, 274; sons of, 278
Old Sarum, Wilts, camp, 181; ley, 181, 183, 223, 244-6
Old Winchester Hill, Hants, 318
Oliver, Mike, 40, 42-43, 45
Omand, Dr Donald, 269
Omphalos, omphali, 95
Origen, 313

Paradise place-names, 41
Peggy o' th' Lantern, 301
Pelochin, Seffrid, abbot of Glastonbury, 313
Pennick, Nigel, 181
Pennine Way, 301-3
People of Hexe, aims and history, 180-4, 186, 304, 319; events post 1991, 308; and Norfolk, 174, 178, 320; and Romanian earthquake, 188, 190, 278, 280; and Stonehenge barrow cemeteries, 223, 225, 244-6, 281; and Trident Fork, 295, 299; and Walking Bone, 243-5, 252; and Whitby, Yorks, 265-6, 270, 273-4, 280-1; 285, 287, 323; in Yorkshire, 252-3, 264, 272, 301
Phillips, Graham, 127, 185
Phoenicians, 221
Potter, Chesca, 133-6, 144, 311
Prior, Derek, 128
Priscillian of Avila, 202

Psychic News, 30
Psychic questing, 10, 106-7, 109, 121
Ptah, Egyptian god, 220; as Stonehenge guardian, 220, 222-5, 238, 246
Purfleet, Essex, Carfax estate, 267

Quarley Hill, Hants, 318
Queen of Sheba, 312
Queen of the South, 312
Qumran, Israel, 203

Ragnarok, age of, 195-7, 272, 279-80, 282, 286, 304
Randles, Jenny, 301
Random Century, 254
Rankine, Dave, 44-6, 49
Ravenscroft, Trevor, 209
Read, Ian, 323
Redmayne, David, 193, 320
Reeve, Angela, 323
Revelation, St John's book of, 36
Ritman, J.R., 208
Ritual child abuse, 12
Roedean school, E Sussex, 155
Romanian shamanism, 188-90, 194-7, 279
Romanian earthquake of 30.5.90, 188-95, 277, 279, 320
Ronan, Stephen, 314
Rosenberg, Alfred, 321
Royston, Herts, beehive cave, 311
Runes, 182, 298
Ryan, Mark, 253

666, root of, 36
Sabbatic Goat, 117
Saint,
    Anne, 23, 244-5
    Basil, 311
    Bernard of Clairvaux, 313
    Catherine of Alexandria, 85, 87, 98, 118, 133-5, 310-13; cult of, 134-5, 311; sun of, 133, 141, 144, 311
    Denis, 127
    Dunstan of Glastonbury, 23
    Edith of Wilton, Eadgyth, 23, 126-7
    Helen, 122, 125, 129-30, 132, 134, 301
    James the Just, 201
    Margaret of Antioch, 312
    Martin, 323
    Mercury, 98
    Thomas Didymus the Apostle, 62
St Anne's Hill, Wilts, 244
St Benet of Holm Abbey, Norfolk, 173-4, 177
St Catherine's Down, Chale, Isle of Wight, 316
St Catherine's Hill, Christchurch, Hants, 316
St Catherine's Hill, Winchester, Hants – see Winchester
Salisbury Cathedral, 181
San Fransisco earthquake of 1989, 193
Santiago de Compostela, NW Spain, 201-2; cathedral of St James, 201-2
Sardinia, 183
Saward, Jeff, 92
Seal, clay, seen by Bernard, 199-200
Second Coming, 282
Seraphica, Sister, nun, 55
Seven Swords of Meonia, 128-9, 144, 169, 305
Sevenoaks, Kent, 82
Shamans, intro; 10; bird shamans, 212-3
Sibiu, Romania, 194
Silbury Hill, Wilts, 97, 103, 120

INDEX

Sobek-nofru-re, Egyptian female king, 269
South Downs, Sussex, 42-3, 318
South Downs Way, 212
Soviet Union, break up of, 194
Spear of Destiny, Spear of Longinus, 32, 184, 209-10
Stein, Johannes Walter, 209
Steiner, Rudolf, 321
Stephen of Blois, king of England, 312
Stoker, Bram, and *Dracula*, 197, 263, 265-70, 280, 283, 288, 296, 322-3; and *The Jewel of the Seven Stars*, 269
Stone, J.F., 221
Stonehenge, Wilts, 95, 181, 217, 219, 221-4, 244-5, 281; Cursus, 221, 230, 245
Stukeley, William, 221
Sunderland, Marion, 281
Swanwick, Hants, ritual pit, 320

Tepes, Vlad, 266, 268
Tintagel, Cornwall, church of St Materiana, 169
Transylvania, 193, 195, 266, 279-80
Trident Fork, found at Whitby 2.11.91, 299; discovery of, 288, 292-4; symbols on, 295, 297-8, 323
Trimarco, Cara, 55
Tuatha de Danann, 174

UFOs, at Clapham, W Sussex, 33; and Helen, 81; in the Pennines, 301-2

Vampires, 263-4; in Romanian folklore, 197
Varna, Bulgaria, 267
Venus statue, found at Danbury, 71-5, 155

Vesey-Fitzgerald, Brian, 316, 318
Vienna, Austria, 193, 209
Vietnam, folklore of, 56
Visualisation techniques, 40-1, 211
Voodoo, 322
Vortigern, British Dark Age chieftain, 169
Vrancea, Romania, 193

Walker, Charles, 33-4, 40, 53, 318
Walking Bone, 238-44; interpretation of symbols, 243-4, 295
Waltham Abbey, Essex, 225
Watkins, Alfred, 181, 244
Werewolves, 262-4
West Bank, Israel, 203
Westenra, Lucy, 267-8, 288
Weston, Paul, 40, 42-3, 45, 112-5, 119, 125, 128, 133, 135-9, 141, 143, 147, 175, 228, 233, 235-6
Wheel, the, 185, 204, 245, 304-5
Whitby, N Yorks, abbey, 273, 275-7, 283-4, 286-96, 299, 323; and barguest hound, 269-70; and Bram Stoker's *Dracula*, 263-70, 273, 285; church of St Mary, 274, 284, 288; Church Steps, 285, 288; Church Street, 270, 286; East Cliff, 270, 283; Tate Hill Pier, 274
Wilkinson, William, 268
Wilsford barrow cemetery, Wilts, 181, 223-4
Wilsford Pit, Normanton Gorse, Wilts, 180-2, 218, 223, 229-30, 246, 319-21
Wilson, Steve, 56
Wilton Abbey, Wilts, 22-3
Winchester, Hants, 33, 85-87, 90-2, 131, 185; and Camelot, 131; and cathedral monastery of St Swithun, 310; and church and

hospital of St Cross, 134, 136; and medieval 'Dark Council', 185; and Miz-maze, 85-6, 88, 98, 137, 313, 323-4; St Catherine's Hill, 85-8, 90-3, 95-8, 103-4, 112, 118-9, 125, 129-41, 143-4, 146-7, 185, 209, 310-13, 316-9, 324

Wise, Caroline, 31, 44-5, 133-4

Wolsey, Cardinal, 92

Wolverhampton, W Mids, 127

Wolves, and lycanthropy, 279; in Ragnarok story, 195-6; in Romanian superstitious lore, 197, 279

Woodhenge, Wilts, 96, 98, 221, 318

Woolbury, Hants, 318

Wulfrida, 127

Wyrd, Web of, 39, 70, 244

York, duchess of, 53

You magazine, 225, 227, 231-3, 321

Young, Carole, 55

Yugoslavian earthquake of 30.5.90, 194

Zoroastrianism, 89, 112, 209, 321

Zosimos of Panopolis, 119